THE DAWN OF SCOTTISH
SOCIAL WELFARE

An Edinburgh water-caddie

after David Allen, reproduced from *The Edinburgh and District
Water Supply*, by James Colston : Edinburgh 1890

THE
DAWN OF SCOTTISH
SOCIAL WELFARE

A survey from medieval times to 1863

THOMAS FERGUSON

THOMAS NELSON AND SONS LTD

LONDON EDINBURGH PARIS MELBOURNE
TORONTO AND NEW YORK

THOMAS NELSON AND SONS LTD
Parkside Works Edinburgh 9
3 Henrietta Street London WC2
312 Flinders Street Melbourne C1
91–93 Wellington Street West   Toronto 1

THOMAS NELSON AND SONS
385 Madison Avenue New York 17

SOCIÉTÉ FRANÇAISE D'EDITIONS NELSON
25 rue Henri Barbusse Paris V^e

———

First published 1948

PREFACE

THIS is not intended to be a text-book, or to cover in any comprehensive way the development of social services in Scotland. Rather is it an attempt to outline the main problems of health and social welfare as they have arisen there, and to show how various solutions have been evolved. The aim has been to draw illustrations from events in different parts of the country, preserving as much as possible of original background : sometimes straying into quiet backwaters and meeting quaint characters. What the books loses in completeness as a result it may gain in general appeal, and in stimulating the reader to explore for himself those fields in which he is specially interested. The story has been carried up to 1862–63, years marking the close of one era and the opening of a new, with the appointment of the first Medical Officers of Health in Scotland, Dr. Littlejohn in Edinburgh and Dr. Gairdner in Glasgow. Much work awaited these early pioneers, but with the creation of official health departments new sources of official reports and records opened up, as well as a new chapter in our social history.

The preparation of a book of this kind, however simple, involves heavy trespass on the good nature of many people. My thanks are due to my colleagues in the Scottish Public Health Service for much help, ungrudgingly given, and particularly to Dr. J. G. Galbraith, formerly Medical Officer of Health of Ross and Cromarty, and to Dr. Bloch of Glasgow Health Department ; to the Librarians of the University of Glasgow, the Royal College of Physicians of Edinburgh, the Public Health Department of the Corporation of Glasgow and the Mitchell Library, Glasgow ; to Drs. Honeyman and Henderson of Glasgow Art Galleries. And, above all, to my wife.

T. FERGUSON

Glasgow, 1947

CONTENTS

vii

CONTENTS

CONTENTS

ix

LIST OF ILLUSTRATIONS

THE DAWN OF SCOTTISH
SOCIAL WELFARE

CHAPTER I

THE FOUR MAIN PROBLEMS

I

MANY of the social problems that have faced administrators through the ages have hinged on the control of infectious disease, the relief of destitution, the improvement of environmental hygiene and the provision of medical care for the people. The relative emphasis placed on each of these has varied from time to time, and often widely within quite short periods of time, but they have been closely inter-related, and from them our health services have emerged.

The old Scottish Bills of Mortality demonstrated clearly how badly children fared at the beginning of the nineteenth century, the great part played by the major epidemic diseases in destroying life, and the pernicious influence of over-density of population in shaping mortality statistics. In his First Annual Report the Registrar-General, examining mortality experience during the year 1855, had something to say about the influence on mortality of what he called " external agencies " ; and among the factors he regarded as modifying profoundly the course of disease were the state of trade, including the wages paid and the extent of unemployment, the price and quality of provisions, and the weather. He accepted it as a well-established fact that a bad harvest, which raised the price of all kinds of provisions, was, in general, attended by an increased mortality ; and throughout Scottish history the ill years have been marked by a strong tendency to increased epidemic prevalence. These early demonstrations of the influence of social conditions on disease and death ultimately helped to stimulate the public conscience to remedial action.

The great epidemics of the major infectious diseases paralysed national life in the Middle Ages, and continued to influence the

I

whole national economy well into the nineteenth century. Leprosy, plague, syphilis, smallpox, typhus fever, and cholera in turn, and sometimes together, demoralized the country, and were responsible for much sickness and death. The reaction of the people to them was a curious mixture of panic and vicious zeal to combat infection and of a fatalistic belief that epidemic prevalence was to be accepted as a visitation of Providence best countered by religious fasts; that somewhere behind the plagues, especially those that affected children mostly, there was probably an element of benevolence—the kind of outlook that regarded smallpox as the poor man's friend because it saved him the trouble of bringing up a family and thought that little was to be gained by removing one major cause of the death of children, because some other disease would promptly come along to take its place —the so-called Doctrine of Replacement. There was little real conception of the prevention of disease, in the modern sense of the term, and certainly no sustained attempt at disease-prevention in the periods between the years of high epidemic prevalence ; though from time to time, when great epidemics threatened, there was a flurry of vigorous, if evanescent, effort to ward off the threatened plague. On such occasions the preventive measures followed a stereotyped course. There were fasts, the isolation of contacts and of victims of the disease, quarantine measures against the importation of infection from abroad, measures to prevent its spread from one part of the country to another, not so difficult in those days of slow-moving transport ; and often these restrictive measures were applied with great severity. In the exercise of measures of this kind Aberdeen had for long a special distinction, with its gibbets for the persuasion of those who might be in danger of breaking the regulations ; and certainly for a long time Aberdeen enjoyed a freedom from plague when other parts of the country were sorely tried by it.

2

The great outbreaks of cholera in the nineteenth century marked the turning-point between the old approach to the prevention of infectious disease and the new. Under the stimulus of cholera, Boards of Health were set up in many towns and villages to promote the welfare of their communities, " by every means which could avert the approach, or effect the extinction of disease."

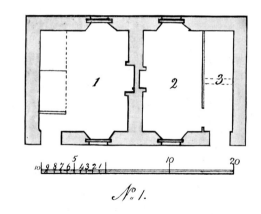

Design by Hamilton, 1822, for a simple type of turf farm-
cottage (see page 46) :

1 kitchen   2   barn or workshop   3   stall for cow

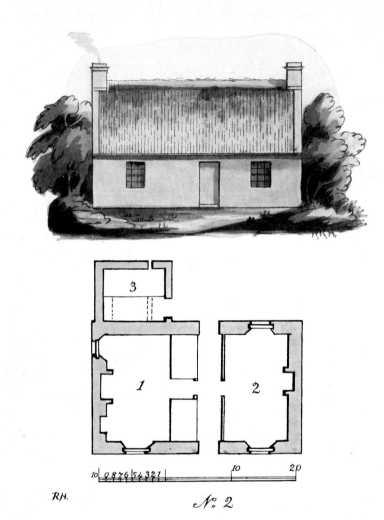

RH.

№ 2

Design by Hamilton, 1822, for a farm-cottage built of
stone and lime :

1 kitchen   2 workshop   3 cow's stall, pigsty, and dungstead

Cholera hospitals were equipped, carriages procured for the transport of patients, the closes and wynds were washed, the houses of the poor whitewashed, and all infected places fumigated, even the precious dunghills were removed, and instructions were issued to the citizens about the prevention and treatment of the disease. But no sooner had an epidemic passed than these measures, adopted in time of crisis, were cast aside, for such interferences with the liberty of the subject, and such a lavish expenditure of money could only be countenanced in a time of real crisis. Of steady remedial action to remove the abuses that were by then well known to beget disease there was none ; and when, as late as 1853, Lord Palmerston suggested that the best course the people could pursue to deserve that the further progress of the cholera should be stayed was to clean up the towns and so remove those causes and sources of contagion, " which, if allowed to remain, will infallibly breed pestilence and be fruitful in death, in spite of the prayers and fastings of a united but inactive nation," his advice was none too well received.

The small size of the administrative units and the slowness of communications between them, while helping to some extent to delay the transmission of epidemic disease, operated against the provision of effective hospital treatment. In early days, when leprosy occurred in a community it was not unusual for the patient to have to live precariously in the fields until a crude hospital hut could be erected for him. Later, when typhus fever was so prevalent in the nineteenth century, the sheer weight of cases of the disease completely swamped the available hospital resources. In those days the young voluntary hospitals treated not only the general sickness of the community but infectious disease as well ; and at some periods of high epidemic prevalence not only were the hospitals themselves filled to overflowing with cases of fever, but huts erected in their grounds and specially erected auxiliary hospitals were also filled, and even then large numbers of patients had to be left without hospital care. Through time it came to be recognized that it was unreasonable to expect the general hospitals to cope with this load of epidemic disease, but it was long before civic authorities showed any willingness to shoulder the burden. Early in the nineteenth century the Managers of the Town's Hospital in Glasgow gave some thought to the matter, but very soon decided that any hospital provision of this kind that was still necessary after the Royal Infirmary was full of cases of fever could properly be left to private charity ; the provision of beds for the treatment of infectious disease was not a thing on which they felt justified in spending public money. So severely were the resources of the voluntary hospitals taxed that their managers, in an attempt to cut down the number of cases, disinfected the houses from which patients had been removed to hospital, and upon occasion made representations to the government of the day to restrict immigration to their areas. These steps marked an early but practical link between preventive and curative medicine ; and about the same time, fully a hundred years ago, Dr. W. P. Allison, Professor of Practice of Medicine in Edinburgh, wrote that the value of a knowledge of the prevention of disease might be expected to increase in course of time, for the conditions necessary for the avoidance of many diseases were in great measure in the power of communities, though still beyond the power of many of the individuals comprising them.

There was often much confusion about the various conditions summarily classified as " fever," so that it was difficult to compare the severity of one outbreak with that of another, and there were wide differences in the fatality of epidemics. It is not surprising, therefore, that there were many conflicting views among the experts of the day as to the nature and cause of the fevers so prevalent in Scotland about 1840, and about the measures that ought to be taken for their control. One view held that the want of good religious training was the cause and that church extension was the remedy ; a second, that destitution was the cause and adequate poor relief the remedy ; a third, that the abuse of intoxicating liquors was the cause and suppression of this the remedy ; a fourth, that want of education was the cause and the establishment of schools the remedy ; and a fifth, that faulty sanitation was the cause and improvement of that the remedy. Cleland, the Glasgow historian, though not so much interested in scientific exactitude, had not been far wide of the mark when, twenty years earlier, he wrote that fever commonly attacked " persons of weak nerves, a lax habit of body and a poor, thin blood ; those who suffered great evacuations, a long dejection of spirits, immoderate watchings, studies, fatigue, etc. ; also those who have used much crude, unwholesome food, vapid impure drinks, or who have been confined long in damp, foul air ; who have broken the vigour of their constitutions by whatever cause."

3

The connection between the great epidemic diseases and poverty was clear enough, and the necessity for the relief of the poor soon came to be appreciated on grounds of expediency, apart altogether from humanitarian considerations. As early as 1424, an enactment of the Scottish Parliament was framed to prevent companies of people from marching through the country, " begging and harbouring." Begging was for long a great curse, and many Acts, severely repressive in tone, were passed in vain attempt to control the " masterful beggars." The practice of licensing to beg those unfit to earn their living otherwise was instituted early, and badges were issued in many Scottish parishes authorizing the holders to beg within their own parish, usually on prescribed days and under prescribed conditions. As the poor increased in numbers, and the size of the beggar bands became more formidable, the urge on the part of the authorities to discourage begging inevitably grew ; and it gave rise to more and more repressive legislation. There was early recognition of the essential difference in point of social deserts between those able to earn their living but unwilling to do so, and those who were unable to earn their living, the " impotent folk and weak folk." The Act of 1579, which for long governed the administration of poor relief in Scotland, was designed " for punishment of the strong and idle beggars and relief of the poore and impotent." One interesting feature was its catholic definition of " strong men and vagabonds." It was no easy matter to enforce these Acts, and poor relief seldom erred on the side of generosity.

The relief of destitution long remained a function of the Kirk Session, and one to which the Church clung tenaciously for many years, even when its resources for the relief of the poor were grossly inadequate. The Reformation, which saw the end of the charitable activities of most of the early hospitias or almshouses, aggravated the plight of the poor, and the growth in the seventeenth century of Houses of Correction made their lot more miserable. Masterless persons and sturdy beggars, young and old, were consigned by the magistrates to these houses, to be " corrected in manner to be appointed " : they were to be compelled to work at such labour as was given to them by the master, and to receive such " entertainment " as he thought their work merited.

In the eighteenth century there were three main sources

available for the relief of the poor in Glasgow. Help might be derived from one of the fourteen Trade Incorporations, if the poor person had the good fortune to belong to one of these ; or from the Kirk Session, generally only if his needs were comparatively modest ; or from the Town's Hospital, which had been set up in 1733, and of which the maintenance was undertaken by the Town Council, the Merchant House, the Trades House and the General Kirk Session, eked out by private benefactions and by a small tax on the citizens. The history of the Town's Hospital in Glasgow is a fascinating essay in social administration, and the records of the deliberations of its Committee of Management shed interesting light on the problems of the times.

With the rapid growth of industrialization, the great movements of population at the time of the construction of railways, the religious sectarianism following the Disruption, and the high prevalence of typhus fever in the early nineteenth century, conditions deteriorated rapidly. The Church became less and less able to meet the needs of the poor, and their plight alike in cities and in country districts was very serious. An increasing number of Scottish parishes, mostly in the larger towns, were driven by sheer necessity to replace voluntary charitable poor relief by the more reliable, if less popular, method of legal assessment ; but things were far from satisfactory, and the government of the day was compelled to set up a Commission to review the whole question of the administration of Poor Relief in Scotland.

The Report of the Commission, issued in 1843, showed that, while conditions varied widely from one part of the country to another, the general standard of care of the poor was low. The Scottish system of relief was essentially an outdoor one, though already there were thirteen poorhouses in Scotland. Medical relief was left almost entirely to private charity, especially in the rural areas. The accommodation for pauper lunatics was grossly inadequate. The Commissioners came to the conclusion that, despite the opposition of the Church, the time had come when it was necessary to introduce a system of legal assessment for the relief of the poor. The recommendations of the Commission became the basis of the Poor Law Amendment Act of 1845, which directed the creation of Parochial Boards, with duty to appoint an Inspector of Poor and be responsible for Poor Relief ; and empowered the Boards to adopt legal assessments to that end. The Act also provided for the establishment in Edinburgh of a central Board of Supervision, charged with general oversight of the administration of Poor Relief throughout the country. The functions of this central Board gradually widened, partly because it was found convenient to charge the Parochial Boards with duties in connection with the prevention of typhus fever and cholera ; and through time lineal descendants of the Board of Supervision came to be the central authority concerned not merely with the welfare of the poor, but also with a widely developing range of health services. The new Poor Law Act was not introduced without considerable difficulty, and the resources of the newly appointed Parochial Boards were sorely strained by the distress following on the failure of the potato crop in 1846. The advent of the new machinery and the new taxation did nothing to discourage local efforts to get rid of the poor as quickly as possible. In Highland counties particularly, much depended on the humanity of the laird, and many cottar houses were pulled down with the avowed object of keeping the undesired poor from developing a domicile in the parish. This artificial creation of a housing shortage had far-flung social consequences, and it certainly helped to stimulate the emigration from Highland parishes that was such a feature of Scottish life in the nineteenth century.

The new Poor Law raised many administrative problems. It appeared that as a result of the new system of assessments, with consequent improvement—though this was only slight—in the amount of the allowances be given by way of poor relief, together with the increase in the number of poor in many parts of the country, the system of outdoor relief no longer worked well. The number of poorhouses began to increase rapidly in Scotland. Their aim was fourfold : to provide a home for the friendless and impotent poor, to arrest begging, to provide a test of the genuineness of applications for relief, and, as a result, to reduce the cost of poor relief. Many of the new poorhouses were indifferently conducted, and their whole atmosphere was quite different from that of the old almshouses. In practice it was found to be extremely difficult to reconcile the two broad functions of a poorhouse, one mainly concerned with meeting the wants of the aged and infirm, the other with furnishing a test of genuineness of need. *The Scotsman* found it necessary to criticize vigorously a system it felt could only be regarded as unsatisfactory, for in practice it was " as difficult for a poorhouse to serve these two purposes as

7

for a man to serve two masters." When, in 1862, information became available for the first time about the average weekly cost of maintenance in Scottish poorhouses, and the figure—for food, fuel, clothing, light, and all other necessaries—was found to be 2s. 11½d., the question was very properly asked whether this could be reckoned sufficient for the proper sustenance of paupers with exhausted constitutions. *The Scotsman* was led to conclude that in Scotland poorhouses had failed, both as tests of poverty and as the means of more effectually ministering to the wants of the aged and infirm poor. There was obviously serious cause for misgiving about the whole question of the welfare of the poor in Scotland ; but the Board of Supervision was slow to believe that anything was amiss.

4

It was early recognized that the great waves of epidemic disease that so disorganized the national life played their worst havoc where sanitation was poorest, and where the poor lived their wretched lives in conditions of greatest poverty and over-crowding. So it was that when a particularly violent epidemic threatened there was often a temporary zeal for the improvement of environmental conditions. Visits from distinguished personages also prompted a clearing of the streets of the most obvious filth ; but despite the constant efforts of Parliament and Town Councils it took many years to secure popular recognition of the fact that the improvement of sanitation was the best guarantee of freedom from major epidemic prevalence. Part of the difficulty arose from the fact that the accumulated filth had a financial value ; some-times this fulzie belonged to the owner of the property from which it came, sometimes to the occupier of the house, sometimes to the Town Council for the common good, and sometimes, as in Aberdeen, it was regarded as the perquisite of the police. Just as there was need for a long period of education of the people to an appreciation of the virtues of removal of the dunghills, so, when the introduction of domestic sanitation became practicable, it was found that for a long time many of the citizens fought shy of the new water-carriage system.

The difficulty in securing and distributing an adequate water supply had long been a serious hindrance to improvement of the general sanitary state of the country. The water-supply history of some Scottish towns—and especially, perhaps, Dundee—makes extraordinary reading ; for many years the provision of an adequate supply had to take second place to an unbelievable amount of intrigue and jockeying for possession. Waiting at the wells was perhaps not wholly without its compensations, but it was time-consuming, and a narrow supply of water carried many ills in its train ; the water-caddies of Edinburgh were a picturesque race of people, " characters " many of them ; but a population that had to buy its water, even at a halfpenny per stoup, was apt to measure over-cautiously the amount of water it consumed. Inadequate supplies of water made drainage difficult, and there was no great enthusiasm for the construction of sewers and drains, even when they became practicable. The reason for the opposition was not unconnected with the commercial value of the material carried away by the sewers ; and another example of zeal to exploit the commercial value of manure was to be found in the irrigated meadows of Edinburgh, Dundee, and Crieff—and doubtless other places—which exposed the whole community to dreadful nuisance to enrich the few.

For a short period in the 1840s, following the passage of a Nuisance Removal and Contagious Diseases Prevention Act, the supervision of Scottish sanitation was in the hands of the English Board of Health, and when a Public Health (Scotland) Bill was laid before Parliament in 1848 there were complaints that the local administrative machinery to be set up was again to be placed under the control of the General Board of Health already in existence in London. The agitation created at that time helped to keep within bounds Whitehall domination of Scottish health services in later years.

5

In one important aspect of environment—housing—Scotland has always been fighting an uphill battle. So far as can be judged, Scottish housing has generally been in worse state than that south of the Border, alike in regard to structural defects and to over-crowding. In the old days of feuds and pillaging and burning, there may have been virtue in simple housing that could be replaced in a day or two ; it may even have been a necessity. But despite the outstanding excellence of the New Town of Edinburgh, Scottish housing in the nineteenth century, and especially the housing of the great cities, can only be described as terrible. As the gentility of another generation moved out to the fringe of the rapidly expanding cities, hordes of poor moved into the accommodation thus vacated, and these made-down houses became breeding places of crime and disease that earned the scathing criticism of social reformers. Medical men complained bitterly about the futility of nursing the sick and the hopelessness of practising midwifery in such a setting ; but the simple fact was that the whole business of living was by any decent standard quite impossible in such circumstances. Nor did the new houses hurriedly erected to hold the masses of incomers to the towns do anything to raise the standard ; poorly constructed, they were packed so close together and were at once so overcrowded as to be scarcely at all better than the decrepit mansions of other days. Much of this rush to the towns was associated with the development of manufactures and of railways ; and one service to public health performed unwittingly by the railway pioneers lay in opening up some paths for the iron way through parts of the cities that were urgently in need of ventilation. Housing was to be seen at its worst in the wynds and in the common lodging-houses, and these latter came to be so well recognized as foci for the spread of epidemic disease that the importance of some regulation of them was readily conceded ; but Russell, the great Glasgow sanitarian, said with truth that but for the risk in point of infection which these common lodging-houses represented to the better-off sections of the community, there would probably have been much less zeal for the improvement of conditions in them.

6

Some Scottish towns early recognized the need for attracting to them physicians of good repute, and in sufficient numbers to look after their citizens, and especially their poor. There are records of appointments of this kind in the sixteenth century in Aberdeen, Edinburgh, and Glasgow. These appointments were often precarious. Sometimes there was difficulty in securing suitable men, even in cities, and sometimes, when times were hard, the magistrates felt constrained to sacrifice their physicians on the altar of economy. This happened in Glasgow in 1684, when, though dispensing with a physician and a surgeon, the authorities retained in their employment a stone-cutter, whose job it was to treat stone in the bladder, a condition apparently then common. There was a curious provision to the effect that though medical men would no longer be retained, the magistrates could still refer an individual case to a physician if satisfied that the patient was unwell and " deserves to be cured," which seems to have placed an unenviable responsibility upon the bailies.

For a long time many parts of the country were badly off for medical care, though of amateur doctors there was no great scarcity, from the king downwards. Many Scottish parishes had their " bleeders " of repute, and farmers, and more particularly clergy, for long were wont to assume medical functions as well as their other duties. In the middle of the nineteenth century, following the passing of the Poor Law Amendment Act, there was difficulty in providing outlying parishes in some parts of the country with the parochial medical officer required by the new legislation, and representations were made to the authorities in Edinburgh urging them to take steps to improve conditions in Wester Ross and Inverness, where there were large tracts of country without any qualified medical man. Indeed, the problem of how best to provide an efficient medical service in the Highlands and Islands was one that continued well into the present century, and was not adequately met until the Highlands and Islands Medical Service, projected in 1912-13, was brought into operation soon after the end of the First World War.

In these days when new health services are under discussion, it is interesting to recall that there was considerable heart-burning in medical circles about conditions of service under the Act of 1845. In the discussions that arose, Dr. (later Sir) J. Y. Simpson played a leading part. It was apparently recognized that the remuneration of a parochial medical officer ought to have reference not only to the number of persons he might be called upon to attend, but also to the distances he had to travel. The professional negotiating committee of those days pointed out that, in fixing the doctor's remuneration, it should be remembered that his clerical work would be greatly increased under the new Act ; they suggested that it should not be permissible to appoint new medical officers by tender, and that payment should be by capitation fee—" the sum liable to alteration by the distance he has to go, but not by the number of his visits." The doctors of 1845 had for long been expected to give their professional skill free, or for nominal remuneration, in the care of the poor, and while they declared that they were anxious to help to carry into effect the new legislation, they thought that the calls made upon them in the past had been unjust, and that in future the medical care of the poor should be put on a more reasonable basis.

About this time it began to be appreciated that if there were to be any sustained effort to improve the health of the people, the establishment of permanent local Boards of Health, and the employment of medical officers, or " medical police," as they were sometimes called, were necessary. It was first suggested that one of the chief duties of the new Medical Officers of Health should be to ascertain the cause of death in every case, but it was soon recognized that the real value of such appointments lay rather in securing sanitary improvements. Some of the early advocates of a " medical police " envisaged a combined preventive and curative service, where the supervision of sanitary regulations and the medical care of the sick poor would be entrusted to the same doctor, in the reasonable belief that the one duty might be expected to aid the other. The first Scottish Medical Officer of Health was appointed in Edinburgh in 1862.

7

Though there had been hospitia or almshouses, largely concerned with the care of old people, long before the Reformation, and though from time to time, in seasons of great epidemic prevalence, accommodation of a kind, usually primitive, had been hastily erected for patients suffering from such diseases as leprosy and plague, it was not until the eighteenth century that the great voluntary hospital system had its beginnings. For long these new hospitals, confined to a few cities and sorely taxed with the many cases of fever clamouring for admission, could only hope to touch the fringe of the need for hospital care. It was not until the beginning of the nineteenth century that hospitals began to be established outside the cities, though a little earlier, in 1782, there had been a combined provision for mental and physical illness at Montrose, where an asylum was opened, together with an infirmary and dispensary for the sick poor. Several of these early Scottish hospitals had their origins in dispensaries for the outpatient care of the sick, the provision of " houses of recovery," as they were sometimes called, following a few years after the establishment of the dispensaries. Soon afterwards there began, in a small way, the provision of hospital accommodation for certain specialized types of case, such as eye, venereal, and children's diseases.

As long ago as 1681, Lord Fountainhall wrote about the lack of any provision in Scotland for the care of lunatics. It was a century later before the first asylum in Scotland was established at Montrose, chiefly because the " compassionate inhabitants " of the town were greatly grieved at conditions in the Tolbooth, in which lunatics were usually confined. Soon afterwards other asylums were founded in Aberdeen, Edinburgh, Glasgow, Dundee, Perth, and Dumfries. These voluntary hospitals for the care of mental disease set a standard which was, in general, high, and a very great improvement on anything that had been available previously. From the beginning they seem to have appreciated the value of occupational therapy and of recreational facilities, and the reports of the early superintendents contain much of interest in relation to the treatment of mental disease. Yet there still remained a great deal that was unsatisfactory in the care of the insane. Accommodation for their reception was badly lacking in some parts of the country. There were cells for lunatics in Inverness Infirmary, used chiefly for the detention of patients until they could be sent to asylums in the south, but much more resembling dungeons than accommodation for the care of sick people. Conditions in that part of Perth prison occupied by criminal lunatics also left much to be desired ; there patients were commonly kept under severe restraint, and of treatment as such there was little or none.

The Report of the Royal Commission on Lunacy described arrangements for the care of the insane as they existed in Scotland in 1855. The houses into which lunatics were received fell into two groups : houses into which they were received under cognizance of the Sheriff, and those into which they were received without such cognizance. There were in Scotland at that time twenty-four private institutions licensed for the reception of the insane, fifteen of them in the Musselburgh area. Conditions in these houses were often unsatisfactory, and the Royal Commission complained that licences had been granted to persons who had no knowledge whatever of insanity and had no experience of nursing. The houses varied greatly in size and contained anything up to ninety patients. Nearly all were overcrowded. The Commissioners decided that there was need for complete revision of all the arrangements for the care of the insane in Scotland, and from their recommendations, made in 1857, there emerged a few years later the District Asylums, and the introduction of measures designed to exercise a more effective check over the whole treatment of the insane.

8

These were some of the problems confronting early Scottish pioneers in social medicine. Progress was slow and delays often vexatious, due partly to the absence of administrative machinery and partly to the unreadiness of the people for progress. The rapid industrial developments of the first half of the nineteenth century exaggerated nearly all the great social problems and compelled an attempt at their solution. Many of the historians of those times viewed with dismay the effects of industrial development on the health and welfare of the people. Sinclair, writing in 1825 his Summary Volume on the Statistical Account, saw obvious objections to the effects of manufactures on health ; generally they involved " too early to work," in addition to which, " eager application, scanty food, and want of proper exercise enfeebles the constitution, produces nervous disorders, and brings on various infirmities which render their lives uncomfortable and hurry them on to premature old age." James Cameron, surgeon in Tain, writing of conditions there in 1840, said that the period of daily labour extended from five o'clock in the morning to six o'clock at night, and that among adults amusements or games of every kind had almost disappeared. " Doubtless they have of late greatly improved as to enterprise and habits of steady industry ; but while they have lost much of that laziness and waywardness imputed to the unmodified highlander, I fear they have lost also much of his free and serenely joyous spirit." Lord Cockburn, in his celebrated letter to the Lord Provost of Edinburgh on the best ways of spoiling the city, wrote in 1849 that mercifully Edinburgh had almost no manufactures, with their legacy of tall brick chimneys, black smoke, a population precariously fed, pauperism, disease, and crime, all in excess.

But forces were stirring, and things were already on the move. There is much of interest in the early struggles, and something of value, for history has a habit of repeating itself.

Chapter II

FOOD

I

Hector Boece (*c.* 1468–1536)—not, perhaps, the most reliable of authorities—was one who believed that things were not what they had been. Strength, vigour, and sovereign virtue had failed among the people as they declined from the temperance of their elders, whose food was prepared with little labour or cost, and whose bread was made of " sic stuff as grew most easily." Their victuals were not sifted into coarse and fine to make them delicious to the mouth, but were all ground together into one form. Their common meat was fish. They breakfasted early in the morning with a small meal, and went on from then till supper-time, never being too overfilled to prevent them from going about their business. At supper they ate more ; howbeit " they had but ane course." The common drink was ale. In their frequent forays they used an iron ration in " ane gret vessel wrocht full of butter, cheis, mele, milk and vinegre temperit togidder." They used strong measures to enforce temperance in those days. " All dronkattis, glutonis, and consumers of vitallis mair than was necessar to the sustentation of man were tane, and first commandit to swilly their fouth of quhat drink they plesit, and incontinent thairafter was drownit in ane fresch rever." Even earlier, Isidore had written that the Scots were a nation of sparing diet, sustaining hunger very long, and rarely indulging in food before sunset, contenting themselves moreover with meat and food prepared from milk ; and there had certainly been legislative efforts to control drinking, for in 1436 the King and Three Estates ordained " that no man in burghs be found in taverns at wine, ale or beer after the stroke of nine o'clock, or be put in prison or fined a shilling."

But now, in 1527, according to Boece, all was changed. Where our elders had sobriety we have " dronkennis " ; where they had plenty with sufficiency we have " immoderat curses with superfluite " ; that man is held most noble and honest who can " devare and swelly maist." We seek for delicacies, provoking our stomach to receive more than it can digest, filling ourselves, day and night, so full of meat and drink that we are unable to follow any virtuous occupation ; not content to have more extravagant dinners and suppers than our elders, we must even satisfy " our schamefull and immoderit voracite with duble dennaries and sowparis," with the result that many of us are fit for no other business than to " fil and teme oure wembe."

Not all visitors to Scotland in those days found the same opulent gluttony. Perlin (1551–52), after observing that the country was plentiful in provisions, " which are as cheap as in any part of the world," wrote that the poor people put their dough between two irons to make it into bread and then made it what was esteemed good food in that country, and tolerably cheap. Ray, a hundred years later, was frank in his criticism : the Scots had neither bread, cheese, nor drink of good quality. " They cannot make them, nor will they learn. Their butter is very indifferent, and one would wonder how they could contrive to make it so bad."

2

A measure of official control of food supplies and food policy was at hand, and that of a kind that would have gladdened the heart of the melancholy Boece. Stimulated by one of the periodic dearths, the Privy Council in 1550 appointed a Commission " to make prices of all manner of victuals and stuff, as well men's as horses' meat, and to decide what order should be made to cause the country bring in the same for the furnishing of our Sovereign Lady's lieges." The Commission took the view that the country should tighten its belt, and proceeded to draw up a schedule of rationing which, however, was based on class distinction rather than on physiological need. No archbishop, bishop or earl was to allow himself more than eight dishes at his mess ; no lord, abbot, prior or dean more than six ; no baron or freeholder more than four ; no burgess or other " substantious man," spiritual or temporal, more than three ; and there was not to be more than one kind of meat at each course. For breach of these regulations fines and moral punishments were prescribed, so that perhaps there had been substance in the complaint of Boece ; but exemption was made in favour of certain high days and holidays, weddings, and banquets given officially to strangers from other realms. The Privy Council inserted in the same Act a clause regulating the price of game : wild goose " of the greet kind," 2s. each ; woodcock, 4d. ; rabbits, 12d. (Scots) ; and of poultry, hens being valued at 8d. and chickens at 4d. (Scots) each. The scarcity of provisions was greatest in Edinburgh, and the Provost was instructed to deal summarily with those unscrupulous and grasping individuals who bought up the commodities " necessary for the sustentation of mankind " for the purpose of retailing them at largely increased prices.

In 1551 a measure was passed to prevent the export over the Border of fish, flesh, cattle, sheep, cheese, butter or other provisions, and the grazing of foreign cattle on Scottish pasture; and in the following year it was reported that the price of all manner of corn victuals had come down to reasonable levels, but that meat was still too dear. In pursuance of this policy of economy, the Kirk Session of Glasgow decreed that there should be " no superfluous gatherings as banquets or marriages, that the price of the dinner should not exceed eighteen pence (Scots), and that persons married shall find caution to that effect."

The year 1562 saw the introduction of the " political Lent," certainly not the last occasion on which an attempt was made to clothe administrative expediency in the respectable garb of science or religion ; the law ordained that none of the lieges, of whatever state or condition, save such as " are visited with extreme weakness," should eat any kind of flesh meat from 12 February to 29 March, the preamble explaining that " in the Spring of the Year called Lentryne all kinds of flesh debilitate, decay and grow out of season, so that in that tyme they are no wise commodious to be eaten." The enforcement of this Act proving difficult, during the following sixty years many changes had to be made, that of 1610 setting out that God in His wisdom having appointed fish as well as flesh for the nourishment and sustentation of man, and there being a great number of the lieges who followed the trade of fishing, it became all modest and good subjects with thankful hearts to embrace God's good benefit, and to use the same for the weal and advantage of the country.

3

In 1602 the Government was called on to settle a dispute that centred on the food provided for the masters and students in the University of Glasgow. The Magistrates of the City and the

Masters of the College being at variance, the King appointed a Commission to inquire into the sufficiency of the masters for their functions, " as well in life as in letters." Barbé says there seems to have been a suspicion that the masters, as they were called in those simple days, looked more after their creature comforts than was consistent with their duty or their position. The findings of the Commission set forth the allowance appropriate to the Common Table of the College. According to the prescribed allowance, the five masters were to have for breakfast one white loaf of 1 lb. weight in a " sowpe," with the remains of a piece of beef or mutton left over from the day before, and a glass of ale each. Their dinner was to consist of a sufficiency of white bread, with five chopins of good ale—better than " the common sell ale in the town." In addition there was to be a dish of broth, and, presumably as an alternative, another of kail or skink (" a strong soup of cows' bones "). Further, " a piece of sodden (boiled) mutton, another of beef, salt or fresh according to season, a roast of veal or mutton, with a fowl or rabbit, or a pair of pigeons or chickens or suchlike second roast, as the season allowed of." Even if some of these viands were meant to be alternatives, the professors could not complain of being underfed in this early rationing period, for they sat down to a similar meal in the evening. It is true that there were meatless days, and on these breakfast was limited to a dish of eggs, " with bread and drink sufficient," while for dinner and for supper the fare consisted of kale, a dish of eggs and three dishes of " weill grathit fish or other equivalent."

The lower table was for bursars. On ordinary days their dietary was to include, for breakfast, " tea and coffee and one oat loaf in a sop," and it was laid down that the loaves should be of such weight that eight score of them could be made out of a boll of meal, so that each of these university loaves must have weighed fourteen ounces. At each of the other two daily meals the fare officially prescribed consisted of two oat loaves among four, one dish of pease or broth, one piece of beef and one quart of ale. For dinner and supper on meatless days the students were to have with their bread and drink, three dishes—one of kale, one of eggs and another of fish. A distinctive luxury of the masters' table was the white or wheaten bread instead of the oat loaf with which the students had to be content : porridge was wholly absent from the official allowance.

4

According to Brown (1795) consumption of herring was very great in the sixteenth and seventeenth centuries among " the middling and common ranks." " At that period they were the principal food of the reapers at harvest, and the sole sustenance, for five days in the week, with oaten cake, of the numerous class of seamen employed in the fishery. Seven large herring per man, to a meal, was the allowance. The times are changed, and the descendants of these hardy fishermen must have the same victualling as if on a voyage to the coast of America."

5

There are many reports of years of dearth in Scotland before 1600. In the ninth and eleventh centuries particularly, famines were very numerous, and such was the difficulty attending the rapid transport and exchange of goods, that the failure of crops in a district meant starvation for many of the inhabitants ; often the only method of escape open to the poor farmer was to sell himself and his family for bread. When the English king went to Scotland in 1322, about the feast of St. Peter (29 June), " though he met not with resistance, he lost many of his men by famine and disease."

During the seventeenth and eighteenth centuries lean years kept recurring with monotonous regularity, culminating from time to time in periods of acute starvation. In 1622 a Fast was proclaimed in Aberdeen for " the present plague of dearth and famine and the continuance thereof threatened by tempests, inundations, and weets likely to rot the fruit on the ground," and in an entry of the Chronicle of Perth, about the same time, was written : " In this yeir about the harvest and efter, thair wes suche ane universall seikness in all the countrie as ellyke hes not bene hard of." There was another such period towards the end of the reign of King William, the seven lean years at the end of the seventeenth century, reaching a climax in the dreadful famine of 1698–99. It does not appear that any public measures were adopted for the welfare of the poor at this time, nor were any uncommon exertions made by the Kirk Sessions, then responsible for poor relief, until the crisis was nearly over. In one district so many families perished from want that for six miles formerly well inhabited there was not within the year an inhabited house remaining. Women were found dead upon the public roads, and babes in the agonies of death suckling at their dead mothers' breasts. In the parish of Duthel many, feeling the near approach of death, crawled to the churchyard so that their bodies might not long be left exposed. Many were buried where they died, as the few surviving relations had neither strength nor means of carrying them to the common burying-place. In some parishes the inhabitants were diminished by death to one half or less of the former number. Many had to subsist on herbs and on the seed of the wild mustard which they ground into meal. Others frequented the churchyard to pull a mess of nettles, and often had to struggle with rivals for the prize : nettles, being the earliest spring greens, were greedily used as food, commonly boiled, without either meat or salt. There was much excessive drinking at this time, and, according to Sibbald, potations of ale or spirits on an empty stomach, especially in the morning, relaxed the fibres and induced " eratic fevers of a bad type, bastard pleurisies . . . dropsies, stupors, lethargies and apoplexies." In one parish (Torryburn) great numbers of fish were thrown up on the coast. Of these the people ate immoderately from want of other food " and became thereby the prey of dysenteries and other putrid disorders." There are repeated references in Scottish social history to outbreaks of disease following excessive consumpt of fish.

Andrew Fletcher of Saltoun writes that in 1698 there were, besides a great many poor families very meanly provided for by the Church boxes, with others who, living upon bad food, fell into various diseases, 200,000 people from a total population not exceeding one million, begging from door-to-door, the number being " perhaps double to what it was formerly, by reason of the present great distress."

The famine of 1740–41 was not so severe, but again many died of starvation, and it was not unusual to find dead bodies on highways and in the fields, " while others from long fasting expired as soon as they tasted food." Scarcity was so great that many offered in vain to serve for bread, and it is reported that in the parish of Monquhitter a number of stout men were glad to accept twopence each per day in full for their work. At this time lack of employment was the great cause of distress, and by way of relief Kirk Sessions allowed eight pounds of meal per week only to young persons and those unable to work.

There was another great famine in 1782–88, when on account of severe weather the crops failed. The municipalities of Glasgow and Edinburgh imported grain for the public benefit. A government committee was appointed to inquire into the state of Highland districts and the prospect of supplying them with grain, and on 6 June 1783 the House of Commons resolved to present an address

beseeching his Majesty to be graciously pleased to give such directions as may tend most effectually to avert the evils that are to be apprehended from the calamitous state of the northern parts of Scotland and assuring his Majesty that this house would make good such expenses as shall be incurred by his Majesty in relieving the misery to which his Majesty's unhappy subjects may be reduced by so deplorable a calamity. (*Comm. Journals*, vol. xxxiv, p. 459)

The sum provided amounted to £15,259, and was used to purchase meal and grain which was distributed in the counties of Argyll, Dunbarton, Perth, Forfar, and all the counties north of these, the largest amounts going to the counties of Inverness, Aberdeen, and Perth, where the need was greatest.

6

In houses of the well-to-do county squires in the eighteenth century, breakfast was served at eight o'clock, and consisted of " skink " or water gruel, supplemented by collops or mutton washed down with ale. The bread consisted of oatmeal cakes or barley bannocks. Dinner was at twelve or one o'clock. The fare was monotonous, " ill-served and worse cooked," and consisted incessantly of broth or kail, or of beef or mutton. Fresh meat could be had in summer and autumn only, and from November to May salted meat alone was available, though game occasionally varied the menu, and strong ale was in ample supply. At seven or eight o'clock came supper, " a substantial meal of the dinner type with ale and claret."

By the middle of the eighteenth century in the southern part of the country even the ploughmen usually had meat twice a week, but, according to Graham, " Milk had to be sparingly used, for the yield from the ill-conditioned cows was low, about two Scots pints (approximately $6\frac{2}{5}$ imperial pints) a day." Up to this time milk and butter were little used by the rich : they were essentially the food of the poor, and often of bad quality. Smollett, quick to appreciate the lack of sanitation in his time, wrote : " But the milk itself should not pass unanalysed, the produce of faded cabbage-leaves and sour draff, lowered with hot water, frothed with bruised snails ; carried through the streets in open pails, exposed to foul rinsings, discharges from doors and windows, spittle, snot, and tobacco quids from foot passengers ; overflowings from mud carts, spatterings from coach wheels, dirt and trash chucked into it by roguish boys for the joke's sake ; the spewings of infants, who have slobbered in the tin measure, which is thrown back in that condition among the milk, for the benefit of the next customer ; and, finally, the vermin that drops from the rags of the nasty drab that vends this precious mixture, under the respectable denomination of milkmaid."

In the second half of the eighteenth century city-dwellers of many classes, " solid traders and spendthrift youths, judges and clerks, men of law, men of letters and men of leisure," met of an evening in clubs bearing many strange names in many strange taverns to eat their favourite dishes—minced collops, rezared haddocks or tripe, a fluke or roasted skate and onions, for which the sum of sixpence was commonly charged. Sir Walter Scott describes such a roystering in *Guy Mannering*, when Pleydell, the man of business, met his Edinburgh cronies ; in Glasgow there were the same cheerful evening gatherings, and the same concentration on the delicacies of the day—" hen broth, black beans, a haggis, a crab pie, with ample punch." Among the fashionable clubs at the end of the century was the Medical Club, which met in a tavern in Princes Street, kept by one Mrs. Pollock. Entry was very strict, all the members being determined that no cantankerous person should gain entrance. On one occasion, when a well-known practitioner of uncertain temper made application for membership, his proposer, doubtful whether his nominee would be an asset to the harmony of the club, intended to drop in the one black ball that was required to keep him out, and was embarrassed when the counting showed a universal black-balling.

Though diet in the Highlands, so far as can be judged, was always rather lacking in variety in those days, Dr. Samuel Johnson in his *Journey to the Western Islands of Scotland* (1774) wrote that " If an epicure could remove by wish in quest of sensual gratification, wherever he had supped he would breakfast in Scotland " ; and in 1782 Francis Douglas, speaking of the diet of small farmers in the north-east, remarked that though flesh was rarely seen in their houses except at Christmas or Fasten Ev'n they were strong and active, slept soundly, and lived to a good old age.

During the eighteenth century periods of dearth compelled the magistrates of Scottish towns to buy meal in bulk for the relief of distress among the citizens. In Glasgow in 1740, the year of the great frost, owing to the backwardness of the seasons the price of meal rose to sixteen pence the peck, and the Town Council approached the Merchants' House, the Trades House, and the General Sessions of the kirk with the proposal that together they should purchase up to ten thousand bolls of meal and sell it to the poor at cost price. A similar relief procedure was adopted in 1765 following a bad harvest in that year, and again in 1782, when the Town Council opened a guarantee fund, to which it contributed £500, and appointed a committee to import grain, meal, and other provisions and distribute these to the citizens.

The closing years of the eighteenth century were hard, as had been the case a hundred years earlier, and Johnston reports that thousands died of starvation, while many suffered from ague, asthma, consumption, and rheumatism, or " pains " as the condition was commonly called. Many communities took action to relieve the want of the poor. In Edinburgh about one-eighth of the population were fed by charity. A public proclamation specified the exact quantity of bread which each family ought to consume—according to Cockburn a loaf for each individual weekly. This dearth saw the first introduction of public kitchens and " cooking committees " in the city. The Town Records of Dingwall contain an entry, under date 8 March 1800, that Bailie Munro reported that he had lately had a conversation with Lord Seaforth upon the present alarming scarcity and high prices of meal and victual, and that his lordship had suggested the propriety of the magistrates opening a subscription for the purpose of raising a fund to enable them to provide meal and to sell the same to the necessitous poor within the burgh at a reduced price. The meeting, having considered Mr. Munro's representations, authorized him " to purchase for them a quantity of meal not exceeding two hundred bolls at 30s. sterling, if it cannot be had cheaper, and in the event ready money could not otherwise be had to pay for it, they directed Mr. Munro to borrow money from the bank upon the credit of the burgh for that purpose " ; and a subscription paper was opened at the same time to enable the magistrates to sell the meal to the poor at a reduced price.

From Sinclair's Statistical Account it is possible to obtain a fair idea of the food of the people at the end of the eighteenth century. Diet " in some districts " was not very wholesome. In summer the people lived mainly on fish and milk, a mixture that, it was supposed, contaminated the blood and occasioned putrid fevers. There is a curious story told of Inveraray, where " there was a remarkable herring fishing in 1791, in consequence of which many of the people fed entirely on fish. The consequence was that they were visited by a fever, and their blood was so much vitiated that, when they let blood, it had the appearance when congealed of a nauseous kind of jelly. Their breath smelled strongly of fish. In proportion as they had fed on it, voraciously or temperately, the fever was more or less severe. Such as lived mostly on herring, or other strong food, suffered dreadful agony. Those who lived chiefly upon water-gruel, suffered very little."

Of the Glasgow cotton-weavers it is said that they and their families were accustomed to make potatoes the bulkiest part of their food : many of them could get little else. Potatoes had become a field crop in the south of Scotland about 1735, though not introduced into the Hebrides until thrust upon the unwilling islanders of South Uist by the Chief Clanranald in 1743. Oatmeal porridge or pease-brose with buttermilk or " swatts " (weak small beer) once formed the breakfast and supper of the weavers, but many now substituted potatoes, which were cheaper. Herring, cod, or ling, sometimes flesh and broth, with potatoes or oatcakes used to be their dinner, but many were now at a loss to get even potatoes and salt. As a result, the consumption of oatmeal decreased, and " few now get the luxury of wheaten bread, but many still take a tea or coffee breakfast, with bread and butter. When dinner-time comes, tea or coffee again, with white or red herrings or other animal food if they can get it : to supper potatoes with salt, or porridge, or sowens and buttermilk." But tea and sugar were dear. A good plateful of porridge for a working man with salt, buttermilk, butter or treacle might cost in all 1½d., but a coffee meal cost 3d.

Those with whose constitutions porridge did not agree, and whose purses could not afford tea or even coffee, used a substitute for the latter sold in Glasgow at 7d. per pound under the name of " Radical Coffee " (so-called because favoured by some of the disaffected), and consisting of horse beans, rye or wheat, partially carbonized and ground down. Only some of the houses had fuel, and in cold weather neighbours flocked to these to get their food boiled.

Salt duties were first exacted in England in 1702. At the time of the Union it was conceded that Scotland should remain free from the duty for a period of seven years, and that when it was imposed, in 1714, it should be at a modified rate. Even so, the tax amounted to many times the value of the salt, and was a burden to people of slender resources. As Langdon Brown wrote : " A salt tax is a tax on health, levied on these who can least well afford it, and deserves as much censure as the old iniquitous Window Tax, another example of the perverted ingenuity of the Inland Revenue." The Salt Duty was finally remitted in 1825.

7

Scurvy and scrofula were common, and the increasing prevalence of scrofula was loudly lamented. The disease was reported to be especially prevalent in districts where the climate was cold and damp, and where the living of the inhabitants was poor and principally vegetable in nature. It was attributed in part to the great quantities of farinaceous food consumed by the labouring classes as porridge, as " hasty pudding," and boiled potatoes, with milk, but rarely any other mixture of animal diet. Following the Napoleonic War unemployment and distress were prevalent, and Hamilton, writing in 1822 about conditions in the west of Scotland, said that many thousands of poor people had for years past been confined to short allowance ; " and, in many cases, they have been obliged to satisfy nature with less than half the quantity of their former consumpt." Sinclair wrote in his *Analysis of the Statistical Account* : " It has been ascertained by actual weight and measurement that a ploughman consumes at breakfast 2½ lb. avoirdupois of porridge containing 10 oz. of oatmeal, 30 oz. of water, and 1 lb. of milk. Flatulence and indigestion often arise, which gradually debilitate the system, occasion swellings in children and scrofulous complaints in adults. Labourers are often deprived by scrofula of the power of earning their subsistence. . . . For the poor, who have strong stomachs, biscuits are much more wholesome than fermented bread, they are not so easily dissolved in the stomach and more nourishment is extracted from them."

But while they might have become more prevalent, scrofula

and scurvy were no new diseases in Scotland. In 1640, during the Civil War, Edinburgh Castle was besieged from 1 April to 18 September. Of the original garrison of three hundred men, one hundred and sixty died from scurvy, while the casualties by fighting numbered only twelve. Hunger reduced the defenders to extremities and compelled them to surrender. There was no bitterness : " The last scene took place on the 18 September, when the leaders of both sides met in the banqueting hall of the Castle, where, with excellent good spirit and complete cordiality, the struggle was finished in the partaking of an elaborate banquet."

8

Sinclair thought that the principal changes that had occurred in the mode of living of the people at the end of the eighteenth century arose from the use of potatoes and tea, and from the greater abundance of spirituous liquors. The better sort of potatoes, he wrote, properly prepared, could be used with perfect safety, and where the inhabitants lived much on salted provisions the use of potatoes was of great service in preventing scorbutic complaints ; but potatoes were often inferior and unwholesome, and might occasion disease, especially in late spring or early summer, " when they have no milk, meat, onions, or salt to eat with them." When potatoes were consumed in great quantities, pepper should be taken with them.

Tea, in moderation and of a good quality, might be taken without injury ; but the poor used a very coarse type of black tea, drank it very strong and often without milk or sugar and frequently " so hot that it produced the most fatal results on the nervous system." " The poor stint themselves in many essential necessaries of life, in order to procure this article of luxury. They are therefore less vigorous and healthy and their children not so stout as they were before the introduction of tea when they lived upon porridge."

But in no respect was the alteration in diet to be regarded as more injurious than in substituting ardent spirits for ale, in regard to both health and morals. Many became tipplers, neglected their business and were ruined, consumptions, stomach complaints, bilious and dropsical complaints, insanity and a multiplicity of nervous disorders were more frequent than formerly.

There was no lack of corroborative evidence of the ill-effects of tea and ardent spirits. Twenty or thirty years after Sinclair wrote, Inspectors of Poor were still attributing the decadence of the Scottish people and the increasing amount of pauperism among them to the baneful habit of tea-drinking. This custom of tea-drinking had to meet opposition from many quarters— from the patriotic, the old-fashioned, and the robust; from magistrates, ministers, and doctors. While commended in lethargic diseases, headaches, gout, and gravel, it was regarded—not altogether unjustly—as liable to cause "trembling and shakings of the head and hands, loss of appetite, vapours, and other nervous diseases." As for spirits, there is general agreement that their excessive consumption contributed largely to the squalor and poverty of the nineteenth century, and was in turn aggravated by these factors. It was estimated in 1840 that the amount of spirits consumed in Scotland was equal to twenty-three pints per head of the population per annum, as compared with seven pints in England and thirteen in Ireland ; and it was stated that when the drunkards of Glasgow became too poor to satisfy their appetite for spirits, they resorted in great measure to laudanum, which, in an adulterated state, was consumed in considerable quantities and regularly sold by many of the chemists. Symon wrote in 1840 that Glasgow was unhealthy because of the bad mode of building and the bad habits of the people—they drank a good deal, and that reduced them to a scanty diet so far as meat was concerned. They lived principally on potatoes, sometimes stewed up with a little bit of meat or fowl, the proportion of meat varying in accordance with the means.

9

Many descriptions of the food of the people about 1840 are to be found in evidence submitted by doctors in connection with a government inquiry that year into the sanitary conditions of the labouring classes in Scotland.

James Cameron, surgeon in the town, reporting on the condition of the people of Tain, wrote that the common food of the inhabitants was chiefly vegetable, consisting of potatoes, oatmeal porridge, cakes, and brose. The labouring classes seldom tasted flesh or fowl except on particular occasions, such as weddings, christenings, and funeral dinners, and on New Year's Day, which was their only holiday. They were able occasionally to buy fish, which was both plentiful and cheap, salt herrings and dried fish in winter and cod and haddock during the summer season. The poorest class were obliged in seasons of scarcity to draw their substance from shell-fish such as crabs (partans), limpets, periwinkles, cockles, mussels, and from seaweed. Some of these indeed appeared at the tables of the rich, and were considered delicacies. The potato was unquestionably the chief article of diet. The people were almost wholly engaged in its cultivation during the months of April and May, " and there is probably no part of the United Kingdom that produces potatoes more grateful to the taste, or of a more nutritious quality." Tea and coffee were the principal luxuries, though they had now become so common as hardly to deserve that name. Among the men the habit of snuff-taking was almost universal, and of those who did not take snuff, the greater part smoked, the tobacco pipe having come more generally into use since the visitation of cholera in 1832.

Speaking of food in St. Andrews, John Adamson, a surgeon there, said that the breakfast food was porridge, with milk or small beer ; sometimes, but not often, tea, etc. The dinner was broth made with pork and vegetables, or coarse pieces of beef, fried pork with potatoes, often salt herrings or fresh fish, which were abundant and cheap. The people were usually well supplied with vegetables from their gardens, such as green kale, cabbages, carrots and onions. The bread in common use was made with a mixture of pease and oatmeal (bannock), or of oatmeal alone (cake) ; either this or common wheaten bread was eaten with tea in the evening, and for supper, potatoes or porridge. This was the best style of living of the labouring men. Many of them, with wages 6s. to 12s., were not able to live in this way ; they had the same breakfast and evening meal, but their dinner was inferior, consisting of potatoes, with herrings or melted hog's lard, pork broth and sometimes pork. The almost invariable possession of potatoes arose in part from a common practice among the farmers of allowing their reapers a small portion of ground for the planting of potatoes, in lieu of part of their harvest wages. The poor occasionally complained of stomach complaints, which they attributed to their poor fare, and some complained of not having enough.

The food of the colliers was worse. The doctor at Inveresk

wrote that the miners there subsisted principally on potatoes and herrings, and on what were called " sowens " (water poured on oatmeal and allowed to stand till sour, the thick part being then washed, boiled, and eaten or supped with milk), occasionally supplemented by milk from the charitable. The doctor was satisfied that insufficient food was the cause of much disease.

This general reliance on potatoes as the primary source of food had catastrophic consequences when the crop failed in 1846 : there were bread riots in Glasgow in 1848. Potatoes had furnished some two-sevenths of the total food consumed by the populace, and a small patch of land which grew enough potatoes to feed a family would, if sown with oats, yield barely sufficient substance for three months of the year. With the failure of the potato crop, meal came to be the staple food of the poor. Sometimes it was taken as gruel, and sometimes made into cakes, very often washed down with tea. It was common enough to find two adults living for a week on a peck of meal (9 lb.), a few potatoes and tea ; it is recorded of a typical family comprising a labourer, his wife and four children of ages ranging from five to ten years, that they were accustomed to live for six weeks on a boll of meal and a boll of potatoes, $i.e.$ $3\frac{1}{2}$ lb. of meal and $10\frac{1}{2}$ lb. of potatoes per week for each individual.

10

Allowances to the poor were paid in money or in kind, almost invariably meal or Indian corn. With rising prices, more and more parishes came to pay their allowances in meal, and a common basis of allowance seems to have been 1 lb. of meal per day per individual, sometimes " a degree less " to adult females. Sometimes the allowances were paid weekly, sometimes monthly, and sometimes at still longer intervals. In some parts of the country there was great difficulty in ensuring a regular and sufficient supply of meal. In Barra there was very seldom enough meal at the mill, or indeed any at all, as in winter the water might be frozen, and in summer there might not be a sufficient quantity to put the machinery in motion ; even if going constantly one mill could not supply the necessary quantity of multure to provide the paupers with their allowances. In some parishes the actual distribution of the meal caused difficulties even when supplies were available. The usual practice was to expect the paupers or their representative to collect the meal at some central point, often ten or even twenty miles distant from their homes. So much was this hardship felt that some of the paupers requested that allowances might be paid at longer intervals in view of the time and labour expended in their collection. The remedy for this evil introduced by some parochial boards was to install large boxes or " girnels " in each part of the parish, where a store of meal was kept, and the inspector called to make distribution at stated intervals.

Observers in various parts of the Highlands reported that they saw the effects of want in the appearance of the people, and many of the poor complained that from insufficient nourishment they were unable to do a day's work ; but Dr. Rae, the Inspector of Poor in the parish of Kilbrandon, said that he had never seen anything in that parish to compare with the misery and destitution that he had witnessed in the course of his professional career in Edinburgh. He thought that none of the people had the appearance of starvation in their countenances, though scrofula and land scurvy were prevalent among them. The parish minister of Kintail reported that not only the poor but the smaller class of tenantry were very much pinched, though he did not think that any were yet bordering on starvation. In the village of Dornie, in that parish, a soup kitchen was opened at which all the paupers were supplied, each being allowed one pint of soup per day. There were similar soup kitchens at Portree, to which everyone on the Poor Roll had access on three days of the week, receiving a chopin, or imperial quart, of soup each ; at Oban, where the soup kitchen was run by an association of ladies who provided soup at a price of 1d. per quart, with a floured scone ; at Tarbert, where the soup kitchen was open three times a week and the poor were given a quart of soup each with a roll ; and doubtless at many other places. This scarcity of food was not confined to Highland parishes. In Dumfries, for instance, the articles of food on which the poor so much depended were dear and of an inferior quality, and Dr. McLellan reported that he had seen many diseases in children induced by scarcity and improper food. A soup kitchen had been established in the town for some years, and continued open for two or three months in winter and spring, according to the inclemency of the weather and want of work.

In their Report, published in 1857, the Lunacy Commissioners described the diet of the poor in Scotland. They believed that there was no doubt that poverty and underfeeding were powerful agents in the production of some varieties of lunacy, especially in the Highlands.

"The diet of the poor in Scotland varies considerably in different districts. In the Highlands it principally consists of oatmeal and potatoes, with the occasional addition of fish ; but on the west coast, and in the Western Islands, the supplies even of this food are scanty, and the people are often bordering on starvation. On the whole, the Highland population must be considered as poorly fed. In the rural districts of the Lowlands also, oatmeal and potatoes constitute the chief part of the diet of the peasantry, with the addition of milk and garden vegetables. Bread is occasionally used, but butcher meat very seldom forms part of the living. The cottars generally, in both the Highlands and the Lowlands, have small patches of potato or garden ground.

"In the manufacturing villages and country towns, bread and tea have, to some extent, especially with the women, taken the place of porridge ; but with the men and children, porridge and buttermilk still constitute the general morning and evening meal. Broth and potatoes, with fish when it is plentiful, or perhaps bread, form the usual dinner of the manufacturing classes in such localities. In the large towns, such as Glasgow, the consumption of butcher meat has latterly greatly increased, and the high wages of the mechanics are frequently entirely expended on their living."

II

In the 1860s Robert Hutchison of Carlowrie, Kirkliston, investigated the dietaries of Scottish agricultural labourers and prepared a report on the subject for the Highland and Agricultural Society. He concluded that as a class the Scottish agricultural labourer and his family were plainly but well fed, that in all the districts of Scotland the average dietary was considerably above the amount necessary for the bare sustenance of life and vigour, and that the nutritive value of the average rural dietary in Scotland was very high, considerably exceeding that of the dietaries of England and Ireland usually adopted by similar classes of the population. But he went on to make certain suggestions for the improvement of the dietary of the Scottish agricultural labourer and his family : that a more general use should be made of pease-meal, and where no butcher meat was available a larger quantity of cheese should be consumed ; that to each rural labourer's family a Scotch pint of sweet milk (3⅛ imperial pints) should be allowed daily, and that to improve the cooking of the peasants' diet coals should be supplied as part of wages and each cottage provided by the landlord equipped with a " fixed-in " grate for cooking, with a boiler attached.

These observations of Hutchison—adopting a line of investigation that has gained popularity in recent days—were based on a survey of the dietaries of fifty-six peasant families from many parts of Scotland, and the author commented upon the difficulty encountered in the collection of these returns, " for the lower classes, especially in country districts, are generally averse to divulge the secrets of their domestic arrangements and mode of living—regarding the process of weighing and measuring their food with superstitious awe and fear." His survey led Hutchison to conclude that farm-cottagers should not be allowed to keep lodgers, as they interfered with the living space so necessary for the continued health and vigour of the cottager : " If crowding and airlessness be permitted, filth and disease are engendered ; and if this state of matters exists along with insufficient food, the low dietary then becomes the certain aggravator of a predisposition to disease."

Information is available about the standard of feeding in various institutions for the poor. One such was the Town's Hospital of Glasgow, opened in 1733 to care for the destitute in that city. Its dietary (reproduced) certainly lacked variety: it observed the traditional reliance on meal, and contained only a very small amount of animal food. In 1766, on being asked for a donation to extend the hospital, the Faculty of Physicians and Surgeons thought fit to attach certain conditions, which were accepted by the Directors ; one of these was that the diet be entirely in the hands of the medical ; attendant but to prevent any alarm on the score of possible extravagance, it was explained that " a proper diet would in most cases turn out cheaper than the common allowance of the hospital." On 15 November 1734 the hospital contained one hundred and forty inmates, who were maintained at the daily expense of one penny and seven-twelfths of a penny sterling each.

The rapid multiplication of poorhouses following the passing

FOOD

DIETARY OF THE TOWN'S HOSPITAL, GLASGOW, 1733

THE DIET FOR ALL PERSONS UNDER FIFTEEN YEARS OF AGE

	Breakfast	Dinner	Supper
SUNDAY	Pease-meal Pottage with Milk or Butter	Bread and Butter	Broth with Bread and Cheese or Butter
MONDAY	Oat-meal Pottage with Milk or Ale	Bread and Broth without Flesh	Oat-meal Pottage with Ale or Milk
TUESDAY	Ditto	Ditto	Ditto
WEDNESDAY	Pease-meal Pottage with Milk or Butter	Ditto	Ditto
THURSDAY	Oat-meal Pottage with Milk or Ale	Ditto	Ditto
FRIDAY	Pease-meal Pottage with Milk or Butter	Ditto	Ditto
SATURDAY	Oat-meal Pottage with Milk or Ale	Ditto	Ditto

THE DIET FOR ALL PERSONS ABOVE FIFTEEN YEARS OF AGE

	Breakfast	Dinner	Supper
SUNDAY	Oat-meal Pottage and Ale	Bread and Ale	Broth with Flesh and Bread
MONDAY	Ditto	Broth made without Flesh, Bread and Butter, or Cheese	Oat-meal Pottage and Ale
TUESDAY	Ditto	Broth made without Flesh, Bread and Herring	Ditto
WEDNESDAY	Ditto	Broth made with Flesh, and Bread	Ditto
THURSDAY	Ditto	Broth made without Flesh, Bread and Cheese	Ditto
FRIDAY	Ditto	Broth made with Flesh, and Bread	Ditto
SATURDAY	Ditto	Broth made without Flesh, Bread with Herring or Butter	Ditto

33

of the Poor Law Act in 1845 gave rise to many difficulties and complaints. Drs. Allison and Christison of Edinburgh were asked to examine and report, after consideration of the dietaries in vogue in the poorhouses of Scotland, England, and Ireland. They were unable to recommend for the Scottish charity workhouses any of the dietaries advised by the Poor Law Commissioners for the English and Irish poorhouses, because most of the articles composing them were different from those the working classes lived on in Scotland. They found wide variation in existing Scottish dietaries. The lowest, that of Edinburgh Canongate Workhouse, contained 12½ oz. dry nutriment (" nutritive proximate principles perfectly dried at 212° F."). Drs. Allison and Christison thought that for elderly paupers, who constituted the great majority of the inmates of Scottish workhouses, an average of 14½ oz. was sufficient. The dietaries also differed as to the amount of food allowed from day to day. Those of Edinburgh, Paisley, Dunfermline, and Lanark allowed very little variety. Those of Glasgow and Montrose were more diversified, and that of Aberdeen admitted of a considerable variety in the meals of each day. " We prefer in this respect the diet adopted at Edinburgh, for experience has proved at Edinburgh that the degree of variety allowed there is sufficient for health, and not unsatisfactory to the inmates ; and any further variety beyond this holds out an additional inducement to apply for admission, besides complicating unnecessarily the domestic details, as well as the accounts." In the opinion of the reporters none of the inmates of workhouses should be allowed any articles of diet at discretion, for many will eat more than enough and waste can scarcely be avoided under such a practice. In 1848 the Board of Supervision found that the diet in St. Cuthbert's Poorhouse, Edinburgh, was " inferior to that which we had sanctioned," and called on the Parochial Board to remedy the defect, and to keep suspended in each ward a printed table of the daily diet that the inmates were entitled to receive. Improvement was secured on the threat that until these steps were taken an offer of admission to the poorhouse would not be held to be a tender of adequate relief.

In the Rules for the Management of Poorhouses issued by the Board of Supervision in 1850, a dietary was laid down for the inmates, who were divided for this purpose into seven classes : (A) aged, healthy but not working, (B) adults, not aged, healthy but not working, and children between the ages of eight and fifteen, (C) adults, either sex, working, (D) infirm, either sex, (E) children aged five to eight, (F) children aged two to five, (G) infants under two years. For each class except G three meals per day were allowed. As illustrations, the diets for classes C and F are reproduced :

Class C	Breakfast	Meal 4 oz., milk ¾ imperial pint
	Dinner	Bread 8 oz., broth 1½ imperial pints, boiled meat 4 oz.
	Supper	Meal 4 oz., milk ¾ imperial pint
Class F	Breakfast	Meal 3½ oz. and new milk ½ imperial pint
	Dinner	Bread 5 oz. and broth ¾ imperial pint
	Supper	Meal 3 oz. and new milk ½ imperial pint

To the diet-tables certain notes were appended : milk might be buttermilk, where new milk or skimmed milk was not specified. The broth was to be made with 2 oz. meat, exclusive of bone, 2 oz. barley, ½ oz. pease, 1½ oz. carrots, turnips, or other vegetable approved by the Medical Officer, and a due quantity of salt for each ration of 1½ imperial pints.

On not more than three days a week there might be substituted for broth at dinner 1½ pints of peasoup ; and, on not more than one day a week, 3 oz. of skimmed milk cheese, or for the broth and meal together, 4½ oz. Not more than twice a week there might be substituted for the broth at dinner 2 lb. of boiled potatoes and ¾ imperial pint skimmed milk ; or for bread, broth and meat together, 3 lb. of boiled potatoes with 1 imperial pint skimmed milk. The rules contained no other provisions for varying the diet.

In the Annual Report of the Board for the following year (1851) the dietary in use in the Easter Ross Poorhouse was set out with obvious approval (page 36).

Treacle-water does not suggest great palatability, but it doubtless had its uses. The dietary in the Easter Ross Poorhouse did not differ much from that set out in the Rules of 1850 ; it had the disadvantage of fixing standard and recurring

DIETARY, EASTER ROSS POORHOUSE, 1851

	Sunday	Monday	Tuesday	Wednesday	Thursday	Friday	Saturday
Aged and Infirm Persons Breakfast and Supper (same)	Meal 3 oz. Milk or Treacle-water ½ pt.	Same as Sunday	Same as Sunday	Same as Sunday	Same as Sunday	Same as Sunday	Same as Sunday
Dinner	Potatoes 1½ lb. Barley-broth 1½ pt.	Oatcake 6 oz. Peasoup ½ pt.	Potatoes 1½ lb. Milk ¾ pt.	Oatcake 6 oz. Barley-broth ½ pt.	Oatcake 6 oz. Rice ¼ lb. with Milk or Treacle ½ pt.	Potatoes 1½ lb. Milk ¾ pt.	Oatcake 6 oz. Peasoup 1½ pt.
Children Breakfast	Meal 4 oz. Milk or Treacle-water ¾ pt.	Same as Sunday	Same as Sunday	Same as Sunday	Same as Sunday	Same as Sunday	Same as Sunday
Dinner	Potatoes 1 lb. Barley-broth 1½ pt.	Oatcake 6 oz. Peasoup 1½ pt.	Potatoes 1½ lb. Herring	Oatcake 6 oz. Barley-broth 1½ pt.	Oatcake 6 oz. Rice 3 oz. Milk or Treacle ½ pt.	Potatoes 1½ lb. Herring	Oatcake 6 oz. Peasoup ½ pt.
Supper	Meal 3 oz. Treacle-water ½ pt.	Same as Sunday	Same as Sunday	Same as Sunday	Same as Sunday	Same as Sunday	Same as Sunday
Adult Persons Breakfast and Supper (same)	Meal 4 oz. Milk or Treacle-water ¾ pt.	Same as Sunday	Same as Sunday	Same as Sunday	Same as Sunday	Same as Sunday	Same as Sunday
Dinner	Potatoes 2 lb. Barley-broth 2 pt.	Oatcake 8 oz. Peasoup 2 pt.	Potatoes 2 lb. Herring	Oatcake 8 oz. Barley-broth 2 pt.	Oatcake 8 oz. Peasoup 2 pt.	Potatoes 2 lb. Herring	Oatcake 8 oz. Peasoup 2 pt.

36

fare for each day of the week, a practice persisting until recent years.

In 1854 the Board of Supervision reported that they had sanctioned alterations in the diet-table of two poorhouses. In one, it had appeared from the report of the Medical Officer that the dietary in use in the house was probably too low, especially during the prevalence of cholera. In the other, the proposal to improve the diet, which had appeared to the Board to be sufficient, came from the House Committee, and the change was sanctioned experimentally, " but we are not yet convinced of its expediency."

Nevertheless there must have been a growing recognition that the scales as officially defined left much to be desired, for in subsequent reports approval is given to the " experimental " improvement of dietaries in several poorhouses in different parts of the country. From published accounts of the average weekly cost per head of poorhouse inmates in Scotland it appears that the average inclusive cost of " food, fuel, clothing, light, and all other necessaries " during the years 1860–63 worked out at about 2s. 10½d., rather less than 5d. per day. With a daily food allowance valued at about 3½d., it is easy to agree that residence in a poorhouse could be regarded as an efficient test of poverty. On 7 May 1863 *The Scotsman* had this to say in a leading article on the subject : " The diet is calculated to sustain life and no more ; and so close is the calculation made that doubts will intrude whether it does not really fall short in the amount of nutriment necessary for health and does not subject many of the inmates to slow death from gradual inanition. Moreover, for proper nutrition, mere quantity is not enough. Nature craves for change, but in our poorhouses we greatly fear that both quantity and variety fail." *The Scotsman* went on to say that in prisons the diet was much fuller than in poorhouses, instancing that (reproduced) of the General Prison at Perth, where the allowance of oatmeal for breakfast for female inmates was 8 oz., double that in the poorhouses ; and it expressed a grave doubt whether aged and sick and broken-down paupers could be sufficiently fed on 3½d. a day.

DIETARY OF THE LUNATIC WARDS OF
GENERAL PRISON, PERTH

ORDINARY DIET

Breakfast   Males   8 oz. oatmeal, ⅔ pint sweet milk ; or 12 oz. bread, ⅛ pint sweet milk, ₁⁵₆ oz. coffee, 1 oz. sugar

         Females 8 oz. oatmeal, ½ pint sweet milk, ⅛ oz. tea, 1 oz. sugar ; or 8 oz. bread, ⅛ pint sweet milk, ⅛ oz. tea, 1 oz. sugar

Supper   Males   6 oz. oatmeal, ½ pint buttermilk ; or 12 oz. bread, ⅛ pint sweet milk, ₁⁵₆ oz. coffee, 1 oz. sugar

         Females 8 oz. bread, ⅛ pint sweet milk, ⅛ oz. tea, 1 oz. sugar

DINNER

Sunday	Males	12 oz. bread, ¼ pint sweet milk, 4 oz. barley
	Females	8 oz. bread, ¼ pint sweet milk, 4 oz. barley
Monday	Males	12 oz. bread, 2 oz. ox-heads, 3 oz. barley, 1 oz. pease
	Females	6 oz. bread, 2 oz. ox-heads, 3 oz. barley, 1 oz. pease
Tuesday ⎫ *Wednesday* ⎪ *Thursday* ⎬ *Saturday* ⎭	Males Females	12 oz. bread, 2 oz. ox-heads, 4 oz. beef or mutton, 3 oz. barley, 1 oz. pease 8 oz. bread, 2 oz. ox-heads, 4 oz. beef or mutton, 3 oz. barley, 1 oz. pease
Friday	Males	12 oz. fish, 2½ lb. potatoes
	Females	12 oz. fish, 2 lb. potatoes

This diet is varied in particular cases

12

Already in the sixteenth century there were the beginnings of efforts to improve the quality of food, and to set some standards to that end. In the Statutes of the burgh of Edinburgh (1529–31) all bakers within the Burgh were ordered to bake their bread with good and sufficient stuff, well baked and dried, the twopenny loaf to weigh eighteen ounces and the brown bread in proportion ; and while the Trade Guilds were designed primarily to promote the interests of the Crafts and to take care of decayed brethren, soon they too began to develop a wider civic consciousness. In 1580 the Seal of Cause of the Incorporation of Fleshers in Glasgow contained provisions of direct importance to the public health : " That they cast out nothing of bags, paunches, or tripes upon the street . . . nor yet to buy dead flesh from any person to sell over again . . . nor yet to brode, cutt down, nor blow with the mouth any flesh, nor score mutton except one score in every fore-shoulder." According to old Acts of the Scottish Parliament, when wild beasts were found dead or wounded, the flesh was to be sent to the house of the leper men, if any such happened to be situated near-by ; and similarly, flesh or pork or salmon, found to be corrupt in the markets and accordingly seized, was to be sent to the lepers.

Centuries later, various Police Acts introduced stringent clauses regulating the trade in butcher meat and attaching heavy penalties to the sale of diseased carcases. " These efforts," wrote Littlejohn of his Edinburgh experience, " were attended with little success until the sweeping measure was passed prohibiting the existence of private shambles ; and the Trade was compelled to use the Public Abattoirs at Fountainbridge, which were opened in 1853, and are believed to be the finest in the country. Where there is such a strong inducement to commit fraud, however, constant attempts are made to evade the Police enactments. The traffic is highly remunerative, and one successful run will cover the losses incurred in many unsuccessful ventures."

For a long time prior to 1801 the price of bread in Glasgow was fixed by the magistrates. For a number of years thereafter the public were supplied by the Incorporation Bakers, on competitive terms, until individuals or societies set up extensive bakeries in the suburbs and began to undercut the Incorporation. This they were able to do, according to Cleland, because not only were they exempt from city taxation, but they baked only quartern loaves, and these of inferior quality, whereas the Incorporation Bakers supplied the public with all kinds of bread of the best quality, and also made small and coarse bread for the poor. Later, in 1840, Dr. Sym reported that the bread in Ayr was of superior quality and free from adulteration, due in great measure to the circumstance that the principal baker was a man of the strictest integrity and considerable wealth, the quality of bread which he furnished setting the standard for inferior tradesmen ; but there seems reason to fear that this high standard of honesty was not universal throughout the country.

Chapter III

HOUSING

I

EARLY visitors to Scotland carried away with them impressions of Scottish housing almost as diverse as their impressions of Scottish women. In the middle of the fifteenth century Pope Pius II wrote that the towns had no walls, the houses were for the most part constructed without lime, the roofs of the houses in the country were made of turf, and the doors of the humbler dwellings of the hide of oxen. At the end of the same century, Don Pedro de Ayala reported that the houses were good, all built of hewn stone and provided with excellent doors, glass windows, and a great number of chimneys : all the furniture that was used in Italy, Spain, and France was to be found in these dwellings. But Don Pedro's judgment may have been influenced by his belief that it would be a service to marry the third daughter of Ferdinand and Elizabeth to the King of Scots : " He would be always a faithful ally, near at hand, and ready to assist without causing any inconvenience to Spain. The kingdom is very old, and very noble, and the king possesses great virtues, and no defects worth mentioning." Fifty years later Perlin wrote bluntly that the houses were badly built and proportioned, at least those of the common people, and Sir William Brereton (1636), who like Sir Anthony Weldon was no admirer of the Scots, wrote even more bluntly that their houses and halls and kitchens had such a noisome taste, a savour, and that so strong " as it doth offend you so soon as you come within their wall ; yea, sometimes when I have light from my horse, I have felt the distaste of it before I have come into the house ; yea, I never came to my own lodging in Edenborough, or went out, but I was constrained to hold my nose, or to use wormwood, or some such scented plant." A little later in the seventeenth century, John Ray commented on the method of house construction, remarking that it was a custom to make up the fronts of the houses, even in the principal towns, with fir boards nailed one over another, in which were often made many round holes or windows out of which the people were wont to put their heads. He found that in the best Scottish houses, " even the king's pallaces," the windows were not glazed throughout, but in their upper part only, the lower having two wooden folds that could be shut or opened at pleasure to admit fresh air. But Ray thought little of the ordinary country houses : " Pitiful cots, built of stone and covered with turves, having in them but one room, many of them no chimneys, the windows very small holes, but not glazed. In the most stately and fashionable houses in great towns, instead of ceiling they cover the chambers with firr boards, nailed on the roof within side." In 1704 an English visitor described the houses in the Lanarkshire village of Crawfordjohn : " The houses are either of earth or of loose stones, or are raddled. The roofes are of turfe and the floors of the bare ground. They are but one storey high, and the chimney is a hole in the roof and the fireplace is in the middle of the floor. There seats and beds are of earth turfed over and raddled up, near the fire place, and serve for both uses."

2

In the Middle Ages the materials used for building were always those that were cheapest and most easily to hand. Stone as well as wood was available in the oldest houses, the stones being left unwrought and the spaces between them filled in with mud. Macgregor writes in his *Old Glasgow* that it was probably only after 1175 that any houses in Glasgow other than mere huts began to be built. A fire in Edinburgh or Glasgow in the thirteenth or fourteenth century, when houses were chiefly of wood, was a calamity causing much temporary distress, but comparatively easy to repair. In 1385 Richard II set fire to Edenborrowe, burning up nearly everything except the Castle, but the citizens were apparently not overmuch dismayed ; " For though the Englysshe men brinne our housis we axe but thre deyes to make them agayne, if we may gete four or fyve stakes and bowes to cover them." From the fifteenth century till the eighteenth building timber was a scarce commodity in Scotland. In bleak exposed districts the stunted trees made short joists, and only narrow houses could be built. The so-called wooden houses of this period in Glasgow and Edinburgh were stone houses with their timber balconies boarded up to increase chamber and shop accommodation, and incidentally in the process encroaching on the width of the street. These wooden projections resulted in narrow streets, and were frequently the cause of disastrous fires.

At the burning of a large part of Glasgow in 1652 the flames, driven by the wind, swept along the wooden fronts and nearly a thousand families were left without homes. Another great fire in November 1677 wiped out many houses above the Cross of Glasgow, and again nearly a thousand families were burned out. Following this fire a Minute of Glasgow Town Council, dated 4 December 1677, laid down steps to be taken to reduce the risk of further outbreaks : " That each persone building de novo on the Hie Street, or repairing, sall be obliged to doe it by stone work from head to foot baik and four without any timber or daill except in the inset thereof, quhilk is understood to be partitions, doors, windows, presses. and such lyk."

In 1681 it was enacted that, the thatching of houses in Edinburgh being dangerous for fire, houses there were to be thatched with lead, slate, scailzie (blue slate) or tile, and that " all houses that shall be built in time coming in the Burghs of Glasgow, Aberdeen, Dundee, and Stirling to be thatched with lead, slate, scailzie, or tile and no otherwise." By an Act of 1698 the Dean of Guild in Edinburgh was entrusted with the enforcement of an Act designed to restrict the height of buildings in the city to " five storeys above the causeway." But not until far on in the eighteenth century was there much improvement in the construction of houses in Scotland. The last thatched house in Glasgow was taken down about 1830.

An Act of 1663 deplored the large number of uninhabited ruinous houses in the royal burghs of Scotland, and sought to compel the owners of such property to rebuild it or to sell it to someone prepared to do so ; and in default, the magistrates were empowered to pull down the property and rebuild.

3

Scotland's housing problems are of long standing and twofold in origin, arising from faulty construction and bad repair on the one hand, and from overcrowding on the other. At the census taken in 1821, it was found that the number of families per inhabited house was 1·3 and the number of persons 6·1—figures already higher than those for England and for Wales, though the census returns did not indicate the number of rooms per house, which would probably have placed the Scottish position in still worse light. At the census taken in 1861 it was found that 35 per cent. of families in Scotland lived in one room, and 37 per cent. in two rooms, so that, taking the country as a whole, 72 per cent. of families lived in houses of one or two rooms. The extent of overcrowding varied in different parts of the country : in Glasgow and in Edinburgh 34 per cent. of families occupied one room, in Aberdeen 35 per cent., in Dundee 37 per cent., and in Paisley 42 per cent.

Analysing the results of the 1861 census the Registrar-General found that, taking Scotland as a whole, there were on an average 4·3 rooms with windows to every house, 2·5 rooms to every family, and 1·7 persons to every room. Among Scottish towns overcrowding was worst in Paisley with 2·1 persons to each room ; but Glasgow and Dundee were nearly as bad, each with 2·0, while Greenock and Leith, which came next, had 1·7 and 1·6 respectively. There was at this time in some of the rural counties a degree of overcrowding worse than that prevailing in the towns : Shetland had 3·1 persons to each room, Caithness 2·1, Orkney 2·0, and Argyll, Inverness, Clackmannan and Ross and Cromarty each 1·8.

The influence of the window tax carried a considerable threat to sanitation. By an Act of 1696, every inhabited house owed duty of 2s. per annum, and in addition every dwelling-house with ten windows owed 4s. per annum. In 1746 the basis of the law was changed, the tax being levied on the several windows of a house, so that it fell more decisively than before on tenement houses. In 1803 a change was made back to the original basis of taxation, and the window tax was dropped altogether about the middle of the nineteenth century.

The Registrar-General reported that at the taking of the census in 1861, 7,964 families in Scotland (or little more than 1 per cent.) were each living in single rooms containing no window, the light being admitted by the door, or by an aperture in the roof or side wall answering the double purpose of window and chimney. The Registrar was anxious to make it clear that it should not be concluded that all these 7,964 families were living in an unhealthy sanitary condition simply because they occupied rooms without windows. He thought that if the room were a thatched cottage with an aperture in the roof or side wall, " whatever other supposed essentials the room wanted, it had in full perfection that which most conduces to full health and freedom from disease—viz. free ventilation ; and though not blessed with the cheering rays of the sun inside its walls, it was a room more conducive to health and vigour than thousands of the cottages with windows where such means of free ventilation do not exist." He thought that the truly unhealthy cottages were those having no open chimney to carry off the smoke and permit of ventilation, no matter whether they had windows or not, for the window was always a fixture, incapable of being opened ; it was in such cottages that mortality was high at all ages, " and Dr. Morgan has clearly proved that it is to this cause the high fatality among the infants is to be ascribed—giving rise to trismus during the first week after their birth." He went on to explain that over the whole of the Highlands, wherever the free ventilating opening in the roof was wanting and the smoke escaped by the door, the proportion of deaths from pulmonary consumption and diseases of the lung was greatly higher than among those living in the same locality but under different hygienic conditions. The Registrar-General did not produce the evidence on which he based these statements, nor did he fully realize the health implications of the box bed, which he held in high esteem : it " forms, as it were, a distinct room for the parties sleeping in, so that it affords facilities for a separation of the sexes, and the observance of decency, to an extent which is impossible in a single room where such accommodation is wanting." The early sanitarians spoke with more feeling and certainty of the effects of life in a single room ; but the Registrar-General was doubtless on safe enough ground when he wrote that " in the case of rooms in towns which have no windows, of all unhealthy dwellings they are the most unwholesome, particularly if such be under the level of the street ; and the inhabiting of such cellar dwellings should be strictly prohibited."

4

In the Statistical Account of Scotland there are references to housing conditions in different parts of the country towards the end of the eighteenth century ; they deal especially with the housing of farmers and farm servants. In many parts of the country agricultural workers lived in houses of the most miserable description. Their families and cattle were generally under the same roof and only separated by thin partitions. Scarcely any of their houses had an upper storey, so that the whole family were obliged to sleep on a damp soil, the floor not being so much as paved with stone or flags, and often without a fireplace to draw off moist and stagnant air. Often the walls were built of dry stone, without mortar, and thatched with straw or broom, which it was necessary to renew every two or three years to prevent the roof from becoming useless. Where the houses had not been improved it was found that their coldness, dampness, and dirtiness produced " various disorders which frequently carried off the unfortunate occupiers in early life." Already by the end of the eighteenth century many houses were having a second storey raised and fireplaces provided to aid ventilation ; and farm-houses and offices were rapidly replacing thatched roofs with slates. James Russell, parish minister of Yarrow, recorded in his diary that the farmhouses in that part of the country were at the beginning of the eighteenth century small and low roofed, built very much on one model, having a room in one end, the kitchen in the other, and, through the kitchen, another room generally used as a bedroom. There were occasionally two small attics above, reached by a trap ladder and lighted by a few small panes through the thatch. The cottages for the hinds and shepherds were little better than dark, smoky hovels. Their walls were alternate rows of stone and sods, their floors of earth and their roofs of course timber covered with turf and rushes. Writing of much the same period, George Robertson, an agriculturalist, said that the cottars' houses belonging to the farms were in some cases set down at the opposite end of the midden, but were generally clustered together at some little distance from the farmhouse. They were very mean hovels. The walls, not exceeding five feet in height, were usually composed of round stones and divots in alternate layers. The roof sustained itself independently of the walls, and was retained in position by rough spars or branches of trees on which straw and turf was laid closely in an attempt to make the whole watertight. A cottage of this kind, in all its parts, was constructed in a single day by the gudeman and his servant, the materials having been collected previously. The size of these cottar huts might be about twelve feet square inside, sufficient to contain all the plenishing that in these times was wont to be acquired. When the huts had a chimney, which was not always the case, it was constructed in the same fashion as the lum of a farmhouse ; otherwise the smoke escaped by a hole in the roof, or as often by the door or window. The window was not always furnished with glass, but often consisted of a single shutter, movable on a hinge, while the opening in the wall seldom exceeded twelve inches square. There were many such cottar house in the Lothians in the second half of the eighteenth century, but towards its close cottar houses were beginning to be constructed in better style— the walls, no longer of turf and dry stone, were built of stone and lime, and besides being high enough to permit an ordinary-sized man to enter without stooping, were also considerably enlarged in length and breadth.

As late as 1822, Hamilton, advocating a system of cottage-farms as a remedy for the ills and discontent of the times, prepared sketch plans for several types of farm-cottage. Two of these plans are reproduced. One type was a turf cottage that could be built for £15. It comprised two small apartments, a kitchen and a barn or workshop, as might be required by the occupant, and had a stall for a cow. The other, a more ambitious affair, was a small cottage that could be built of stone and lime for £60. It contained a kitchen, a workshop, and a cow's stall and pigsty with dungstead, etc. ; "Above stairs the garrets are floored over, and may be occupied as found necessary."

In the Schoolmasters' Act of 1803, which compelled heritors to build houses for the schoolmasters, it was stipulated that the houses need not contain more than two rooms, including the kitchen ; and there was difficulty in obtaining even these "palaces for dominies."

The doctors who reported on the sanitary condition of the labouring population of Scotland to the Government Commission collecting evidence on that subject in 1840 had much to say about the housing of farm-workers. Married workers generally lived in detached or connected cottages, each consisting commonly of two rooms and a closet. The unmarried servants lived in barrack-like buildings or bothies, where they themselves prepared their food and often contrived to live cheerfully enough under Spartan conditions. Dr. Alison reported that the cottages inhabited by hinds in the County of Haddington could be divided into two classes, a superior and an inferior, the former constantly increasing and the latter as constantly decreasing in number. He described a cottage of the inferior class as consisting of one apartment, about fourteen feet long by twelve feet broad. The habitation was formed of the front and back walls, about eight feet high, two side walls or gables rising pyramidally to a height of about twenty feet. The roof was composed of thatch or straw, resting upon rafters or beams of wood. There was one fireplace, provided with a capricious chimney. The walls were generally substantial, but the roof in many cases very inferior. The thatch was often quite rotten and pervious to rain and wind, and the rafters in many cottages were much decayed. Some tenants had a portable wooden ceiling, which they carried with them from house to house as a piece of furniture. In some cottages no ceiling of any kind was used, and their appearance was very bad. The floors of these cottages were generally below the level of the soil outside. The walls on the inside were bare or whitewashed. The one window, generally about two feet square, was usually incapable of being opened, and doctors in all parts of the country were constantly complaining of the lack of ventilation in the houses of the people ; but the door was seldom well-fitted, frequently decayed, and readily admitted strong currents of air. The " superior " cottages which were then rapidly replacing the old were, with few exceptions, of much the same size as those replaced ; they, too, had generally only one apartment, and their floors were below the level of the ground outside.

This improvement of rural housing, very much overdue and inadequate as it was, was nevertheless taking place in most of the country districts of Scotland in the early part of the nineteenth century. In 1850, Sir John McNeill, Chairman of the Board of Supervision, reporting on a visit to Caithness, wrote that amongst the cheering evidences of social progress none was more agreeable than the improvement in the dwellings of the working class, and he instanced the cottages of the quarrymen at Castlehill, which, " though perhaps hardly affording a sufficient number of apartments, are very far in advance of the dwellings of the preceding generation." Some of them were models of cleanliness, neatness, and comfort, conveying irresistibly the impression of domestic welfare ; but Sir John had to add that in the progress of this improvement the small crofter had almost disappeared, to be replaced by the farmer and by the labourer for wages who held no land.

5

Housing conditions in the fishing villages were no better than in the country. Writing of Musselburgh in 1840, Wm. Stevenson, surgeon there, wrote that the houses inhabited by the poorer people were generally in narrow lanes or closes, five feet to seven feet wide, and 150–200 feet long. The houses mostly contained two rooms, and each room accommodated one or two families. Floors were below ground level, of clay or earth beaten down, and water ran into the houses. In very few were there any receptacles for filth, " consequently it is just thrown out at the door and allowed to remain there or not, as chance may." Dr. Stevenson went on to explain that people connected with the fishing trade were in most cases very obstinate, and that it was a difficult thing to persuade them that what they were accustomed to was not right and proper. In the houses of the fisher folk he found dirty and uncomfortable beds of straw, very scantily furnished with bedclothes spread on the damp clay floor. Sometimes large stones supplied the place with chairs ; and the atmosphere became intolerably vitiated in time of sickness. The beds swarmed with bugs and fleas and the heads of the children with lice. He concluded that the fishermen (of Fisherrow) " are in general filthy in their habits, both in their dwellings, persons, and families. They are much addicted to dissipation and drunkenness and very improvident."

But probably the occupational group living under the worst conditions was that of the colliers ; in areas like Tranent, where colliers and hinds lived in the same neighbourhood, it was the invariable experience that the houses of the colliers were worse than those of the hinds. Nor did this depend entirely on the structure of the houses, bad though that undoubtedly was. " In many of the houses of the colliers," wrote Dr. Alison of Tranent, " there is great want of necessary furniture. . . . There is a fearful amount of filth . . . which with dirty persons, unwashed rags of clothes, and the hot putrid atmosphere usually present, go far to add to the wretchedness of the scene and to complete the measure of squalid and disgusting misery." Alison recorded that in some of these houses the females were so lazy and so filthy in their habits that they carried their ashes and cinders no farther than to a corner of the apartment, where they accumulated, and had their bulk swollen by the addition of various impurities. He went on to say that he did not believe that there was a single house in Tranent into which water was conducted by pipes, and that indeed there often existed great difficulty in getting water at all.

These criticisms of conditions in the houses of the colliers have to be considered against the background of the history of the mining communities, and the squalid conditions of the mining villages that in the nineteenth century grew up like mushrooms in the black belt of Scotland, destined to form for so long foci of much misery. The mining rows built at that time consisted largely of " single-ends " and two-roomed houses, innocent of water-supply, and in some cases wholly devoid of even the most primitive sanitary facilities.

6

Housing in the towns was little better. Dr. James Sym, reporting in 1841 on the sanitary condition of the town of Ayr, wrote that while Ayr was a very open town, having not more than eighteen families per acre, the benefits held out to the opulent by the hygienic advantages derived from nature and the general structure of the town were to a great extent precluded from reaching the poor. " Scanty, uncertain, and innutritious food, insufficient clothing, squalor of person, incessant labour, sinking of the heart, cold lodgings, filthy beds, or harsh substitutes for beds, the atmosphere of their dwellings confined for the sake of warmth, and poisoned by too many breaths, or polluted by noxious exhalations, these hold the vital functions too rigidly and cruelly in their grips to permit the more remote influences of climate to be in any appreciable degree effective either for good or for evil." He found that the houses in which the labouring classes resided varied in different parts of the town. Some in the old royal burgh were sadly out of repair and the rent of a single room was from 30s. to £2 per annum. Almost all the poor houses were thatched with straw and the roofs in bad repair. The windows were generally fixed, and most of the glass was so much broken that its place was taken by boards, rags, and old hats. The ceilings were low and without plaster. There was usually a bedstead at each side of the door, often much shattered, and beneath it all sorts of rubbish and lumber were hurled together, as well as the store of potatoes for the family, when they possessed so much wealth. Sometimes even a heap of horse-dung was to be found under the bed, collected by the children from the streets to be sold when a sufficient quantity had been accumulated. Cleaning under the beds was never dreamt of, nor could it easily have been effected, for they were generally boxed in on three sides and were invariably infested with bugs. The bedding consisted of straw or chaff, with a scanty supply of dirty blankets and mats but no sheets ; one or two broken chairs and stools and a fir table constituted the remaining part of the furniture, and the possession of an old chest indicated some degree of opulence. The greatest nuisance was the filth collected about the houses of the poor : the back premises of the poorer portions of High Street had their narrow alleys used for necessaries, and the ordure with which they were thickly studded rendered it difficult to pick one's steps through them without pollution. In Stirling, butchers used as killing booths their back shops, often situated under dwelling-houses ; and occasionally part of a house was used as a residence and part as a slaughter-house.

7

But it was in the great cities that the cumulative effects of bad housing reached their worst. As early as the sixteenth century Edinburgh had its " gardyloos," and in spite of repeated orders from the magistrates, fines, imprisonment, the pillory, whipping, and banishment, old habits could not be subdued, and the sounding of the ten o'clock bell from St. Giles's belfry was the signal for a general simultaneous discharge from the windows of every house. Despite all the magistrates' zeal, the gardyloo continued for many long years. Smollett thus described it in *Humphrey Clinker* : " At ten o'clock at night the whole cargo is flung out of a back window that looks into a street or lane, and the maid calls gardyloo to the passengers, which signified ' Lord have mercy upon you,' and this is done in every house in Haddingbourgh, so you may guess what a sweet savour comes from such a number of perfuming pans ; but they say it is wholesome, and I truly believe it is." Glasgow, too, had its " gardyloo," and in 1696 enacted a statute " against nestines " which prohibited the casting out at windows, by day or night, any dirt or filth of any description.

In the seventeenth century King James complained to the magistrates of Edinburgh about the shameful filthiness of the streets, wynds, and closes, and an order was issued that the inhabitants should each clean " fornent their ain bounds " ; but the inhabitants took little notice of the edict. An Act of William I legislated minutely for the cleanliness of streets and dwellings.

It was a big advance on previous Acts, and its clauses sought to enforce removal of dung and fulzie, cleansing of common stairs and areas, the prohibition of keeping of swine in dwelling-houses, and a compulsitor on dealers in rags to fumigate their dwellings ; but while the Act denounced accumulations within dwelling-houses (where there is seldom means of ascertaining their existence) there was an exception excluding, to a great extent, interference with accumulations in the open air.

8

Before 1700 the population of Edinburgh appeared to be almost stationary, but after the failure of the Forty-five it began to move upward : it was about 50,000 in 1750, 100,000 in 1800, and 200,000 in 1850. Formidable geographical difficulties limited Edinburgh's expansion. The Castle and Holyrood House blocked the way to west and east. On the south there was only a negligible strip of ground between the town and the wide Burgh Loch, while on the north was the deep and forbidding valley of the Nor' Loch, with its foreground of middens and slaughter-houses. It was decided to plan a new town to the north, and the design of James Craig was accepted. A Bill for the extension of the Royalty was passed in April 1767, and in October of that year the foundation-stone of the first house was laid—the beginning of a pioneer essay in town planning that remains one of Scotland's great achievements.

Craig planned for a self-contained unit with no regular outlets to east or west. George Street on the crown of the low ridge was planned as the main axis. In an Act of 1781 provision was made that in the new scheme no house should exceed three storeys in height, inclusive of basement and garret, that all plans and elevations must be submitted for approval, that the meuse lanes should be solely appropriated for stables, etc. ; that houses in the intermediate streets (*e.g.* Rose Street) must not exceed two storeys ; and that no storm-windows, or any windows other than skylights, be allowed on the front roofs. The earlier houses were all designed on one model, with little or no external architectural character, but some improvement took place as building progressed westward, and reached its crowning glory in Charlotte Square, designed by Robert Adam and completed about 1800.

The attempt to limit the height of tenement-dwellings in the city doubtless arose in part from experience in the Old Town, where there were many blocks of buildings exceeding ten storeys in height, with common stairs sometimes as filthy as the streets or wynds to which they opened. By their construction they lessened the chance of cleanliness and increased labour of carrying up necessaries, particularly water ; and Dr. Neil Arnott, writing of the fevers so prevalent in Edinburgh and Glasgow in the early part of the nineteenth century, said that " If any malaria or contagion exist in the house, the probability of its passing from dwelling to dwelling on the same stair is much greater than if there were no communication but through the open air." Other writers complained that owing to the close packing of the ancient towns within defensive walls, many houses, especially in Edinburgh, were of gigantic dimensions, and were celled off, as it were, into numerous houses, sometimes enclosing in one tenement a population that would make no inconsiderable village Alexander Miller, Surgeon to the Royal Dispensary, complained in 1840 that the dwellings of the poor were very filthy, often consisting of one small apartment, ill-ventilated, damp, overcrowded, often partially underground, with " miserable scantiness of furniture, or rather, in many cases, the total want of any kind of it," and he protested that the practice of midwifery under such dreadful conditions was a tragedy.

This tendency to the aggregation of large numbers of people in high tenement-houses was the direct means of securing the appointment of Dr. Littlejohn as first Medical Officer of Health of the city. Under the stimulation of the epidemics of the first part of the eighteenth century and the problems created by the great and increasing mass of destitution in the city, the public conscience had been awakened as never before to an interest in the condition of the poor. One early fruit of this new interest was the thorough, though far from systematic, drainage of the town, but with the passing of the Poor Law Act in 1845 public attention slumbered again. It was rudely awakened on 21 October 1861, when a house in the High Street collapsed, burying many in its ruins and killing thirty-five of the inmates : people wondered at the number of persons found to be inhabiting a single house. A public meeting of the inhabitants was held on 25 February 1862, and one of the results was that a deputation was appointed to wait on the Town Council to urge that body to appoint an officer of health, an approach culminating in Dr. Littlejohn's appointment the same year. It emerged that in the districts of Canongate, Tron, St. Giles, and Grassmarket the proportion of population to each inhabited acre varied between 219 and 352. Of the single-roomed houses in Edinburgh, 1,530 had from six to fifteen persons living in each, and 121 of these houses had no windows ; many were cellars, and of a series of houses visited in these areas the average size of room was found to be fourteen feet by eleven. In the Old Town there was to be found an amount of overcrowding, with its natural concomitants of vice and disease, which were not surpassed by any town in Britain : " In the Middle Meal Market Stairs are fifty-nine rooms, almost all separate dwelling-houses, entered by a steep, dark stone stair, common to the whole. In these dwell 248 individuals (adults 197, children under five, 51) divided into fifty-six families, and in this huge congress of dens there is no water, no water-closet, no sink."

The early investigations of Dr. Littlejohn amply demonstrated that the height of epidemic prevalence was related to density of population, and the new Medical Officer of Health was soon waging a campaign against the slum lands of Edinburgh. He saw in Birtley Buildings and in Crombie's Land in the West Port good examples of what would become of the courts and closes should proprietors continue to be allowed to run up skeleton houses of the most rickety description and faulty sanitary construction. Both were inhabited by the very poor ; Birtley Buildings was a refuge for some of the worst characters in the town. Each room was small and overcrowded, and the passages were dark and ill-ventilated. Tried by any standard they were faulty in the extreme. Yet unlike many others formerly inhabited by a richer class, Birtley Buildings and Crombie's Land were modern structures, built specially for the poor, and with an eye to a large rental ; hence the small ill-ventilated rooms, and their great deficiency in sanitary comforts.

In 1851 a first block of houses, appropriately named Ashley Buildings, had been built in Edinburgh by charitable enterprise along lines that originated in London for erecting suitable houses for the working class. Ashley Buildings was placed in the Tron district, in which overcrowding prevailed to a great extent, and on all sides it was surrounded by decaying houses, tenanted by the poor. It not only afforded to the industrious workman a greatly improved habitation, but from its situation formed an example to surrounding proprietors and tenants of the manner in which such houses should be built and kept in a permanent state of cleanliness. Unfortunately it was only the better-off industrial workers who were able to afford the rent of Ashley Buildings, but Dr. Littlejohn was able to point to the pioneer work of Dr. Foulis, who, years previously, had bought a close in the Grassmarket, gutted it, cleaned it thoroughly, and repaired it, in no expensive manner, but in such a way as to afford comfortable housing for the poor, and placed it under such supervision that the inhabitants were taught cleanliness ; should a new-comer not be susceptible of the lesson, after patient trial, he quickly left ; and, " to this hour, the close in question stands out an oasis amidst the wretchedness and filth that is to be met with in other closes of that well-known locality."

9

Because of historical circumstances Glasgow's greatest public health problem is still that of the adequate housing of its citizens ; difficulties arose in an acute form through the rapid expansion of its population in the nineteenth century. The Dean of Guild Court had been constituted in Glasgow in 1605 in a Letter of Guildry, modelled on the Charter already held by Edinburgh, but until the middle of the nineteenth century the civil duties of the Court were chiefly those of securing the proper lining of streets, and the protection of the roads against encroachment by adjoining properties. By the Police Act of 1843 an attempt was made to improve the housing of the city. The Act sought to regulate the frontage line of buildings by a provision designed to prevent encroachment on public footpaths or streets " by new building " ; and an extension of this provision required that houses, to be built or rebuilt, should not project beyond the line of adjacent houses. This Act also conferred power on the Dean of Guild to order the repair or removal of houses that had become insecure, ruinous, or in any other way dangerous to safety. Under this Act many of the worst tenements in the wynds and in Calton, Gorbals, and Anderston were dealt with ; but the policy of the Act aimed only at demolition, and substantial structures could be erected even on the sites of the condemned buildings, so that great overcrowding continued. In 1851 the Dean of Guild laid before the Council the necessity for an Act of Parliament to regulate the erection of future buildings, but forty years were to elapse before his aim was fully realized. Nevertheless the clause of 1843 was applied to some purpose during the great epidemics of typhus fever and cholera in 1847–49. The Glasgow Police Act of 1862 contained some hesitant provisions on the regulation of new buildings, the control of nuisances, overcrowding and cellar-dwellings, but it set up no effective mechanism for carrying out these provisions, and its objects were not secured until the Act was replaced by another a few years later.

By the 1862 Act existing one-apartment houses of less than 700 cubic feet capacity were rendered illegal, and new one-apartment houses were required to be of 900 cubic feet capacity. In two-apartment houses the corresponding minimum requirements for existing and for new houses were 1,200 and 1,300 cubic feet respectively. For three-apartment houses the minimum requirements were 1,800 and 2,000 cubic feet respectively. In addition to fixing a minimum cubic content for houses of not more than three apartments, the Act empowered the Corporation to measure and ticket all such houses if they contained not more than 2,000 cubic feet capacity, and to ascertain the number of persons who might legally sleep in them on an allowance of 300 cubic feet per person over eight years, and 150 cubic feet for a child under that age. This power to " ticket " was a discretionary power, which was exercised by affixing tin-plate tickets on the outer door ; in practice all houses ticketed were one- or two-apartment houses, and almost without exception they were " made-down houses," with inevitable defects of ventilation, lighting, and crowding. They were let by the week or by the month at rates averaging 7s. 11d. per month for one-roomed houses, and 10s. 3d. per month for two-roomed houses, and they were largely peopled by a nomadic population.

In addition to a general provision enabling the Dean of Guild to reject plans for the erection or alteration of buildings failing to provide proper ventilation, the 1862 Act sought to improve the lighting and ventilation of sleeping apartments, by requiring that every such apartment must be provided with a window one-third of which could be opened. The area of window was to be at least 1 foot for every 100 cubic feet the room contained, if the room was of less than 2,000 cubic feet capacity. There were also provisions requiring the preservation of free space in front of windows of sleeping apartments, and it was laid down that no house or other building should be erected within thirty feet of the centre of a turnpike road. Sanction of the Dean of Guild had to be secured before the erection of dwelling-houses exceeding in height the width of the street, and the Dean of Guild was given discretion to secure acceptance of such conditions as he might impose " with reference to the width of the street in relation to the height of the building, or the height of the buildings in relation to the width of the street."

In the early years of the nineteenth century many of the foremost medical figures in the city strongly criticized its housing conditions, with special reference to the continued high prevalence of fever. One of the earliest of these medical writers was Dr. Robert Graham, who referred in 1818 to a visit he had made with one of the district surgeons among every species of disgusting filth, through a long alley, from four to five feet wide, flanked by houses five floors high, with here and there an opening for a pool of water from which there was no drain, and in which all the nuisances of the neighbourhood were deposited in endless succession to float and putrefy and waste away in noxious gases. He invited his reader " to look as he goes along into the cellars which open into this lane, and he will probably find lodged, in alternate habitations, which are in no way distinguished in their exterior, and very little by the furniture which is within them, pigs, cows, and human beings which can scarcely be recognized till brought to the light, or till the eyes of the visitant get accustomed to the smoke and gloom of the cellar in which they live. . . . I saw one closet, measuring twelve feet by less than five, on the floor of which he told me six people had lain, affected with fever, within these two days, and where I saw the seventh inhabitant now confined." Dr. Graham believed that an important step towards ventilation would be effected if it were possible to open up the lanes in which the poorer classes lived, for the hovels they inhabited were collected into dense masses of very great size between some of the larger streets, and he went on to say that he did not think it would be easy to devise a more judicious charity than the building of houses for the poor on an approved plan and in a good situation.

Dr. Cowan, writing in 1837, was of opinion that much of the fever then raging was due to the total want of cleanliness among the lower orders of the community ; to the absence of ventilation in the more densely peopled districts ; to the accumulation, for weeks or months together, of filth of every description in public and private dung-hills ; and to the overcrowded state of the lodging-houses resorted to by the lowest classes. He advocated the establishment in Glasgow of a system of medical police to supervise the sanitation of the city.

Dr. Neil Arnott, in a report written in 1840, spoke of the courts south of Argyle Street in these terms : "There was no privies or drains there, and the dung-heaps received all filth which a swarm of resident inhabitants could give ; and we learned that a considerable part of the rent of the houses was paid by the produce of the dung-heaps. . . . The interiors of these houses and their inmates corresponded with the exteriors." He thought the saving to the community of the cost of supporting the wretched widows and orphans of men who died of fever generated in the place would more than compensate the community for the expense of pulling down the houses.

In 1844 Dr. Robert Perry wrote of the sanitary state of Glasgow that in his experience the prevailing outbreaks of fever had one striking feature : "the overcrowded state of their houses, families of six, eight, and ten individuals crowded into one small apartment, without a bed to lie upon, if we except perhaps a quantity of long-used straw or filthy rags emitting a stench of human impurity so offensive. . . . These small apartments, being often let by the week, are filthy in the extreme. The poor, not having the means to pay for better than they then possessed, must still continue to huddle together in dwellings scarcely fit for pigs." Even in these early days sub-letting was a formidable evil : the construction of the houses showed that they were let to one person as landlord, to be let out again by him at so much per night or week.

A few years later Dr. Sutherland, of the General Board of Health, reporting on measures adopted for the relief of cholera in Glasgow during the epidemic of 1848-49, wrote that it was in those frightful abodes of human wretchedness which lay along the High Street, Saltmarket, and Briggate that all sanitary evils existed in perfection. The houses were so lofty that the direct light of the sky never reached a large proportion of the dwellings. Ordinary atmospheric ventilation was impossible. The water supply was defective ; such a thing as a household supply was unknown. It was said that the Water Companies found it impossible to recover rates, and that, had cholera not appeared, it was in contemplation to have cut off the entire supply from this class of property ! The walls were dilapidated and filthy and in many cases ruinous. " There are no domestic conveniences even in the loftiest tenements, where they are most needed, except a kind of wooden sink placed outside some stair window and communicating by a square wooden pipe with the surface of the close or court beneath. . . . Another matter connected with these districts, and their peculiar liability to epidemic disease, is the great and continually increasing overcrowding that prevails. I have been credibly informed that for years a population of many thousands has been annually added to Glasgow by immigration, without a single house being built to receive them."

Nor did criticism of Glasgow housing in the first half of last century come solely from medical sources. Cleland produced statistics in 1819–20 which showed that the 147,197 people who inhabited Glasgow occupied 31,445 houses with 71,388 apartments, that the average number of persons in each family was 4·68, so that for every apartment in the city there were 2·059 persons. J. C. Symons, an Assistant Commissioner dealing with the condition of hand-loom weavers, reported in 1838 that the low-lying slum districts of Glasgow contained a motley population, consisting partly of people in the lower occupation groups but still more of those whose sole means of subsistence lay in plunder and prostitution. He described the condition of the wynds and closes, and reported that many of the worst houses were dilapidated and in a dangerous state, and had been condemned by the Dean of Guild Court, " a sentence of which the execution appears to be generally postponed, and which renders these abodes doubly desirable to the occupants, as the passing of sentence prevents the levy of rent." His impressions of Glasgow housing were terse enough : " I visited the parts of Edinburgh likewise, where the lowest portion of the community reside, but nothing which can for a moment be compared with the wynds of Glasgow exists there. It is my firm belief that penury, dirt, misery, drunkenness, disease, and crime culminate in Glasgow to a pitch unparalleled in Great Britain."

Captain Miller, Chief Constable of the city, had much to say about the health of Glasgow at the meeting of the British Association in the city in 1840 : " In the very centre of the City there is an accumulated mass of squalid wretchedness, which is probably unequalled in any other town in the British Dominions.

In the interior part of the square, bounded on the east by Salt-market, on the west by Stockwell Street, on the north by Trongate, and on the south by the river, and also in certain parts of the east side of High Street . . . there is concentrated everything that is wretched, dissolute, loathsome, and pestilential. These places are filled by a population of many thousands of miserable creatures. The houses are unfit even for styes, and every apartment is filled with a promiscuous crowd of men, women, and children, all in the most revolting state of filth and squalor. In many of the houses there is scarcely any ventilation, and, from the extremely defective sewerage, filth of every kind constantly accumulates."

Of the many problems facing Dr. Gairdner on his first appointment in 1863 to the health officership of the city, housing was certainly one of the most clamant, and in a report, dated October of that year, to the Board of Police, he wrote that the sanitary evils of the eastern district were entirely due to the most deliberate and systematic violation of all the conditions on which town property, at least, ought to be held. " To meet the rapidly increasing demand for lodgings, by a class of Irish labourers and others by no means delicate in their sense of domestic comfort," he wrote, " a fine open and originally well-aired and pleasant modern street has been rapidly converted into a series of plague-spots, which can hardly be made reasonably safe, in many instances, by any means short of demolition." He described one court, in which a square block of buildings intended for a midden-stead had been roofed over and made into a dwelling-house, and another in which a room built for a washhouse had been similarly occupied. He concluded his report by calling the attention of capitalists to the great necessity that existed for new houses, in accordance with modern sanitary requirements, suitable not only for the better-off members of the working classes, but also for those then paying rents varying from 1s. to 1s. 6d. a week for houses not habitable ; he thought that this could hardly be beyond the commercial resources of a community that had succeeded, through the beneficent enterprise of one of its members, in enabling a working man to eat a thoroughly good dinner for 4½d.

THE EXPENSE OF BUILDING COTTAGES, AND THE RENTS PER ANNUM, IN CERTAIN SCOTTISH TOWNS 1842

Town	Cost of erection of cottages, etc.	Rent of cottages, etc., per annum	Rent paid by labourer to total expenditure
Aberdeen	Houses for six families £250–£300	Garret or attic 25s.–30s. Room and closet 50s.–80s. Two rooms £5 Cottages, etc., £4–£6	8–14%
Arbroath	£60–£80	£3–£6 Garrets 20s.–30s.	11–16⅔%
Ayr	About £30	30s.–£4	About 8⅓%
Dundee	£60–£80	One room 40s.–50s. Two rooms 70s.–100s.	6¾–21¼%
Edinburgh	£60–£80	£2–£4 for one apartment One room and kitchen £3–£5	6–25%
Glasgow	Tenement for sixteen families £800–£1,200, room and kitchen for each	One room £2 Room and kitchen £3–£7 Two rooms and kitchen £6–£9	7½–33%
Inverness	£30–£80	From £1–£3 a room	About 10%
Kirkcaldy	Two rooms £40	One room 30s.–40s. Two rooms £3	6–10%
Kirkwall	£60–£60	£1–£2 for one room	6–16%
Melrose	£60–£80	£4	About 16⅔%
Tain	£10–£20	10s.–60s.	About 5%
Wigtown	£15	30s.–40s.	About 7½%

From the Report of the Poor Law Commissioners on the Sanitary Condition of the Labouring Population

11

Wretched as was the general level of Scottish housing in the nineteenth century, it nowhere reached the depth to be found in the common lodging-houses abounding not only in the cities but in many of the country towns. In these miserable lodging-houses were to be found the most wretched people of the times. " The worst form of barbarism," wrote Sir J. B. Russell, " is that which gathers at the base of civilization, and here we had it in perfection." Lodging-house reform and regulation sprang from the necessity of self-preservation ; typhus and cholera established their headquarters there ; and there was undoubtedly truth in the saying of Russell that if some disease-proof partition could have been erected which would have prevented the spread of the flames of fever, the inmates of the comfortable houses could have thanked God that they were not as these other men, and left the fire to die away among the ashes of its victims.

In Tranent there were from fifteen to twenty regular lodging-houses in which paupers, vagrants, and a few labouring people lived. They were crowded at all hours, but most especially at night. Men, women, and children lived and slept in the same apartment ; in one room about eighteen feet long and ten feet wide there were four beds made up constantly, and when the house was " throng " another was added to the number. These lodging-houses were the headquarters for beggars. In Stirling there were " numerous lodging-houses of the very worst description in various parts of the town, especially in Broad Street, St. John Street, Baker Street, and King Street." There were three lodging-houses in Tain, chiefly occupied by beggars and hawkers. The general charge for such lodgings was twopence per head for the night, with an ample allowance of whisky to the landlord by way of perquisite. These lodgers were the means of introducing to the community infectious diseases such as fever and smallpox, and in 1840 it was reported that " Measures have recently been adopted in neighbouring counties for repressing this grievous nuisance." In Greenock there were " a good many lodging-houses for vagrants " ; the charge for a night's lodging was 2d. or 3d., 2d. being the charge where more than two persons occupied the same bed.

But the lodging-houses were to be found at their worst in the cities, and in Glasgow, particularly, many of the early sanitarians criticized them fiercely. Graham described a lodging-house consisting of two rooms, separated by boards, the first thirteen feet by eleven, the other fifteen by eight, in which " twenty-three of the lowest class of Irish were lately lodged. To-day there are fourteen, of whom two are confined with fever, three are convalescent, and one only has hitherto escaped." There were three beds in this house, one of them in a press half-way up the wall, the others wooden frames, on which were laid some shavings of wood, scantily covered with dirty rags, but most of the patients were lying on the floor. Symons wrote that in the lower lodging-houses ten, twelve, and sometimes twenty persons, of both sexes and all ages, slept promiscuously on the floor in different degrees of nakedness. " These places are generally, as regards dirt, damp, and decay, such as no person of common humanity would stable his horse in." Dr. Smith, one of the district surgeons, wrote that many of the lodging-houses were more fit for pig-sties than dwellings for human beings ; " and in not a few the donkey and the pigs rest at night in the same apartment as the family."

Conditions in these common lodging-houses were described by " Hawkie," beggar, street-orator, and wit, and a well-known Glasgow character in the first half of the nineteenth century. " Hawkie " described one particular lodging-house, " a cele-brated spot called the flea-barracks," and he spoke of those " most notorious characters, lodging-house keepers," who were suffered to take an old house, perhaps an old stable or condemned house, and in it start a lodging-house, which, every second night, returned their original outlay ; he told of a house of two apart-ments, only one having a fireplace, in which he had seen as many as forty lodgers at one time at 3d. per head per night.

Among the early efforts made to control common lodging-houses from the public health point of view was that contained in a local Act applicable to Calton and Mile-end. It decreed that " no keeper of lodging-houses of an inferior description for the accommodation of mendicant strangers and others " should receive such lodgers without the house being inspected and approved by the Superintendent of Police, who was authorized to fix the number of lodgers who might be accommodated. Keepers of such houses, in the event of any person in their houses becoming ill of fever or other disease, were bound under penalty to give intimation of the illness to the Superintendent of Police, so that the disease might be investigated and treated and the patient removed ; further, if there was a reason to apprehend the spread of infectious disease in any such lodging-house, the magistrate could cause the remaining lodgers to be removed and the houses to be disinfected. It was not until 1843 that powers were taken in the city to license common lodging-houses, prevent overcrowd-ing, and secure the reporting of fever by the keepers ; and the machinery for enforcing this Act was imperfect. Another development during the forties in Glasgow was the creation of the " Model Lodging Association," a voluntary organization that established three large houses, later acquired by the Improvement Trust. Very similar measures for the control of lodging-houses were taken in Edinburgh and other Scottish towns. Under police supervision the lodging-houses were registered and inspected, their ventilation and cleanliness controlled, and the keeper of a house required to report forthwith to the police any case of infectious disease among the inmates. A committee of the Royal College of Physicians of Edinburgh, appointed to consider any Bills that might be brought before Parliament for the improvement of the health of towns, regarded it as unfortunate that the Towns Improvement Clauses Act, 1847, did not require keepers of lodging-houses for the labouring classes to report to the authorities the case of any lodger confined to bed by illness for twenty-four hours.

These early measures for the regulation of common lodging-houses were dictated almost entirely by fear of infection ; there was little or no effort to improve the lot of the unfortunate people who frequented such places. An increasing number of Parochial Boards began to set up lodging-houses to which the poor could be sent as an alternative to outdoor poor relief, but the standards of these places appear to have been little better than those run for private profit, and in the Annual Report of the Board of Supervision, issued in 1862, it was stated that from information available to them the Board " should not be justified in holding an offer of admission to any parochial lodging-house as equivalent to an offer of adequate relief."

CHAPTER IV

CAUSES OF DEATH AND SICKNESS:
THE INFLUENCE OF THE GROWTH
OF MANUFACTURES

I

In the seventeenth and eighteenth centuries repeated attempts were made to take a census of the population of different parts of Scotland, and indeed the keeping of parochial registers had become fairly general in the country by 1783, when there was introduced a tax which, however trifling, was fatal to the system. " So odious was this duty," wrote Sinclair, " that though it amounted only to threepence for each article entered, yet the common people, not being compelled to pay it, rather chose to save the trifle than to have either a baptism, burial, or marriage inserted in the register." It was estimated that the total revenue derived from this tax could never have exceeded £15,000 per annum, and was probably much less ; and the tax was subsequently dropped.

At the time of the Union of the Parliaments in 1707, the population was estimated to be about 1,048,000, but not until 1755 was the first comprehensive census of Scotland carried out, namely, by the Reverend Alexander Webster, D.D., minister of the Tolbooth Church of Edinburgh. Dr. Webster persuaded the Society for Propagating Christian Knowledge in the Highlands and Islands of Scotland to require every minister within the bounds of those presbyteries in which the Society had erected Charity Schools " to make and transmit a list of his Parishioners, distinguishing them into Protestants and Papists." To ensure compliance, this order to the ministers was accompanied by a threat to withdraw the schools in default. The adoption of a more propitiatory approach secured co-operation in other parts of the country, and there is cause to believe that Dr. Webster's census was reasonably accurate. It showed the total population of Scotland to be 1,265,380. One of Dr. Webster's objects was to ascertain the number of men likely to be able to bear arms in different parts of the country. He counted as potential fighting men those between the ages of 18 and 56, both inclusive, regarding

64

these ages as preferable to the generally accepted limits of 16 and 60, " the one being generally too Weak to bear the fatigue of War and the weight of Arms ; and the other too Crazy and Infirm, notwithstanding some particular Instances have appeared to the contrary." On this basis he estimated that Scotland could raise of fighting men more than one fourth of the number of souls which it contained. " But as this proportion includes the Blind and Lame, or otherwise diseased, the Author has supposed the Fighting Men in every Parish and Shire to be only one fifth part of the number of the inhabitants, and these He is of opinion may be reckoned effective Men." Webster prepared a table setting out the distribution by age of the inhabitants (page 69), and he realized that this table might serve several useful purposes, " particularly for calculating the probabilities of life and consequently for estimating the value of Annuities in Scotland with more exactness than any table yet extant." The tables then in use in Scotland for calculating annuities were founded either on the births and burials in London or on those in Breslau, the capital city of Silesia, " which can be no just rule in Scotland. Because by comparing them with the (Scottish) table it appears that the generality of people in Scotland live to a greater Age than at London and not to so great an age as at Breslaw." It appeared that at Breslau one half of the people born lived until they were sixteen years of age and one quarter of them until fifty-five years. In Scotland one half of those born lived only to the age of eleven years and one quarter to the age of forty-six, whereas in London, " according to some tables, the one half die before they arrive at the age of eight years, and one fourth of them before the age of forty-three ; and according to other tables they die much sooner, which must necessarily make a considerable alteration in the chances of life and consequently in estimating the value of Annuities."

About 1795 the population of Scotland was ascertained again for Sir John Sinclair's national statistical work, and found to amount to 1,526,492, and in 1801 the first official census of the inhabitants of Great Britain, taken under government auspices, found the population of Scotland to be 1,599,068. The subsequent censuses, taken at ten-yearly intervals, showed a progressive increase in population with an increasing density of the population per square mile, though this affected different parts of the country to a different extent. Thus according to Sinclair the density of population per square mile in Scotland as a whole rose from 42 in 1745 to 69 in 1821, but the increase chiefly affected the "southern division" of the country (that south of Stirlingshire and Dumbartonshire), where the figure rose from 62 to 133 over the period.

Sinclair classified the inhabitants of Scotland as falling into three broad groups : (1) the eleven " productive classes," (2) the eleven " useful, or indirectly productive classes," and (3) the five " unproductive classes " (totals as original report).

It is interesting to note the extent to which the number of professional men was surpassed by the number of innkeepers.

	Families	Persons
1 *The eleven productive classes*		
Agricultural class	130,699	784,194
Fishermen	27,015	120,561
Clothing workmen for the home market .	72,671	218,015
Building class, including makers of furniture .	27,750	111,000
Workers in mines and quarries	13,160	50,500
Manufacturers in various branches . .	73,250	201,425
Commercial class	14,500	51,000
Fisheries not intended for food	2,000	8,000
The monied interest class	500	2,000
The class for the fine arts	400	1,800
The literary class	5,000	20,000
	366,945	1,568,293
2 *The eleven useful, or indirectly productive, classes*		
The political class	70	304
The revenue class	600	2,400
Class for the public defence	100	1,500
The legal class	3,500	16,000
The clerical class	2,000	10,000
The medical class	1,500	6,400
Teachers of youth	3,500	10,500
Inland traders	31,400	188,400
Innkeepers	25,085	97,500
Menial servants, male and female . .	4,500	97,985
Persons who furnish innocent amusements .	500	2,540
	72,555	455,329
3 *The five unproductive classes*		
The insane	—	4,500
Debtors confined	100	420
The infirm poor	10,100	45,762
Adults receiving occasional assistance . .	2,900	10,000
Vagrants and criminals	360	1,152
	13,460	61,834

GENERAL SUMMARY OF THE AGES OF PERSONS IN GREAT BRITAIN, 1821 (after Cleland)

MALES

	Under 5 Years	5 to 10	10 to 15	15 to 20	20 to 30	30 to 40	40 to 50	50 to 60	60 to 70	70 to 80	80 to 90	90 to 100	100 and upwards	Total
England . . .	739762	645735	562209	475052	706757	555713	452514	320092	215263	106697	27052	1995	57	4808898
Wales . . .	51817	48123	41404	34534	49023	37949	29815	22112	16246	8335	2535	258	3	342154
Scotland . . .	137956	125298	115183	95319	137645	101107	82695	60014	42309	19977	5377	620	40	923540
Total of Males	929535	819156	718796	604905	893425	694769	565024	402818	273818	135009	54964	2873	100	6074592

FEMALES

	Under 5 Years	5 to 10	10 to 15	15 to 20	20 to 30	30 to 40	40 to 50	50 to 60	60 to 70	70 to 80	80 to 90	90 to 100	100 and upwards	Total
England . . .	725202	636604	530226	499638	845469	607867	468336	328077	230009	114572	32564	2888	111	5021563
Wales . . .	49487	45853	39140	35931	55869	41640	32641	24083	19175	10076	3751	392	18	358056
Scotland . . .	133711	121573	109247	108306	182712	124380	96991	73518	51868	23298	6734	766	62	1033166
Total of Females	908400	804030	678613	643875	1084050	773887	597968	425678	301052	147946	43049	4046	191	6412785

The Total Number of Persons in Great Britain (not including the Army, Navy, and Seamen in Registered Vessels) was 14,072,331—and the Number of Persons whose Ages were returned was 12,487,377—whence it appears that the Ages of one-ninth part of the Persons therein enumerated, have not been obtained, in compliance with the question to that effect. The Total Number of Enumeration Returns received was 16,819—four hundred and sixty-five of which did not contain any answer to the question concerning Ages of Persons, and are thus marked (→) throughout the Abstract.

67

From the general summary of the census of Great Britain carried out in 1821 it appears that in that year the number of families chiefly employed in agriculture in Scotland was already less than the number of families engaged in trade, manufacture, or handicraft, to an extent somewhat similar to that in England at the time. In Wales the position was reversed, most families being still engaged in agriculture. From the same general survey of conditions in 1821 it appears that the number of families per house in Scotland (1·31) was already greater than in England (1·20) or in Wales (1·08), so that already the bugbear of Scottish overcrowding had begun to be apparent.

GENERAL SUMMARY OF HOUSES, FAMILIES, AND PERSONS
IN GREAT BRITAIN, 1821 (after Cleland)

	England	Wales	Scot-land	Army, Navy, Marines, and Seamen in Registered Vessels	GREAT BRITAIN
Houses Inhabited . . .	1951973	136183	341474	—	2429630
— By how many Families occupied	2346717	146706	447960	—	2941383
— Building . . .	18289	985	2405	—	21679
— Un-inhabited .	66053	3652	12657	—	82364
Families chiefly employed in Agriculture .	773732	74225	130699	—	978656
— in Trade, Manu-facture, or Handi-craft	1118295	41680	190264	—	1350239
All other Families not com-prised in the two preceding classes	454690	30801	126997	—	612488
Persons Males	5483679	350487	983552	319300	7137018
— Females . . .	5777758	366951	1109904	—	7254613
Total of Persons . .	11261437	717438	2093456	319300	14391631

REMARKS

" 1. In the Number of Males attributed to the Army (column 4th) are included certain Militia Battalions which happened to be embodied on the 28th of May 1821, in the following Counties, viz.—in Bedford, 336 men ; in Bucks, 611 ; in Cambridge, 478 ; in Derby, 914 ; in Dorset, 436 ; in Hertford, 509 ; in Huntingdon, 175 ; in Kent, 1208 ; in Middlesex, (London) 526 ; in Northampton, 614 ; in Somerset, 817 ; in Southampton, (Isle of Wight) 66 ; in Stafford, 1134 ; in Suffolk, 999 ; in Surrey, 759 ; in York, 789 ; in Brecon, 213 ; in Carnarvon, 141 ; in Denbigh, 372 ; and in Glamorgan, 413 ; in all 11510 men. These men not having been included in the Enumeration Abstract of the several Counties, the number of males, and consequently the population of those Counties is (strictly speaking) rather understated, as compared to that of the other Counties ; those who serve in the Militia being generally, though not always taken from among the inhabitants of the County for which they serve.
2. The Abstract of the returns obtained from the Islands in the British Seas is not included in the General Summary of Great Britain."

When more information about the occupation of the people of Scotland became available from the census of 1851, the swing over from agriculture to industry was obvious and continued to increase during the following decade.

OCCUPATION OF SCOTTISH POPULATION ; PERCENTAGE OF PEOPLE ENGAGED IN VARIOUS OCCUPATIONAL GROUPS

Occupational Group	1851	1861
Professional	1·45	1·71
Domestic	59·93	56·63
Commercial.	2·58	2·75
Agriculture	13·43	12·36
Industry	18·21	22·66
Indefinite and non-productive . . .	3·76	3·86

2

The age distribution of the people of Scotland varied but little between 1755, when 26·3 per cent. of the people were under ten years of age, and 7·2 per cent. over sixty, and 1811, when the percentages were respectively 25·5 and 7·2. Fifty years later, in 1861, the percentage under ten was still 25·5, but that over sixty had risen to very nearly 9.

AGE DISTRIBUTION OF THE PEOPLE—SCOTLAND

Age	1755[1]	1811	1861
Under ten . . .	322,381	459,826	780,443
Ten . . .	233,813	336,342	630,147
Twenty . . .	210,791	300,660	513,975
Thirty . . .	175,202	249,898	376,961
Forty . . .	134,701	192,130	298,336
Fifty . . .	94,840	135,282	218,917
Sixty . . .	58,911	84,027	151,687
Seventy . . .	25,659	36,598	69,626
Over eighty . . .	7,082	10,101	22,302
	1,265,380	1,804,864	3,062,294

[1] Dr Webster's Census

The oldest person mentioned in Sinclair's Statistical Account was a native of Shetland who had reached his hundred and fortieth year. He married in his hundredth year, and in the very year that he died pulled his small skiff ashore unaided in very severe weather. Of the healthiness and longevity of the Scots in those days Sinclair wrote that from a table constructed by the Reverend Mr. Wilkie, a Fifeshire divine, it emerged that in Scotland the expectation of life in infancy was 40·6 years, whereas the comparable English figure was 28 years. " The people of Scotland," wrote Sinclair, " not only live long, but preserve till an advanced period of life their corporeal and mental faculties. Great wealth and high rank are not favourable to long life." In 1821 Cleland observed that more persons survived to attain the age of eighty years in the northern counties than in the southern ; he found that in Ross and Cromarty 1 person reached that age out of every 93 ; in Aberdeen 1 in 96, in Inverness 1 in 98, in Stirlingshire 1 in 176, in Lanarkshire 1 in 169, and in Edinburghshire 1 in 257.

3

Further information became available about population trends in different parts of the country. For a long time before 1700 the population of Edinburgh appeared to remain almost stationary at about 25,000 ; then it began to turn more and more steeply upward, and for each half-century after that date it doubled, rising to about 50,000 in 1750, 100,000 in 1800, and 200,000 in 1850 : even in the late eighteenth century the population of Edinburgh was nearly double that of Glasgow. The population of the Isle of Skye, Sinclair reported, had been constantly increasing for eighty years, and had so much increased that between August 1771 and October 1790 no fewer than eight large transports sailed from the island with 2,400 emigrants to seek settlements in America, taking with them £24,000 sterling, ship freights included. In the small island of Eigg, containing only 399 souls, no fewer than 176 persons emigrated between 1788 and 1790, the country being so overstocked with people that the lands were unable to supply them with the necessaries of life ; fathers divided their farms, however small, with their sons when they married.

In no county was the increase in population so striking as in Lanarkshire, of which the inhabitants increased from 146,699 in

1801 to 316,819 in 1831, an increase of over a hundred per cent. in thirty years. The population of the thirty-nine landward parishes amounted in 1831 to 114,364, about 35 per cent. of the total. The occupations of the male residents in the landward parishes were classified in the 1831 census : occupiers of land employing labourers, 1,474 ; occupiers of land not employing labourers, 1,286 ; labourers employed in agriculture, 3,679 ; males employed in manufactures, 5,217 ; males employed in retail trade or in handicrafts, 8,350 ; wholesale merchants, capitalists, bankers, professional persons, and other educated men, 840 ; labourers employed by the three preceding classes and in other labour not agricultural, 4,832 ; all other males twenty years old, except servants, including retired tradesmen and masters diseased in body or mind, 1,281.

The earliest reliable estimate of the population of Glasgow was made in 1610, when Archbishop Spottiswood found it to amount to 7,644 souls. In 1660 it was 14,678 and in 1688, at the time of the Revolution, it had decreased to 11,948. In 1708, immediately after the Union with England, the population was 12,766 ; and in 1740 it was ascertained by the magistrates to be 17,034. In 1755 Dr. Webster found it to be 23,546, a figure perhaps slightly inflated ; in 1763 it amounted to 28,300 ; in 1780, 42,832, a figure including for the first time the whole of the suburbs ; in 1791 it was 66,578, and at the first official census the corrected figure was found to be 83,769 ; by 1831 it had risen to 202,426, and the age distribution of the people was as follows : Under 5 years 30,277, 5–9 years 25,707, 10–19 years 41,956, 20–29 years 38,185, 30–39 years 26,419, 40–49 years 18,014, 50–59 years 11,648, 60–69 years 6,920, 70–79 years 2,592, over 80 years 708. The age of the population of the city was already higher than that of Scotland as a whole. Of the inhabitants of the city 35,554 were Irish, 2,919 English, 353 foreigners, and 163,000 Scots.

From an analysis of the occupations in which the population of Glasgow was engaged in 1819–20 it emerged that the largest occupational group was that of weavers and warpers, and that many men were engaged in other manufacturing processes. At the census of 1861 the population of Glasgow was found to be 395,503.

Two factors played a large part in attracting the poor to Scottish cities during the period of their rapid expansion : (1) the hope of getting employment of some kind for parents and children, failing which, the hope of getting succour from public and private charities ; and (2) the practicability of getting house-room, however wretched. Robert Skirving wrote in his book *Landlords and Labourers* (1862) that the boasted peasantry of Scotland had decreased so that " the soil is now to no inconsiderable extent cultivated by the poorest, the most destitute, and too often, I fear, the most degraded class of Irish immigrant," and he went on to lament that it seemed to have got into the heads of most of the owners of the soil that the old houses should be pulled down without replacement ; houses were levelled for the avowed purpose of driving away the inhabitants, largely through fear of increasing the number of paupers. Only a fraction of the inmates of the city workhouses were city born (40–50 per cent.), and the same held true of the hospital population. Dr. Cowan found that in 1840 less than a quarter of the patients in Glasgow Royal Infirmary were natives of the city, and that not more than 15 per cent. of the patients admitted into the Albion Street Fever Hospital, when fever was at its height at that time, were natives ; that 30 per cent. were from Ireland and 40 per cent. from the Highlands and agricultural districts of Scotland. Among these incomers to the cities poverty and distress were prevalent, and the incidence of disease was high.

At the census of 1861 it was found that 90·9 per cent. of the population of Scotland was Scottish, 6·6 per cent. Irish, and 1·7 per cent. English ; the four cities varied widely in the nationality of their citizens :

PERCENTAGE DISTRIBUTION OF NATIONALITY OF CITIZENS

City	Population	Scottish		English and Welsh	Irish	Other
		from county in which town situated	from other counties			
Glasgow	395,503	50·96	30·04	2·66	15·69	0·62
Edinburgh	170,144	57·57	31·46	4·33	5·17	1·45
Dundee	91,664	61·57	20·95	1·35	15·67	0·43
Aberdeen	73,900	76·48	19·31	2·18	1·25	0·76

4

The principal causes of death and incapacity could not be specified until accurate registers of deaths were kept. In 1613 the Presbytery of Glasgow had appointed Bills of Mortality to be kept within their bounds, but it was not until 1694 that this was done with any accuracy, and even then the name and age of the deceased were all that appeared. Yet before the middle of the nineteenth century, mortality bills afforded the only source of information about the causes of death. These Bills of Mortality were taken from the Parochial Registers kept with varying accuracy in different parts of the country. The registration of burials was entrusted to the churchyard wardens, of whom there were twelve in the population district of Glasgow. These officers, who received a fee for their trouble, attended all funerals and made a memorandum of the name, age, etc., of the deceased. Sometimes the alleged cause of death was also recorded, and in any case the accuracy of information available on the subject was for long doubtful, save in a few particular areas and in respect of a few diseases marked by signs and symptoms so gross, or of epidemic prevalence so marked, that little doubt attached to the diagnosis.

It was estimated that the population of Edinburgh in 1732 was about 32,000, and from information available it is possible to obtain a rough indication of some of the important causes of death in the city in 1740 and 1741 :

Causes of Death	1740	1741
All causes	1,237	1,611
Consumption	278	349
Fever	161	304
Flux	3	36
Smallpox	274	206
Measles	100	112
Chincough	26	101
Convulsions	22	16

In considering these figures it must be borne in mind that great distress set in in Edinburgh during the severe winter of 1739-40. The mills were stopped by ice and snow, causing a scarcity of meal ; the harvest of 1740 was bad, riots took place in

October, and granaries were plundered. Creighton points out that the deaths from fever, which were many in 1740, were nearly doubled in 1741, with a considerable increase in the prevalence of fatal dysentery.

One of the earliest complete tables of mortality was that kept by the parish minister of Torthorwald, in Dumfriesshire, for the twenty-seven years ending 1790. During the period there were altogether 280 deaths, and the reputed causes of death, as recorded in the Parish Registers, were as under :

Decay of age	. . . . . .	39
Asthma	. . . . . .	36
Children under 1 year—disease unknown	. . . . . .	29
Fever	. . . . . .	25
Dropsy	. . . . . .	19
Rheumatism	. . . . .	18
Consumption	. . . . . .	17
Palsy	. . . . . .	17
Smallpox	. . . . . .	14
Unknown diseases	. . . .	9
Accident	. . . . . .	6
Internal chronic complaints — obstructed viscera	. . . .	6
Worm fever	. . . .	5
Looseness	. . . .	5
Inflammation of stomach and bowels	. . . .	4
Chincough	. . . . . .	4
Cancer	. . . .	4
Apoplexy	. . . . . .	3
Jaundice	. . . . . .	2
Inflammation of liver	. . . .	2
Teething	. . . . .	2
Measles, Child - bed, Abscess, Atrophy, Scrofula, Idiotism, Ischuria, Carious ulcer, Rupture, Fits, Inflammation, each		1

In Glasgow, mortality from all causes was 31·8 per thousand of the population in 1783, and still 27·6 per thousand in 1861. During the intervening years a figure as low as 17·1 was recorded in 1801, but in several other years, usually associated with high epidemic prevalence, the figures were nearly twice as high. One year with a high death-rate was 1791. In that year 1,508 persons died in the City Parish, in addition to 43 patients in the Town's Hospital ; in Gorbals Parish, the deaths in the same year numbered 361 ; in Calton, 319 ; and in Anderston, 248. Of the 1,508 city deaths, 403 were due to small pox, 274 to consumption, 151 to diseases of old age, 102 to fever, and 101 to bowel hives. No fewer than 694 of the 1,508 deaths were of children under two years of age, and 63 per cent. of all deaths occurred among children under ten. This high record of child-deaths is characteristic of all Mortality Bills of the first half of the nineteenth century : that for 1838, with its 1,347 deaths of infants in the first year of life in addition to 583 still-births, is typical. Year after year, for nearly two generations, the deaths of children under ten accounted for more than half of all deaths in the city ; not until the middle of the century did improvement take place, and as late as 1861 some

WHO DIED OF THE FOLLOWING DISEASES

Abortive	60		Brought up	885
Aged	151	Iliac passion		2
Asthma	62	Inflammation		3
Apoplexy	1	Lethargy		1
Bowel hive	101	Measles		4
Burnt	1	Palsy		7
Casualties	19	Rheumatism		2
Childbed	15	Rickets		3
Chincough	69	Running sores		1
Colic	1	Rupture		1
Consumption	274	Smallpox		403
Convulsions	3	Stopping		69
Cramp	8	Sore throat		20
Dropsy	3	Swellings		7
Fever	102	Teething		71
Flux	11	Tympany		1
Gravel	3	Vomiting		2
Jaundice	1	Water in the head		26
Carry up	885		Total	1,508

From the Bill of Mortality for the City Parish of Glasgow, 1791 (after Brown).

42 per cent. of all the deaths were still of children under ten years of age, a figure in strange contrast to that now prevailing—about 13 per cent.

The population of St. Andrews was 4,299 in 1840, and the total number of deaths there during the five years 1836–40 was 438.

Littlejohn, in his survey of sanitary conditions in Edinburgh in 1863, found ample evidence of the correlation between overcrowding and high mortality : the highest death-rates were returned from Tron, Grassmarket, and Canongate districts, with densities of population per inhabited acre respectively 353, 238, and 220 ; and the lowest rates from Morningside, Newington, Broughton, and Grange, where, by way of contrast, the densities of population per inhabited acre were respectively 8, 40, 49, and 16.

Dr. Begbie, Consulting Physician to the Society, reported on the causes of death among members of the Scottish Widows' Fund Life Assurance Society during the years 1860–66. The Fund embraced all ranks, "from highest to lowest citizenship," but Dr. Begbie found that for a complicated disease the death certificate tended to state some of the symptoms of the disease rather than give its name. During the seven years studied by Dr.

BILL OF MORTALITY FOR GLASGOW, 1838 (after Brown)

TABLE exhibiting, under the different Ages, the Amount of some of the more easily discriminated DISEASES of which the Parties are reported to have Died, and also Proportions which these bear to the whole Number of Deaths during the year, as well as to the Estimated Population

POPULATION ESTIMATED AT 263,000

AGES

DISEASES	Under 1 Year		1 and under 2		2 and under 5		5 and under 10		10 and under 15		15 and under 20		20 and under 30		30 and under 40		40 and under 50		50 and under 60		60 and under 70	
	M.	F.	M.	F.	M.	F.	M.	F.	M.	F.	M.	F.	M.	F.	M.	F.	M.	F.	M.	F.	M.	F.
Accidents	1	—	3	2	11	14	15	12	9	4	12	1	29	5	17	1	19	7	4	3	4	5
Aged	—	—	—	—	—	—	—	—	—	—	—	—	—	—	—	—	—	—	5	7	65	100
Asthma	—	1	—	—	—	—	—	—	—	—	—	1	1	4	9	5	18	29	32	23	30	32
Bowel Complaints	322	246	92	60	21	21	4	3	1	2	—	1	4	1	5	7	2	5	3	4	5	6
Catarrh	5	1	—	3	2	2	1	—	—	—	—	—	—	—	—	3	—	1	1	2	—	—
Child Birth	—	—	—	—	—	—	—	—	—	—	—	3	—	42	—	34	—	10	—	—	—	—
Croup	19	13	17	18	38	22	5	4	1	1	—	1	—	—	—	—	—	—	—	—	—	—
Decline	60	68	59	58	56	54	41	25	25	32	39	48	115	107	76	97	59	87	39	68	12	15
Dropsy	8	4	3	—	13	5	14	13	3	4	2	1	8	8	10	13	10	18	8	16	13	17
Fever	19	34	8	10	23	30	21	18	14	24	24	26	72	56	91	79	102	79	37	31	20	19
Head, Diseases of	45	34	33	29	43	32	16	16	3	2	3	3	10	3	14	6	11	5	17	5	15	8
Heart, do.	1	—	—	—	—	—	—	—	1	3	—	2	5	—	5	—	4	2	6	2	4	2
Hooping Cough	84	64	66	86	65	73	12	15	3	1	—	—	—	—	—	—	—	—	—	—	—	—
Inflammation	42	41	22	15	24	28	16	19	2	3	9	7	10	29	20	20	30	18	10	9	10	2
Measles	37	39	65	59	86	75	15	24	2	—	1	—	1	—	1	1	—	—	—	—	—	—
Nervous Diseases	6	6	6	1	4	4	2	2	2	5	—	4	—	2	—	—	2	—	—	2	—	1
Scarlet Fever	2	1	7	8	25	17	9	8	2	3	—	—	—	—	—	1	1	1	—	—	—	—
Small Pox	58	53	56	43	59	60	14	14	4	—	7	4	7	7	2	2	—	—	1	—	—	—
Miscellaneous Diseases	8	10	4	11	7	4	6	4	6	4	3	4	8	13	11	12	23	22	11	21	20	14
Total Diseases ascertained	717	582	441	403	479	438	191	166	73	85	95	104	271	282	261	281	282	284	173	201	198	221
Diseases not ascertained	25	23	5	8	6	6	3	3	2	—	3	3	4	6	7	4	8	12	4	5	5	—
Total Deaths	742	605	446	411	485	444	194	169	75	85	98	107	275	288	268	285	290	296	177	206	203	221

76

DISEASES	70 and under 75 M.	70 and under 75 F.	75 and under 80 M.	75 and under 80 F.	80 and under 85 M.	80 and under 85 F.	85 and under 90 M.	85 and under 90 F.	90 and under 95 M.	90 and under 95 F.	95 and under 100 M.	95 and under 100 F.	100 and upwards M.	100 and upwards F.	Total M.	Total F.	Grand Total in 1838	Grand Total in 1837
Accidents	2	1	—	1	1	1	—	—	—	—	—	—	—	—	127	56	183	165
Aged	66	103	46	62	39	62	23	31	2	6	—	4	—	2	246	377	623	878
Asthma	10	10	6	2	1	3	—	—	—	—	—	—	—	—	108	110	218	303
Bowel Complaints	1	2	1	1	—	—	—	—	—	—	—	—	—	—	459	363	822	1100
Catarrh	—	—	1	2	—	—	—	—	—	—	—	—	—	—	10	14	21	389
Child Birth	—	—	—	—	—	—	—	—	—	—	—	—	—	—	—	89	139	93
Croup	—	—	—	—	—	—	—	—	—	—	—	—	—	—	80	59	139	129
Decline	3	2	2	1	—	2	—	—	—	—	—	—	—	—	581	662	1243	1562
Dropsy	6	10	5	3	—	2	2	—	—	—	—	—	—	—	99	101	200	208
Fever	4	1	—	—	—	—	—	—	—	—	—	—	—	—	439	377	816	2180
Head, Diseases of	2	2	—	2	2	—	—	—	—	—	—	—	—	—	220	153	373	489
Heart, do.	—	—	—	—	—	—	—	—	—	—	—	—	—	—	30	15	45	38
Hooping Cough	—	1	—	—	—	—	—	—	—	—	—	—	—	—	228	238	400	457
Inflammation	1	—	—	—	—	—	—	—	—	—	—	—	—	—	196	190	386	580
Measles	—	—	—	—	—	—	—	—	—	—	—	—	—	—	208	197	405	350
Nervous Diseases	—	—	—	—	—	—	—	—	—	—	—	—	—	—	22	19	41	59
Scarlet Fever	—	—	—	—	—	—	—	—	—	—	—	—	—	—	46	41	87	79
Small Pox	—	—	—	—	—	—	—	—	—	—	—	—	—	—	201	187	388	352
Miscellaneous Diseases	4	4	4	—	—	1	—	—	2	—	—	—	—	—	117	124	241	263
Total Diseases ascertained	99	137	64	73	43	72	26	31	4	6	—	4	—	2	3417	3372	6789	
Diseases not ascertained	1	—	—	—	—	—	—	—	—	—	—	—	—	—	73	70	143	536
Total Deaths	100	137	64	73	43	72	26	31	4	6	—	4	—	2	3490	3442		

Total Number of Deaths 6932
To which add Still-born . . . 583

Total Number of Burials 7515

77

Begbie the number of lives at risk was 11,112, and the number of deaths 1,398. The principal causes of death were diseases of the brain and nervous system (including apoplexy and paralysis), 314 ; diseases of the respiratory organs (including tuberculosis and broncho-pneumonia), 276 ; diseases of heart and vessels, 221 ; diseases of the digestive organs (including the liver), 172 ; and epidemic and contagious diseases (chiefly continued fever, cholera, and dysentery), 144. Two facts from this mortality experience particularly struck Dr. Begbie : (1) the frequency with which concealment of the real cause of death was practised in alcoholism and in cancer, and (2) the increasing mortality from consumption up to age 45, and its subsequent gradual decline. Dr. Begbie analysed by age the deaths occurring among members of the Fund between the years 1815 and 1866 :

SCOTTISH WIDOWS' FUND LIFE ASSURANCE SOCIETY— MORTALITY EXPERIENCE, 1815–66

Age at Death	Cause of Death		
	All Causes	Consumption	Heart Disease
20–30	124	37	1
30–40	437	89	25
40–50	694	73	59
50–60	914	54	117
60–70	852	23	138
Over 70	650	—	86
Not ascertained	34	—	—
	3,705	276	426

In his first detailed annual report, published in 1861, the Registrar-General examined Scottish mortality experience during the year 1855 and came to the conclusion that if the mortality of that year could be accepted as reasonably average, Scotland was one of the very healthiest countries on the face of the globe. He found that, taking Scotland as a whole, the percentage of deaths to population was higher under five years of age (5·88) than at any other age under 70 ; and the occurrence of child deaths was, except in Aberdeen, considerably higher in the great cities than in the country as a whole, being approximately 12 per cent. in Glasgow, 7·5 per cent. in Edinburgh, 10 per cent. in Dundee, 8·5 per cent. in Paisley, and 14 per cent. in Greenock. The Registrar-General concluded that there are three modes of estimating the comparative healthiness of a district : first, by estimating the proportion of annual deaths to the living population ; second, by estimating the proportion of deaths under five years to the number living under five years ; and, third, where the number of the population is lacking, by ascertaining what proportion the deaths under five bear to the total deaths.

The chief groups of disease responsible for deaths in 1855 were, in order, the zymotic diseases, tuberculosis, respiratory diseases and diseases of old age. The zymotic diseases causing most death, were typhus fever, scarlatina, whooping cough, diarrhœa, smallpox, and measles.

In this first report the Registrar-General had something of interest to say about the influence of external agencies on mortality : " Besides the specific diseases, which are the more immediate gateways (or trapdoors) through which our race drops into the grave, there are other agencies which powerfully modify these diseases and their action on mankind. Of these, the most important to consider are, the state of trade (including the question as to the wages paid, and the fullness of the occupation), the price and quality of the provisions, and the weather." He recognized it as a well-ascertained fact that a bad harvest, which raised the price of all kinds of provisions, was in general attended by an increased mortality, and he noted that the year 1855 was not one in which trade was dull or employment scarce as evidenced by deposits in Savings Banks during that year. The necessaries of life were abundant ; the people felt no want, " and had a sufficient supply within their reach of nitrogenous or muscle-producing foods "; yet the year 1855 was one of high comparative mortality, and the Registrar-General looked for the explanation in another factor—the weather. He took exception to the prevailing sanitary doctrine that in Scotland " epidemics seemed to be generally combined with summer or hot weather," and pointed out that except for one single class of diseases—bowel complaints—the prevalence and fatality of almost all epidemics in Scotland was at a minimum during the warmest months and increased with the increase of cold. He was convinced that in Scotland it was cold that killed, not heat, and that the mean temperature most favourable to health was one not above 60° F. nor below 50° F.

A Registrar-General of later days (1936) compared the expectation of life in Scotland for 1861–70 with that prevailing in 1930–32. He found that the expectation of life at birth had increased during that period by nearly sixteen years; and he particularly noted that as a result of the decline in mortality in early childhood the age at which expectation of life was at a maximum had shifted from four years in 1861–70 to two years in 1930–32. By the rates of mortality prevailing in 1861–70, male children were reduced to 75 per cent. of their original number at the age of four and a half years, whereas on the rates prevailing in 1930–32, a similar reduction did not take place until the age of forty-five years was reached.

5

For hundreds of years the whole life of Scotland was dominated by the visitation of repeated outbreaks of the major infectious diseases, which tended to obscure the more common everyday ailments of the people. Sometimes, as during the seven " ill years " at the end of the seventeenth century, great privation prevailed. Many people died of starvation, and many more were able to maintain life at a bare existence only. It is not surprising that under such conditions of privation many sought solace in potations of ale or spirits, which in turn begot " dropsies, stupors, lethargies, and apoplexies." Sibbald wrote that the peasantry of those days had poor food and hard work and were subject to many diseases : " Heartburn, sleeplessness, ravings, hypochondriac affections, mania, dysentery, scrophula, cancer, and a dire troop of diseases which everywhere now invades the husbandmen that were formerly free from diseases." Consumption was prevalent, as were fevers of various kinds.

In the year 1730 there started in Edinburgh a practice, soon discontinued, of publishing annual accounts of the reigning maladies. Thus in the winter of 1731–32 there was much worm fever, comatose fever or convulsive fever occurring chiefly among children, though not entirely limited to them. It was marked by intense pain in the head, sometimes with raving, sometimes with stupor, tremulous movements and leaping of the tendons. Many of the children affected passed worms and recovered, the fatalities among young people being few.

Sinclair in the Statistical Account had much to say about the diseases prevalent in Scotland about the end of the eighteenth century. The general impression was that disease had become more prevalent than formerly ; in earlier years, he said, diseases had been few in number, and, with the exception of smallpox, rarely distinguished by violence, a circumstance attributed by Sinclair to the plain mode of living of the people, their remoteness and their healthy constitution.

Rheumatism was then, as now, very prevalent : " there is not a parish in Scotland in which it is not now very generally felt." In the beginning of the eighteenth century rheumatism was but little known, but now, according to Sinclair, " the disorder seems to gain ground." Several factors were held to be responsible for this increased prevalence of rheumatism. One was the climate, and the condition was believed to be most common in the wet west and on the east coast, where the north-easterly winds occasioned it in spring. Another factor was the nature of the houses, " miserable cold damp huts, often made of sods and very imperfectly roofed, damp, badly ventilated, often earthen floors : ill-supplied with fuel and well constructed stoves." Also responsible were the close timber beds in which the common people slept ; " few can be convinced of the vast advantage of having their bedclothes exposed to the fresh air, or the danger of sleeping in places too confined." Clothing, too, left much to be desired. Many found it impossible to avoid continuing to wear wet clothes throughout a long working day, and some were unwilling to shed their wet clothes even at the end of the day's work. Sinclair reported that a circumstance to which importance was commonly ascribed was the disuse of flannel or woollen sheets, and the substitution of linen ones. Among still other factors were the improvident practices and neglects of the people and their increasing pursuit of a sedentary mode of life ; while some attached much importance to the increasing use of potatoes, " a less nourishing diet than oatmeal," and to the immoderate use of spirituous liquors among the males and the great consumption of tea among the females, " which must enervate the constitution, and render it more liable to colds of the rheumatic sort." Sinclair recognized the great social and economic importance of rheumatism. " There is no subject," he wrote, " to which the real philanthropist can direct his attention with a greater prospect of doing good, than by endeavouring to alleviate the distresses which rheumatism occasions among so many thousands of his fellow subjects ; for it almost universally renders the decline of life a state of increasing misery." As was to be expected, innumerable recipes for the cure of rheumatism had been recommended, and

Sinclair gave details of one which he regarded as among the simplest and best : " One ounce and a half best sulphur, one ounce best calcined magnesia ; to be put in an English quart or a Scotch chopin bottle and filled up with whisky : Take a wine glassful morning and night, shaking it well before taken."

In 1816 William Balfour, an Edinburgh physician, published his " Observations with cases illustrative of a new, simple, and expeditious mode of curing rheumatism and sprains, without in the least debilitating the system." Eleven years later he published another work in which he set out details of a hundred cases, " of Rheumatism and Complaint allied to it successfully healed by Compression and Percussion after all other remedies had failed." From a key to the identity of his patients it appears that they numbered many of the distinguished people of the day—one, a Right Honourable Baronet, aged seventy, apparently none other than Sir John Sinclair himself, who " felt debility making gradual inroads upon him . . . was evidently apprehensive his most active and philanthrophic career was drawing to a close " : in a month the worthy Baronet was restored to perfect health. Another patient was a Right Honourable Lady, aged seventy-one, apparently Lady Seaforth : she, too, was cured in a month. Dr. Balfour was not slow to push his claims : " to the honour of discovering the utility of Compression and Percussion in Rheumatism —to the honour of discovering and introducing into practice, the Power of Percussion," he wrote, " I have an exclusive claim ; and I venture to assert, that it will be found a discovery of no ordinary importance."

Sinclair reported that the ague formerly prevailed over a large proportion of Scotland, having been so common in spring and autumn, and sometimes even in summer, that the farmers found it difficult to obtain sufficient labour. In several parishes (e.g. Careston, Kirkden, Barrie, and Abernite) the inhabitants, with few exceptions, had an annual attack. By the end of the eighteenth century the ague was less common and entirely banished from a number of districts, a change chiefly attributed to rapid improvement in agriculture and especially to drainage : " hence the inhabitants of districts, formerly distinguished by an emaciated and jaundiced look, and who rarely reached seventy, and still more rarely ninety years of age, become so robust, healthy, and long-lived, as to attain the advanced age of from ninety to a hundred years."

It was reported that the nature of the prevalent fevers had changed greatly about the end of the eighteenth century ; whereas formerly " pleuritic and inflammatory " types prevailed, now they were " low, lingering, and nervous." Sinclair thought that this alteration might arise from the fact that his contemporaries lacked the hardiness of their forefathers ; they had " become effeminate and laboured more severely, by which the mind is depressed, from the anxieties of life and the difficulty of procuring a subsistence." He found that little attention was paid to cleanliness ; even after the fevers were subdued, relapses were frequent, as the people were not at pains to wash the bedclothes when they had recovered. Slow and nervous fevers were found to be most prevalent after seed-time and harvest, especially in cold, rainy seasons. They were frequently brought on by lowness of spirits occasioned by excessive fatigue, without proper food or accommodation to prevent its bad effects. Sinclair regarded as worthy of all condemnation the custom of visiting the sick when they were suffering from an attack of infectious fever : " it would be highly desirable therefore, that every minister in Scotland should annually deliver a discourse from the pulpit against a practice which, if it exists in his parish, must be the source of so much calamity."

Consumption was thought to be more frequent among the young at the end of the eighteenth century than it had been formerly, " and carries off the greatest number of persons about the middle period of life." Old people affirmed that in their forefathers' days consumption was extremely rare and seldom fatal. The increased prevalence of the condition was ascribed to (1) coldness and dampness of the houses, (2) change of clothing from thick and warm Scotch plaiding to fine but cold English cloth, (3) the increase in sedentary employment of factory workers, especially weavers who toiled in damp, badly ventilated work-shops, and (4) " spinning also, which is the employment of the young women during the winter months, is justly reckoned the occasion of consumption among them, by the waste of saliva requisite in that laborious employment."

In his first detailed annual report, the Registrar-General had much to say about consumption, as well he might, for in 1855 phthisis was responsible for 7,129 deaths in Scotland, or about 2·6 deaths per thousand persons living. The Registrar pointed out that tuberculosis was known to be encouraged by all those causes tending to enfeeble the human frame, and that it was particularly prevalent in the large towns, Greenock and Glasgow being worst in this respect. He referred to the old tradition that the Western Isles of Scotland were remarkably free from consumption, and he thought his figures, though inconclusive, lent support to that view ; one difficulty he encountered was that in many of the islands there were no doctors, and entries of the cause of death were made by the relatives, who often used the word " consumption " as a common term to express any illness which reduced the strength and wasted the body of its victim, such as the decay produced by the infirmities of old age. But the Registrar was satisfied that the Western Isles enjoyed a freedom from consumption surpassing that of any locality to which it was fashionable to send consumptive patients, and he thought these islands might be developed as centres for the treatment of tuberculosis. He studied the effect of unwholesome trades and occupations in the production of consumption, and concluded that such trades play a part exactly analogous to an unhealthy site or locality, by diminishing the general health of the individuals exposed, and thus rendering them more liable to the attack of whatever disease may happen to overtake them.

Sinclair reported that the increase in prevalence of scrofula was loudly lamented in the land, especially where climate was cold and damp, and the food of the inhabitants poor and principally of the vegetable kind. The disease was frequent in southern Scotland, owing partly to the prevailing cold east wind, " which obstructs perspiration," and partly (it was supposed) to the consumption of great quantities of farinaceous food, as porridge or hasty pudding or boiled potatoes.

It was the experience of Sinclair's day that new diseases were frequently occurring : in the country districts gout, until lately unknown, was becoming prevalent, while everywhere palsy and dropsy, formerly very rare complaints, were becoming very common. " It has been justly remarked," Sinclair wrote, " that in proportion as civilisation advances in a State, the number of diseases is augmented. Hence, that the profession of medicine acquires greater respect and estimation from its more extensive utility."

Mr. Cameron, surgeon in Tain, reported in 1840 that the most prevalent diseases among the poor in that district were fevers, to which the people were predisposed by insufficient, meagre, or unwholesome food, or distempers proceeding from exposure to

84

cold or damp ; and he added that in these parts old persons, when attacked by illness, however slightly, generally betook themselves to bed with the expectation and intention of not rising again ; " this baneful custom, which prematurely prostrates strength and causes much inconvenience, ought to be discountenanced." In the same year Dr. Adamson of St. Andrews recorded the relative frequency of some of the more common diseases in his practice. In a series of 824 patients, he saw 141 suffering from scarlatina, 90 from measles, 27 from influenza, 7 from whooping cough, 81 from continued fever and typhus, 33 from symptomatic fever, 66 from bronchitis, 29 from pneumonia, 25 from phthisis, 74 from stomach complaints, enteritis and peritonitis, 51 from diarrhœa and dysentery, 18 from organic disease of the brain and apoplexy, 8 from inflammation of the brain or membranes, 17 from hydrocephalus, 22 from ophthalmia, 23 from erysipelas or erythema, 23 from rheumatism, 45 from diseases peculiar to females and hysteria, 51 from diseases of the heart, and 1 from smallpox.

In the year between Martinmas 1840 and Martinmas 1841 Mr. Tait, surgeon in Edinburgh, inquired into sickness experience in the wynds and closes of that city. About 180 families were visited, but only 117 of them had been one year and upwards in their present dwelling. In these 117 families were 335 persons, and a record was made of such diseases as threw the persons affected out of employment. There were many cases of slight and continued ailment of which no notice was taken ; for example, no case of rheumatism was recorded unless so severe as to lay the person entirely off work. No record was taken of the sickness of children under ten years of age, such children being intentionally excluded from the survey.

Of the 335 persons at risk, 83 were incapacitated from work for more or less lengthy periods during the year, 23 of them from disease of the lungs, the average duration being $5\frac{1}{2}$ weeks ; 15 from fever, with average duration of incapacity of $5\frac{1}{4}$ weeks ; 9 from rheumatism, average duration 9 weeks ; 9 as the result of accidents, average incapacity $4\frac{1}{2}$ weeks, and smaller numbers from such conditions as palsy, smallpox, lumbago, and inflammation of the stomach.

Early hospital records sometimes afford an indication of the disease prevalent more than a hundred years ago. Thus the 35 patients treated in the first year of existence of Edinburgh Royal Infirmary suffered from conditions such as consumption (5),

cancer (4), flux (4), scorbutic ulcers (3), ague (3), hysteric disorders (2), and chlorosis, some of them conditions now relatively
uncommon and some not now treated in general hospitals.

Of 790 patients admitted to Greenock Infirmary during the
year ending 1 May 1841, 588 were cases of fever ; 74 suffered
from injuries, sustained for the most part as the result of accidents
in the shipbuilding yards ; 37 from ulcers ; 19 from syphilis ;
13 from rheumatism ; 11 from consumption, and 23 from other
lung diseases ; 12 from erysipelas, and 7 from scurvy. Dr. Laurie,
a practitioner in the town at that time, gave it as his opinion that
the inhabitants of Greenock were more subject to scrofula and
rheumatic affections than the inhabitants of towns farther inland,
probably from the moist and relaxing atmosphere that prevailed.

At the census of 1861 it was found that 2,820 persons were
described as blind (=1:1086 of the population). The age distribution of these blind people was quite different from that
prevailing now : in 1861 as many as 1,160 of the 2,820 blind were
under thirty years of age, whereas to-day only a small percentage
of the blind are under thirty. In 1861, 2,335 persons were
classified as deaf and dumb (=1:1311 of the population), blindness and deaf mutism being alike most common in the more rural
counties.

These figures may have been understatements, for whereas,
according to the 1861 census, there were in Scotland 4,966 lunatics
and imbeciles, the number of such patients in that year, according
to the Fourth Annual Report of the Scottish Commissioners in
Lunacy, was 8,136 (=1:376 of the population).

6

In the course of the development of manufactures in Scotland
the question of the effects of industry on health was bound to
claim attention. Long before the industrial revolution and
the coming of the machine age, Scottish craftsmen had their
Guilds and Incorporations to safeguard their interests in professional matters, and to look after the welfare of their decayed
brethren. The common chests of the Incorporations were sustained in several ways, partly by entrance fees, partly by membership dues, partly by charitable contributions and partly by fines
imposed on members for breaches of the Incorporation code ;
and in many cases the Guilds came to play an important part in

civic administration. One of the many interesting crafts was that of the pynours, an ancient Aberdeen body later known as the Shore Porters' Society. The pynours were first mentioned in the Burgh Records in 1498. Up to 1636, admission to the Society was easy and unrestricted ; but in that year a candidate for admission had first to undergo a professional trial before being accepted as a full and privileged member. Such professional trials were by no means uncommon in other crafts, but the special interest of the test to be undergone by budding pynours lay in the fact that it was a test of strength, to which the candidate was subjected under the supervision of the Water Bailie ; and only candidates who passed the test were licensed by the Magistrate. It is believed that this strength test lay in ability to carry, without resting, one hundredweight of a back lift from the Block House at the Harbour Mouth to the Braid Gutter up in the heart of the town. The test was primitive but severe, when the distance, a long mile, and the elevation were taken into account ; and it must rank as one of the earliest Scottish examples of a test of physical capacity for work to be undertaken. No class of the community had more need to provide for old age and infirmity than the pynours, for each man's stock in trade was his physical strength, and when that failed he became dependent on others. In 1660, the pynours established a " Gild Brethren's Box." It was agreed that each member of the Craft would contribute one penny Scots weekly to a common fund on which decayed brethren might have a legal claim in case of need, and the Town Council hanselled the box with a contribution of twenty pounds Scots.

Even in the seventeenth century the character of Scottish towns was beginning to be influenced by their trade and by the occupations of their inhabitants. Richard Frank wrote in 1656 that Aberdeen streets and alleys were cleanly swept and paved, but contrasted the position in Dundee, where pernicious vapours nauseated the air, " whereby it becomes almost infectious . . . because it debilitates both the native and the inhabitant, and would certainly incapacitate them of health and long life, did not custom and a country-habit plead a prescription, both as to physic and diet : Insomuch, that neither gass or blass nor any nauseating suffocating fumes, nor hardly death itself can snatch them from Scotland ; where some natives have lived to a prodigious age."

Sinclair's analysis of the occupations of the people of Scotland at the end of the eighteenth century showed that while the largest individual group of occupations was still that associated with agriculture a considerable number of persons were already employed in manufactures of various kinds and in building, and that

OCCUPATIONS OF THE POPULATION OF GLASGOW, 1819–20

Occupations	Number in the Royalty	Number in Barony & Gorbals	Total in Royalty, Bar. & Gor.
Weavers and Warpers	3,523	8,632	12,155
Shopkeepers	1,866	1,125	2,991
Labourers	1,852	1,578	3,430
House Carpenters, Cabinet-makers, and Glaziers	1,096	604	1,700
Boot and Shoemakers	956	378	1,334
Publicans licensed to retail Spirituous Liquors	885	728	1,613
Tailors and Upholsterers	746	175	921
Blacksmiths, Whitesmiths, and Coppersmiths	712	334	1,046
Manufacturers of Cotton Cloth . . .	574	165	739
Porters	560	88	648
Calenderers	504	58	562
Masons and Bricklayers	424	361	785
Bakers and Biscuit-makers	348	249	597
Carriers and Carters	319	346	665
Writers and Attorneys	265	87	352
Physicians and Surgeons	176	52	228
Fleshers	175	76	251
Teachers	158	81	239
Coopers	145	67	212
Skinners, Tanners, and Curriers . . .	118	15	133
Gardeners	100	236	336
Barbers and Hair-dressers	90	28	118
Dyers	82	281	363
Farmers and Farmers' Male Servants . .	19	301	320
Principal and Professors in the University .	18	0	18
Clergymen having cures in the Establishment	14	6	20
Clergymen connected with the Dissenters .	15	10	25
Clergymen of the Episcopal persuasion . .	2	0	2
Clergymen of the Roman Catholic persuasion	1	0	1
Professors in the Andersonian Institution .	3	0	3
Rector and Masters in the Public Grammar School	6	0	6
Pawnbrokers	6	0	6
Persons engaged in various employments not before enumerated, and at Cotton Mills, Foundries, Distilleries, Breweries, Sugar-Houses, Soaperies, Coaleries, and other Public Works	6,355	5,371	11,726

already over thirteen thousand families were dependent for a livelihood on work in mines and quarries. An analysis of the occupations pursued by the inhabitants of Glasgow in 1819–20 showed, as was to be expected, an even higher proportion of the people to be engaged in manufacturing work. There was as yet little interest in the welfare of workers, and the conditions under which they laboured were often very bad ; but Robert Owen's mills in New Lanark were among the first in Britain to begin to raise working standards, conditions there evoking much interest— and some controversy—among industrialists south of the border (*see* Appendix to this chapter), and a little later (about 1840), James Smith's cotton factory at Deanston, near Stirling, was even more advanced. Smith built his factory with special attention to ventilation and heating ; he protected the shafting of his machinery to reduce the risk of accident, and he provided well-built houses near the factory for his workers. He employed a medical man to examine the work-people from time to time, to " give them timely advice, and, as far as possible, to prevent disease " ; this must be amongst the first recorded instances in this country of the employ- ment of a works doctor.

In the dawning British interest in industrial medicine, Scottish doctors played their part. In 1831 Dr. Gregory reported the case of a collier from Dalkeith whose lungs showed a peculiar black infiltration throughout, and this first report was followed by a series of papers on the same subject. Dr. Hamilton of Falkirk described a similar case in 1833, his patient being a man who had been employed for forty years by the Carron Company as a moulder, " in which occupation the workmen are continually exposed to the inhalation of a fine powder, composed in great part of very finely ground charcoal." Dr. Girdwood of Falkirk had two other moulder patients similarly affected. Dr. Graham of Glasgow described a similar condition in a collier from Polmadie, as did other doctors in the west of Scotland ; Dr. Thomson of Perth, who had formerly worked in Tillicoultry, described a similar case that he had seen in mining practice there ; and Dr. Archibald Makellar dealt with conditions as he saw them in the coalfield of East Lothian. " The collier," he wrote, " at last unavoidably falls a victim to lesions within the cavity of the chest, arising from the nature of his employment." He found that the ventilation of the mines in East Lothian was very much neglected, that for a generation past coarse linseed oil had been burned in the miners' lamps instead of whale oil, with greatly increased production of smoke, and that from blasting operations the men inhaled much gunpowder smoke.

Dr. Stevenson of Musselburgh wrote in 1840 of the colliers there that " almost everyone is affected more or less with dyspepsia ; they are also very subject to diseases of the lungs

(I would say that one in three are affected with asthma) ; but the nature of their work I should consider as often producing these, more especially as they are frequently accompanied by a kind of spit, only known I believe among colliers—I mean what is called the black spit, produced I should suppose by their inhaling small particles of coal along with the air in the pits. I was at the dissection of a young man, a collier, last winter, who died of enlargement of the heart, and on examining the lungs we found them completely gorged with fluid, which, when squeezed out with the hand, had just the appearance of ink : this young man had not been at the pits for some weeks previous to his death." Dr. Stevenson advocated the provision of improved air in collieries, with, if necessary, the use of respirators, as well as control of colliery accidents and of the employment of children in collieries ; he thought that mines should be under similar control to factories. A neighbouring practitioner, Dr. Allison of Tranent, also knew well that mining was an unhealthy trade. From a statistical survey of thirty-five colliers' families he found the average age for each male head of the family to be thirty-four years only ; the average age of thirty-five male heads of farmer-families in Tranent was over fifty-one years. Many of the miners were in bad health, suffering from " difficulty of breathing, cough, with expectoration of a black-colour resembling ink, and are affected with greater or less emaciation." In the thirty-five miners' families studied, taken without any selection, Dr. Allison found that there were no fewer than ten widows.

A little later, in 1851, Professor Bennett tried to sum up experience of lung disease among miners as it occurred in Scotland. He found that the disease was common in colliers and in moulders of iron and copper ; " yet it is curious that whilst it is common among the workmen of some coalpits it is unknown among those employed in others. For instance it exists to a great extent among the colliers of Fife, Haddingtonshire, and Midlothian, but is unknown at Newcastle, Paisley, or Alloa, although the dust and powder is as finely levigated in one place as in another." He found that miners doing stone work in the pits were particularly liable to the condition.

7

Sinclair recognized that the growth of manufactures might be injurious to health, and he summarized the objections to manufacture from the health point of view as being generally those of "too early to work ; in addition to which, eager application, scanty food and want of proper exercise enfeebles the constitution, produces nervous disorders, and brings on various infirmities, which render their lives uncomfortable and hurry them on to premature old age."

From the point of view of the health of the general community it was soon found that the control of nuisance from the new factories was no easy matter. Where a man could show that his neighbour, either by the direct effect of operations or the neglect to remove noxious substances, occasioned risk to his health or property or rendered life uncomfortable to him, there was power to require removal of the cause of annoyance ; the ground of complaint was generally that manufacturing operations polluted water or tainted the atmosphere. In a case occurring in 1808 a Dean of Guild Court made a remit to medical men, "that they report as soon as they conveniently can whether the operation of manufacturing glue is, from the nature of the materials used or otherwise, attended with injurious consequences to the health of persons living in the vicinity of the places where the manufacture is carried on." The finding was " that the glue-work proposed to be erected by the defender, although not necessarily hurtful to the health of the inhabitants of the neighbourhood, will render the enjoyment of life and property uncomfortable to the inhabitants, and will lessen the value of the adjacent tenement, and therefore finds that the proposed erection is a nuisance." It was held that the mere existence of noxious manufactures did not justify the erection of additional buildings for such a purpose approaching closer to the vicinity of persons complaining of them ; but apparently where the operations were of a nature to be gradually and imperceptibly enlarged, there was no remedy.

In his first report as Medical Officer there, Dr. Littlejohn complained that Edinburgh, though not a great manufacturing city, had already suffered from the fumes of manufacture, and he gave two particular instances. The city gas-works had been placed at such a low level in the district of Canongate that the fumes from them rendered almost uninhabitable the houses skirting the Calton Hill, and to remedy this nuisance a new chimney stalk had to be erected of such gigantic proportions as to form a landmark and eyesore from whatever quarter the city was approached. Again, the amenity of the West End as a place of residence had been greatly interfered with by the erection of the Caledonian Distillery, said to be the largest in the kingdom ; refuse from the distillery found its way westwards for a distance of three hundred yards, polluting the atmosphere of the western districts of the city until it reached the Water of Leith, then flowing eastwards through the city for a distance of three miles, so that the inhabitants were again subjected to annoyance from it. Dr. Littlejohn thought that the chief nuisance connected with the Edinburgh factories was the amount of smoke they discharged into the atmosphere ; the Smoke Nuisance Abatement Act seeming to be a dead letter, not only was the air contaminated, but free ventilation of the houses in the neighbourhood was discouraged.

There were, however, some trades to which he took specific exception ; one was the extensive tanning industry carried on in close proximity to the High Street and St. Mary's Wynd, the other the manufacture of catgut from the intestines of animals. There were two factories in Edinburgh engaged in this latter trade, and both had been the subject of repeated complaints, " but without avail, seeing that a large amount of testimony, ordinary and scientific, was forthcoming, to speak as to the innocuous character of the manufacture." A special by-law applicable to Edinburgh was passed in 1848, providing that " all persons dealing in bones and rags shall, at all times, keep their shops and cellars, and other premises, in a cleanly state, to the satisfaction of the Inspector of Cleansing," but unfortunately the rags were defined in it as " woollen," so that the by-law proved totally inoperative.

To meet the unhealthiness of the conditions under which bread was baked, the Bakehouses Act, passed in 1863, made provision for the sanitary state of the workshops and the comfort of the workmen engaged in baking.

APPENDIX TO CHAPTER IV

1 The dimensions of spinning-rooms, especially the height ?
2 Number of spindles in a room ?
3 Modes of ventilation and purification ?
4 Number of boys and girls in one room ?
5 Hours of labour, of rest, and for meals ?
6 Rules of cleanliness, and for health ?
7 Time and manner of teaching the children to read, and of religious instruction ?
8 Mode and time of hiring ?
9 Whence the mills are supplied with labourers ?
10 Means employed to prevent or correct the typhus fever ?
11 Mode of lodging and feeding the children ?
12 What are they fit for when too big for the spindles ?
13 Are they commonly strong for labour, or otherwise, etc. ?

MR. DALE'S ANSWER TO THE SAME

1 The spinning and all the other rooms are of the whole extent of the buildings, without any sub-divisions, and are from 120 to 150 feet long ; from 26 to 30 feet wide, and all of them in height 10 feet from floor to floor, or 9 feet clear of the beams.

2 The spinning rooms contain each about 2,000 spindles.

3 Ventilation is greatly promoted by the rapid motion of many parts of the machinery. Fresh air is introduced by regularly opening the windows at top, on both sides of the house. To increase the circulation still more, air-holes six inches square, on a level with the floor, are opened below every other window through the walls, at the distance of fourteen feet from each other ; but these are only of advantage in summer, as the cold in winter precludes the use of them. The means of purification in use are washing the walls and ceilings of the rooms at least once a year with new slacked lime, weekly washings of the floors and machinery with scalding water, and frequent and constant brushings of the walls, ceilings, and floor.

4 The greatest number of persons in one room is 75, in some there are only 50.

5 The hours of labour are eleven and a half each day, viz. from six o'clock in the morning till seven o'clock at night, with half an hour of intermission at nine o'clock for breakfast and a whole hour at two for dinner.

6   The only rules of cleanliness and health are such as enjoin the practices above mentioned, in answer to the third query.

7   Seven is the hour for supper ; in half an hour after at most, and as much sooner as possible, the teaching commences, and continues till nine o'clock.   The schools at present are attended by five hundred and seven scholars, in instructing whom sixteen teachers are employed ; thirteen in teaching to read, two to write, and one to figure, besides a person who teaches sewing, and another who occasionally teaches church music.   The mode of teaching is as follows :   The course is divided into eight classes, according to the progress of the scholars ;   to each of these classes one or more teachers are assigned, as the numbers in that stage of advancement may require.   To the teachers is specified in writing how far they are respectively to carry forward their scholars ;   which, so soon as they have accomplished, the scholars are transferred to the next highest class, and the teacher receives a premium for every one so qualified.[1]   In their respective classes, the teachers promote emulation in the usual way by making the top of the class the post of honour, which is still further kept up by the distribution of rewards every half-year to such as, from an account taken once a fortnight, appear to have been most frequently uppermost.   On Sundays that part of the children who cannot go to church for want of accommodation are kept busy at school ;   and in the evenings, after public worship, the usual teachers spend regularly three hours in giving religious instruction, by causing the Scriptures to be read, catechizing, etc.   As there is accommodation at church for only 150 children, they all go to it in rotation.   Besides the night schools there are two day schools for children too young for work, which, as well as the night one (except the providing their own books), are entirely free of expense to the scholars.

8   The time of hiring differs with the different descriptions of children.   Those who agree for a stipulated weekly wage, and who are generally such as live with their parents, are commonly engaged for four years ;   while such as are received from the workhouse in

[1] The following is a statement of the number in each class at present, which affords an accurate view of the general state of their education :

In the first or latter class there are 65 scholars

,,	second	,,	,,	85	,,
,,	third	,,	,,	76	,,
,,	fourth	,,	,,	65	,,
,,	fifth	,,	,,	44	,,
,,	sixth	,,	,,	44	,,
,,	seventh	,,	,,	51	,,
,,	eighth	,,	,,	80	,,

The eighth or highest class are all good readers, and employ half of their time each night in writing.   Such as stand in no need of further instruction in reading, of whom there are about twelve boys and twelve girls, employ the remainder of their time, after writing, in learning arithmetic and sewing, except on occasional nights appointed for revising their reading.

Edinburgh, or who are otherwise without friends to take charge of them, and who, in lieu of wages, are maintained and educated, are bound four, five, six, or seven years, according to their age, or generally till they have completed their fifteenth year. The mode of hiring is generally by contract of the parents or curators of the children in their behalf.

9 The supply of workers for the mills comes either from the native inhabitants of the place ; from families who have been collected about the works from the neighbouring parishes, and more distant parts of the country ; or lastly, from Edinburgh or Glasgow, by the number of destitute children these places constantly afford.

10 When fevers, or any epidemical distempers, appear in the boarding-house where that description of workers who do not receive their wages are accommodated, the means used to prevent the spreading of the infection are the immediate removal of the sick to a detached part of the house, and frequent sprinkling and fumigating of the bedrooms with vinegar. Typhus fevers have not appeared there for years, but have, during that time, been in the village, though never general ; yet in no case, so far as circumstances afforded the means of judging, did it appear to originate in the mills, or even to be communicated by the intercourse the workers have there with each other.[1]

11 The greatest part of the workers are lodged in their parents' houses in the village, in the immediate neighbourhood of the mills, or in the town of Lanark, one mile distant. The principal part of their food, as is usual in the country, consists of oatmeal. Those who get their maintenance in lieu of wages are lodged all together in one house. They consist, at present, of 396 boys and girls. There are six sleeping apartments for them, and three children are allowed to each bed. The ceilings and walls of the apartments are white-washed twice a year with hot lime, and the floors washed with scalding water and sand. The children sleep on wooden bottomed beds, on bed-ticks filled with straw, which is in general changed once a month. A sheet covers the bed-ticks, and above that are one or two pair of blankets, and a bed cover, as the season requires. The bedrooms are carefully swept, and the windows thrown open every morning, in which state they remain through the day. Of late, cast-iron beds have been introduced in place of wooden ones. The upper body clothing in use in summer, both for boys and girls, is entirely of cotton, which as they have spare suits to change with are washed once a fortnight. In

---

[1] The following statement of the number of children in the boarding-house, at different periods, and the annual deaths there, best evinces their general state of health.

In 1792	.	.	.	.	272 boarders	2 deaths
,, 1793	.	.	.	.	288 ,,	1 ,,
,, 1794	.	.	.	.	306 ,,	0 ,,
,, 1795	.	.	.	.	384 ,,	6 ,,
						9 deaths

winter the boys are dressed in woollen cloth, and they, as well as the girls, have complete dress suits for Sundays. Their linens are changed once a week. For a few months in summer both boys and girls go without shoes and stockings. The provisions are dressed in cast-iron boilers, and consist of oatmeal porridge for breakfast and supper, and milk with it in its season. In winter its substitute is a composition of molasses, fermented with some new beer, which is called swats. For dinner the whole of them have every day, in all seasons, barley broth made from fresh beef. The beef itself is divided among one half of the children, in quantities of about seven ounces English to each ; the other half is served with cheese in quantities of about five ounces English each : so that they have alternately beef and cheese for dinner, excepting now and then a dinner of herrings in winter and fresh butter in summer. To the beef and cheese is added a plentiful allowance of potatoes or barley bread, of which last they have also an allowance every morning before going to work.

12 and 13 As far as observation, with regard to these two queries, has extended, the workers, when too big for spinning, are as stout and robust as others. The male part of them are fit for any trade. A great many, since the commencement of the war, have gone into the army and navy, and others are occasionally going away as apprentices to smiths and joiners, etc., but especially to weavers ; for which last trade, from the expertness they acquire in handling yarn, they are particularly well fitted, and of course are taken as apprentices on better terms. The females generally leave the mills, and go to private family service when about sixteen years of age. Were they disposed to continue at the mills, these afford abundant employment for them at reeling, picking, etc., as well as to many more young men than ever remain at them.

CHAPTER V

CONTROL OF INFECTIOUS DISEASES

I

THE steps taken for the control of the major epidemic diseases in the Middle Ages were among the earliest Scottish essays in social medicine. Some of these diseases, notably plague, completely upset the life of the country for long periods, and while there is no precise information available about the prevalence of leprosy, probably the earliest of the epidemic diseases, it is abundantly clear that this, too, filled the people with terror ; while the drastic attempts made to control plague and cholera fairly reflected the dread of them in which the people stood. Early efforts at control took the form of forcible isolation and harsh repression. Of constructive attempts to remove conditions responsible for the diseases there was little evidence.

The modern conception of preventive medicine arose only very gradually. It is little over a hundred years since Dr. Robert Cowan, Professor of Medical Jurisprudence and Police in the University of Glasgow, wrote that the prevalence of epidemic disease depended upon various causes, " but the most influential of all is poverty and destitution." In his view the next cause of the diffusion of epidemic disease was the state of the districts in which the poor lived. Shortly afterwards, Dr. W. P. Allison, Professor of Practice of Medicine in the University of Edinburgh, wrote that if the human race was destined to possess greater wisdom and happiness, the knowledge of the prevention of disease might be expected to increase in course of time, " because there are many diseases which the experience of ages has brought only partially within the power of medicine, but the causes of which are known, and under certain circumstances may be avoided ; and the conditions necessary for avoiding them are in great measure in the power of communities, though at present beyond the power of many of the individuals composing these."

It was a long time before there was any organized attempt to preserve the communal health, though occasional unexpected glimpses of a hygienic outlook are to be seen in very early days, as for instance, in the Statutes of the Burgh of Edinburgh (1529–31), where alongside a regulation governing the quality of bread is one " anent the Servandis that wesches Clais," stipulating that servants must not under penalty mix up other peoples' washing with that of their master and mistress, for " it is unpossable to keip the toune clene gif sik thingis be usit," and there were similar regulations in other Scottish towns.

2

Leprosy claims consideration first. Reference is made elsewhere (see p. 256) to the leper hospitals that used to be scattered throughout Scotland, at Aldcambus in Berwickshire, Aldnestun in Lauderdale, in Glasgow, Edinburgh, Elgin, and other places. Nearly all our knowledge about leprosy in Scotland is due to the researches of Sir J. Y. Simpson, whose classical paper on the subject was communicated to the Medico-Chirurgical Society of Edinburgh in 1841. Simpson recalled that a special enactment of the Scottish Parliament held at Perth in the year 1427 " anent lipper folke " illustrated both the apparent prevalence of the malady at that time, and the fact that the burghs of the kingdom were then spoken of as obliged to possess lazar houses of their own : " that na Lipper Folke sit to thig [beg] neither in kirk nor kirkzaird, nor other place within the burrowes, but at their own hospital, and at the port of the towne and other places outwith the burrowes." It is not possible to estimate the number affected by leprosy in Scotland—partly because the disease was at its height during the eleventh, twelfth, and thirteenth centuries, just when the Scottish Records are most defective—but there can be no doubt about its extent and severity ; it was referred to as " the mickle ail." In the Burgh Records of Glasgow of 1581 it was entered that Patrick Bogle was ordered to be inspected for leprosy ; and eight years later " Robert Bobill, sone to Patrick Bogle " was reported to be an inmate of the leper-house. There is reason to believe that the disease continued to prevail in Scotland long after it had disappeared from England, and that it continued in the northern islands of Scotland long after it had disappeared from other parts of Great Britain. In Shetland it was known for centuries. It persisted in Lerwick as late as the latter part of the seventeenth century, and in some parts of the islands it continued still later. Apparently most of those affected either belonged to, or were sent to, the Island of Papa. The Session Books of the Parish of Walls show the expenses incurred in keeping the lepers at Papa from 1736 to 1740 : four of them died during these years, and two of the entries are for the tobacco used at their funerals, perhaps as a disinfecting agent. Though the Session Records of Walls in 1742 bore a long entry earnestly enjoining a day of public thanksgiving for the supposed total deliverance of the country from leprosy, in fact the disease was not entirely eradicated, and the parish minister, in a report for the Statistical Account of Scotland in 1798, described " several miserable cases of the disease," and added that in many instances there was reason to suspect a heredi-tary taint. It is recorded that in Papa about the year 1778 a leprous woman was put out and died in the fields before a leper-house could be built ; that about the same time there were leprous persons in the district of Watless ; and that the son and daughter of a man, Henry Sinclair, were infected and sent to the hospital in Edinburgh. As late as 1798 a male patient from Shetland was for some time in the wards of Edinburgh Infirmary under the care of various physicians before being finally diagnosed as a case of leprosy : the patient, John Berns, was twenty-eight years of age, and some of his ancestors had been affected with the same disease.

Though probably not all the supposed cases of leprosy in those days actually suffered from the disease, there seems to be strong evidence that King Robert the Bruce was really affected with, and died of, leprosy.

There exist in the old records of Scotland many enactments enforcing the seclusion of lepers. The Scottish " Burrow Lawes," drawn up in the twelfth century for the government of the first four Royal Burghs of Scotland (Berwick, Roxburgh, Edinburgh, and Stirling), contained some regulations regarding " lipper men " : any man stricken with leprosy who had substance of his own was to be put in the hospital of the burgh where he dwelt ; if he had nothing on which to live the Burgesses of the burgh were to collect the sum of twenty shillings for his keep. An Act of the Perth Parliament of 1427 ordered the dignitaries and officers of the Church to search diligently in their parish visitations for any persons affected with leprosy, and to commit them to the keeping of the civil or ecclesiastical authorities. Earlier, in the thirteenth century, the ordinances of the Provincial Councils of the Church had said on the subject of giving advice to lepers :

Regarding those affected with leprosy and who by general consent are separated from the communion of their fellows, we ordain that when such transfer themselves to solitary places they be effectively reminded by the presbyters in their retirement that they visit the Parish Church according to their ability ; but if they cannot be induced to this, let no force be applied to them, since affliction should not be heeped upon the afflicted, and they ought rather to be pitied for their misfortunes.

Lepers were compelled to seek the asylum of the lazar hospitals in consequence of laws prohibiting any citizen from keeping in his house a person suffering from leprosy, and were prevented from entering the gates of towns and villages. The old Burrow Lawes had stringent clauses to that effect, and by a later Act of the Parliament of Perth, lepers were prohibited from entering towns except to purchase victuals—and then only on three days a week, on Monday, Wednesday, and Friday, " fra ten hours to twa after noone," but where fairs and markets fell on these days they were to delay their visit to the town until the morrow. It was directed that flesh of pork or salmon found to be corrupt in the markets and accordingly seized should be sent to the lepers. The fear of contagion was very great, and towns in proximity to the larger leper hospitals had many local rules designed to prevent contact between the inhabitants and the lepers. Thus the burghers of Prestwick were in constant fear of infection from the near-by leper hospital at Kingcase, and the burgh records contain many entries dealing with citizens who tried to carry on trade with the lepers ; some of the erring ones were banished from the town. There were similar regulations in Edinburgh, and as late as 1530 the Magistrates of the Burgh decreed " that na manner of Lipper persone, man nor woman, fra this tyme furth, cum amangis uther cleine personis, nor be nocht fund in the kirk, fische market, nor flesche merket, nor na other merket within this burghe, under the pane of burnyng of their cheik and banasing off the toune."

In Glasgow, leprosy was so prevalent that at the chief courts regular lists of those affected were delivered to the Magistrates, whose duty it was to issue orders for their seclusion. The task of visiting the lepers and making returns of their number and names devolved on the Water Bailie. The lepers were first " delatit as Liper," *i.e.* legally accused or informed upon as being infected with the disease and thereupon ordained to be visited, and if found to be leprous, to be " secludit of the town to the hospital at the brig end." The Presbytery of Glasgow in 1599 refused to allow a man to contract marriage because he was a leper. The lepers were permitted under certain stringent conditions to issue forth to the town to solicit alms : they were then clad in a gown with hood and sleeves closed to the finger tips, and they were provided with " clappers," which they were obliged to rattle as they went along. A Town Council Edict of October 1610 ordained " that the lipper of the hospital sall gang onlie upon the calsie syde near the gutter and sall haife clipperis, and ane claith upon their mouth and face, and sall stand afar of qll they resaif almous, or answer under the payne of banischeing from the town and hospital."

3

It appears that plague was present in Glasgow as early as 1330, but up to the middle of the fourteenth century Scotland was almost completely free from the disease. Its appearance in 1349 was recorded by Wyntoun, and of this outbreak Fordoun wrote : " By God's will this evil led to a strange and unwonted kind of death, in so much that the flesh of the sick was somehow puffed out and swollen, and they dragged out their earthly life for barely two days." The disease attacked especially the common people, seldom the magnates, and it filled the populace with fear : " Men shrank from it so much that, through fear of contagion, sons, flee-ing as from the face of leprosy, or from an adder, durst not go and see their parents in the throes of death." The pestilence came from the east. For a time its progress was stayed at the Scottish border, and " the foul death of the English " afforded the Scots malicious pleasure ; but from a reckless raid into England they brought the Black Death into their own country, where it was estimated that it destroyed one third of the population.

The next visitation, in 1362, was comparable with the first ; to avoid it King David and the Bishop of St. Andrews retired to Kinloss and Elgin respectively, and the King improved the shining hour by taking Kildrummy Castle from the Earl of Mar during his visit to the north. The third outbreak of plague in Scotland was in 1380 : it followed a foray by the Earl of Douglas and twenty thousand men as far south as Penrith, when, along with much booty, they brought back plague. The next visitation, in 1401, was apparently worse than any of the previous ones and gravely interfered with the daily life of the country ; in 1402, for instance, only one bailie from Dundee attended the exchequer audit at Perth, the others having died of the plague. The next recorded outbreak was in 1430–32, when the disease broke out in Edinburgh. The Parliament held in Perth in 1431 enacted that the collectors of the land-tax should present their accounts on 2 February next to come, provided the pestilence were not there ; but if it were there, the accounts were to be rendered at St. Andrews. The year 1439 in Scotland was a year of famine. It was marked by outbreaks of dysentery and of plague, which was first reported from Dumfries, and was responsible for many deaths, " for there took it nane that ever recoverit, but they died within twenty-four hours." There was another outbreak in 1455, and in the following year the Scottish Parliament passed an Act, the Rule of the Pestilence, which represented the first administrative attempt at the control of the disease. In the outbreak of 1475, apparently not for the first time, a plague hospital was maintained on Inchkeith in the Firth of Forth.

In 1498 the Magistrates of Aberdeen warned the citizens of certain measures to be taken to preserve the town from pestilence : during the day a guard of citizens was to be posted at each of the four gates, and at night the gates were to be " lockit with lokis and keis." Plague was fairly general in Scotland in 1499 and 1500, in March 1500 Sir Patrick Hume, the Comptroller, being granted an extra allowance " for his great labour in collecting fermes in different parts of the kingdom in time of the infection of the plague."

The next outbreak, in 1503, affected chiefly the Edinburgh area. The Lord High Treasurer disbursed ten shillings for " translating " the lining of some of the King's gowns, " for caus William Ferry, furrour, was suspect with pestilence." In July of the following year the King gave three shillings to the poor folks of Linlithgow, " that wer put furth of the toun," and in the same year, from 23 August to 18 October, Curry, the King's jester, being " suspect of pestilence," was, together with his man, kept " furth beside Stirling." On their discharge, he and his man were provided with coats, shoes, and blankets, presumably to replace others that had been burned with a view to preventing infection. The Preceptor of St. Anthony's in Leith wrote to the General of the Order that the plague had carried off all the brethren except himself and another ; their lands in town were untenanted, their fields untilled, and they themselves deprived of the Alms of the faithful ; they were unable, through poverty, to attend the general Chapter of the Order.

In April 1514 further orders were made in Aberdeen for keeping the town clear of the pestilence. Lodges were erected on the Links and Gallowhill, where infected or suspected persons were to remain for forty days. In 1515 sixteen persons were banished from the town for a year and a day for disobeying the Orders against the plague ; and in 1539 there were more Orders designed to avoid the " contagious infeckand pest callit the Boiche, quilk ryngis in diverse partis of the same [Realm] now instantly."

In 1545, Hertford's invasion of Scotland was aggravated by the introduction of plague, which had broken out in his army and spread through the border land. The Session of the Law Courts was transferred to Linlithgow because the plague was in Edinburgh, and in December of 1546 an Aberdonian with the unlikely name of David Spilzelaucht was ordered to be " brint on the left hand with ane het irne " for not showing the Bailies " the seikness of his barne, quilk was seik in the pest." In 1548 the plague was at Perth.

It is reported that on the fourth day after George Wishart was driven by religious persecution from his ministry in Dundee the town was visited by the pestilence. Contagion spread from house to house and from street to street, until the whole town was involved in one general calamity, and the mortality reached incredible heights. Wishart returned to Dundee from Ayrshire, and on the following day preached at the East Gate in the Cowgate. Many of the sick had been carried outside the gate and lodged in booths at a spot near the river, later called the Sick Men's Yards. Afterwards the gate was locked and the separation between the diseased and the healthy rendered complete.

In 1574 the Magistrates of Glasgow, in order to prevent the spread of plague to the city from the east coast of Scotland, where it had been virulent, forbade all intercourse with Leith, Kirkcaldy, Dysart, and Burntisland, and required " testimonials from persons coming from Edinburgh." Public officers, called *searchers*, were appointed, to each of whom a special district was allotted within which he went from house to house searching for the sick. It was ordained that all cases of sickness should be reported to the searchers, and the responsibility of reporting was placed by the magistrates upon the master of the house. The last item in this code of ordinances was directed against the breeding places of disease—" Ordanis the Schulehous Wynd and all the wennallis to be simpliciter condampnit and stekit up." On 31 October the Scots Privy Council at Dalkeith issued an Order designed to check the spread of the plague, and in the same year the Kirk Session of Edinburgh appointed an eight-day Fast against the threat to the whole realm. The Wardens of the Marches were instructed to prevent Englishmen from crossing the Border, and the fairs held periodically at Duns and Kelso, to which people of both countries resorted, were prohibited.

One of the most serious epidemics raged from 1584 to 1588. The Privy Council issued order after order in an attempt to stop all traffic from places north of the Forth except by licence ; sails were to be taken out of the ferry-boats. Between September 1584 and August 1585 no fewer than 1,437 persons died from plague in Perth. The infection reached Edinburgh in May 1585, and orders were given that all filth, filthy beasts, and carrion were to be removed from the highways, and these cleansed and kept clean. The Mint was transferred to Dundee, and when plague broke out there, it was moved to Perth, where the disease had by this time burned itself out. The Court of Session moved to Stirling. The outbreak was severe in St. Andrews, causing the dispersal of the students. In Edinburgh it continued until the beginning of 1586, when all the citizens who could leave the town did so, " nevertheless there died of people which were not able to flee fourteen hundred and some odd."

In 1586 Dr. Gilbert Skene, who had been a lecturer at King's College, Aberdeen, wrote the first treatise on plague in "the English." He was induced to do so by seeing the poor " succumb without assistance," all men avoiding speech or communication with them : " Every ane is become sae detestable to other (whilk is to be lamentit) and specially the puir in the sight of the rich, as gif they were not equal with them, touching their creation, but rather without soll or spirit, as beast degenerate from mankind." Dr. Skene enumerated the causes of plague : stink, corruption, and filth, " greit reik of colis without vinde to dispache the sam."

If sanitation was practically ignored in those days, there was no lack of zeal and vigour in the efforts of the government to prevent the introduction of plague when the disease was known to be prevalent in any country with which Scotland held intercourse. Merchants coming from infected or suspected ports had to remain on shipboard with their goods or go to some quiet place away from intercourse with the lieges. It was a capital offence for the crew to come ashore until pronounced free from infection. " Because most danger appeared to be amongst the flax," ships from the Baltic were unloaded on Inchcolm and the bales opened to the wind every other fair day for from six to eight weeks. Other articles in the cargo were to be cleansed by allowing the sea to overflow them at one or two tides. The ship itself was to be bored, so as to let sea water into it ; all this at the expense of the owners. In addition to Inchcolm, there were quarantine stations on Inchkeith, Inchgarvie, and May Island. After all these precautions, sailors had to obtain a licence from the magistrates before attempting to hold intercourse with the citizens. If a " foul " ship entered a Scottish port, the Master was arrested and orders given that the inhabitants were to have no truck with any members of the crew under pain of death.

In the plague of 1585 James VI headed the exodus of the panic-stricken. He went to St. Andrews, then to Falkland, then to Tullibardine, then to Stirling, as the plague followed him, apparently without much confidence in his own expressed opinion that " the pest always smites . . . such as flies it farthest and apprehends deepliest the peril thereof."

The measures adopted by Local Authorities in those days were intended to prevent the spread of disease rather than to relieve those already stricken. Under pain of death the master of a house in which any person fell sick had to report the case immediately to visitors or searchers. The death penalty was often exacted, as it was with an Edinburgh tailor who was brought to execution " on a gibbet before his own door," for having failed to report the illness of his wife who died of the disease ; but, the rope having broken, " at the will of God, he eschapit," and was banished from the city forever. Women offenders were drowned. When plague broke out in a family the members not affected were compelled to remove to a plague-camp where they were housed in wretched huts, as described in Chapter XI.

During an outbreak of plague, owners of dogs and swine were often forbidden to allow the animals to wander at will. Meetings of all kinds were prohibited, and, as has been shown, the administration of public business was generally transferred to some town that had escaped. No-one might hold school under pain of banishment, and children under fifteen were liable to be put into the stocks and to be scourged with rods if they used their enforced leisure to play " on the gaitt or in the streets or in the kirk." It was made a capital offence for the destitute in a plague area to beg for their living, and if voluntary contributions proved insufficient for their maintenance, special taxation might be levied for the purpose.

In 1598 Dumfries was affected from Cumberland, and in 1600 plague was prevalent in Moray. In 1601 Renfrewshire was affected, and Crail in Fife ; later in the same year Glasgow and Edinburgh were also involved. A ship owned in Crail arrived in the Forth on 30 July 1602 from the Baltic with three or four dead of the plague, and was quarantined at Inchkeith.

It was estimated that during the second half of the sixteenth century the plague years in Scotland covered in the aggregate at least a third of the whole period. During this time the city of Aberdeen enjoyed an extraordinary immunity, perhaps due to the very drastic measures taken against the disease : in May 1585 the Magistrates erected three gibbets, " ane at the Merkat Cross, and other at the Brig of Dee and the third at the Haven Mouth, that in case ony infectit person arrive or repair by sea or land to this Burgh, or in case ony indweller of this Burgh receive house or harbour, or give meat or drink to the infectit person or persons, the man be hangit and the woman drownit."

Plague continued in the south of Scotland in the early years of the seventeenth century, affecting Edinburgh, Leith, St. Andrews with most of the other Fife coast towns, and Closeburn (Dumfriesshire). The worst year appears to have been 1606 : " it raged so extremely in all the corners of the kingdom that neither burgh nor land in any part was free." The burghs of Ayr and Stirling were almost desolate. Two houses on the line of the great road from the south towards Aberdeen, situated on opposite sides of the Dee, were suspected of having received the infection, and the gentlemen of the county met and resolved to send to Dundee for two professional " clengers " or disinfectors, giving a bond to the burgh of Dundee for 500 marks for the services of its clengers. Dundee and Perth were affected a year or two later, and a few cases occurred in Edinburgh in 1624, though there was no great epidemic in Scotland at that time.

After the storming of Newcastle by the Scots Covenanters in October 1644 the plague appeared in Edinburgh, Kelso, Bo'ness, Perth, and other places. At Edinburgh the plague-stricken were housed in huts in the King's Park below Salisbury Crags. In Glasgow too the plague was serious, making havoc in the city from 1645 onwards, and not disappearing entirely until the autumn of 1648. The most determined efforts were made to stamp out the disease. Daily house-to-house visitation was eventually adopted, and when this measure failed it was resolved to fall back on the old expedient of transporting the infected out of the town to the Muir—believed to have comprised the wastelands to the north of the town. Intimation was to be made " be touk of drum that na manner of persone goe out to the Muir quher the foull persones are without leave of the Magistratis." Unclean folks on the Muir were to be visited by James Robiesoune, baxter, and in the minutes of the Town Council there were several entries regarding the inspection and care of the unclean folks on the Muir and the precautions to be taken in respect of the herring-boats coming from Renfrew and Govan to the Broomielaw. The University authorities migrated in a body to Irvine, where the Principal, Regents, and Bursars of the College were boarded in 1645 and part of 1646, when they moved to Paisley. Local trade was almost at a standstill. Nearly all who could leave the town did so, and the burgh tacksmen had to beg to be excused from the payment of their rents, " in respect of the seïknes." In 1647 the plague scattered St. Andrews students ; it was also in Edinburgh and in the north. Not even Aberdeen escaped, for the infection reached the city in April 1647, and there were straggling cases as late as November 1648. Among the regulations made by the Town Council in April 1647 was one requiring " poysone laid for destroying myce and rattons," almost as if the City Fathers had anticipated more modern knowledge about the part played by rats in the spread of the disease. The deaths from plague in the city at this time were put down at sixteen hundred, besides one hundred and forty in the adjacent fishing villages of Futtie and Torry. This enormous mortality took place despite the adoption of all the usual rigorous measures—the removal of the infected to huts on the links and Woolmanhill, a guard of soldiers to shut them in, a gibbet for the disobedient, and clengers to disinfect the infected houses. The last case of plague in Scotland occurred in 1648.

4

Venereal disease was early reported. Within three years of the arrival of Columbus at Palos from the New World it had made its appearance in Scotland. The first notice of it was contained in an Edict of the Town Council of Aberdeen, dated 21 April 1497 :

> The said day it was statut and ordanit be the Alderman and Consale for the eschevin of the infirmitey cum out of Franche and strang partis, that all licht woman be chargit and ordanit to decist fra thar vices and syne of venerie, and all thair buthis and houssis skalit, and thai to pas and wirk for thar sustentacioun vndir the payne of ane key of het yrne one thair chekis, and banysene of the toune.

This early Aberdeen edict showed that the common mode of infection of the disease was recognized to be the same as all acknowledge it to be at the present day, though later statutes were apparently based on less accurate knowledge of the mode of its transmission.

In 1507, among a long list of statutes passed by the Council of Aberdeen were two referring to the introduction and spread of syphilis. By the first of these it was enacted :

> That diligent inquisitioun be takin of ale infect personis with this strange seikneis of Nappillis, for the sauptie of the town ; and the personis beand infectit therwith be chargit to keip thaime in their houwssis and vether places fra the haill folkis.

The other was evidently apprehensive of the spread of the disease by simple contact. It ordained :

> That nayne infeccht folkis with the seiknes of Napillis be haldin at the common fleschouss, or with the fleschouris, baxteris, brousteris, ladinaris, for sauete of the toun, and the personis infectit sale keip thame quyat in thar houssis, zhardis, or vther place, quhill thai be haill, for the infectioun of their nichtbouris.

There was an early Edinburgh Edict aiming at the control of syphilis, and dated 22 September 1497. It was drawn up by the Privy Council under the title " Ane Grangore Act," and was apparently sent to the Magistrates to be put into operation. Like the earlier Aberdeen Edict, it was designed to meet the prevalent danger of the infection of the lieges " fra this contagius seiknes callit the Grandgor," but its line of approach was different. It ordained that all persons within the burgh who were infected or had been infected with this contagious disease should gather on the sands of Leith at a certain hour in the morning to be taken by boat to the Inch, there to stay until they were cured ; and that any person who took it upon himself to cure the disease should go to the Inch with the sufferers, and stay with them there, apparently as a measure against spread of infection ; and there were the usual threats of penalties of burning on the cheek with the marking-iron and banishment.

The measures adopted in Aberdeen and Edinburgh failed to arrest the spread of the disease, and it seems to have found its way into most of the sizable towns in the country within a year or two of its first introduction to the country. The accounts of the Lord High Treasurer of Scotland contain records of payments made by the king in 1497 to persons suffering from the disease in Dalry, Linlithgow, Stirling, and Glasgow.

The records of the Privy Seal of Scotland contain a Minute regarding the punishment of a medical man in whose hands a dignitary of the Church had died while under treatment for syphilis ; he was banished from the town for nineteen years. Simpson, in his *Antiquarian Notices of Syphilis in Scotland*, observed that clerical morals were still confessedly in a sad state about the time that syphilis first appeared in the country. Queen Mary seems to have regarded the health of the high Church dignitary who baptized her son, James VI, with considerable suspicion ; she said that " she would not have a pokie priest to spet in her child's mouth." An Edict of the Edinburgh Synod exhorted the clergy not to keep their own illegitimate children in their company, prohibited their promotion of them in the churches, and forbade their endowment with baronies out of the Church's goods. Patrick Hepburn, Bishop of Moray, had seven illegitimate children " all acknowledge in one day " ; and according to the testimony of Marjoribanks, " in the yeir of God 1533 Sir Walter Cowpur, chaiplaine in Edinburgh, gate of pynte of vyne, a laiffe of 36 unce vaight, a pock of aite-meill, a pynte of aill, a schiepe-hede, ane penny candell, and a faire woman of ane XVIIId. grote."

In 1592 a Minute of the Kirk of Session of Glasgow directed " that the hous beyont the Stable Grein Port for women affectit with the Glengore be looked efter," so that probably the method adopted to check the spread of this disease was again that of isolation. A Minute of the Session of 17 April 1600 bore that " after the morning preaching the Session consulted how the infection of the Glengore within the City may be improved. Some sent to the Council to deplore the infection that's in this city by the Glengore, and some to convene again in the Blackfriar's Kirk anent it, and the whole Chirurgeons and Professors of Medicine to be present. So much was given to a man for bigging a lodge without the Stable Green Port to the women that hath the Glen-gore." Another Town Council Minute dated 3 May of the same year was to this effect :

The provest, baillies and counsale hes appoyntit Weddinsdye nixt efter the preiching to convein thamselffis for taking tryall of the inhabitantes anent the greit suspicioune of sindry personnes infectit with the Glengoir, quilk, gif it be nocht preventit will endanger the haill toune, and has ordanit the haill chirurgiones to be warnit to that effect to compeer in the Greyfrein Kirk and qu'haeher beis warnit (and comes nocht) to pay fyne £1 of vnlaw.

The outcome of these deliberations is not known, but apparently they did not control the spread of syphilis. The town's surgeon, Mr. Peter Lowe, had written in 1596 a book on the disease, which he had called *The Spanish Seiknes* : in it he said he had cured the disease " by the help of God and my Confection."

About the middle of the seventeenth century a " new disease " was recognized in Scotland, viz. *sibbens*, which had been introduced by the soldiers of Cromwell. It spread through the counties of Aberdeen, Banff, Moray, and Inverness, and reached Orkney, Shetland, and Lewis. It gradually spread to the south and reached the Solway Firth. By the end of the century cases were few, but in 1825 it broke out again in epidemic form in Ayrshire, lasting till 1835, and sporadic cases were noticed almost a decade later. A contemporary writer said of it : " Great are the perplexity and distress, the suspicion and terror caused by it wherever it comes : and hitherto nothing has been able to prevent the spreading of it." It produced an extensive itchy ulceration of the skin, sore throat, ulcerated tonsils, hoarseness, and occasionally destruction of bone. The condition was extremely contagious and quarantine was adopted as a matter of course. In the northern islands huts were built in the fields and sufferers jealously isolated. In the south an infected cottage often had its guard of soldiers. All this naturally led to concealment, and sometimes deliberate infection of others took place. In the Highlands, servants were stripped naked and carefully examined for sibbens before being engaged. It was believed that sibbens could be spread by the air or by sleeping in contaminated bedding. Epidemics frequently occurred in autumn when the country was overrun by wandering companies of harvesters. The possibility of contagion through sexual con-nection was often overlooked, sometimes asserted, sometimes denied. For prevention, cleanliness was recommended and the use of separate spoons. Wet nurses were not to be engaged without strict investigation. " The disagreeable custom of lying two in one bed should be discouraged." The medical treatment consisted in purging, blood-letting, and dosing with mercury, which was often given to excess.

The striking similarity between sibbens and syphilis was noticed from the beginning, and later researches made it clear that sibbens was in fact syphilis.

5

Another scourge was smallpox. The Kirk Session Records of Aberdeen record an outbreak of it there in the summer of 1610 :

There was at this time a great visitation of the young children with the plague of the pox.

Apparently outbreaks of the disease occurred at intervals during the century following, and the epidemics introduced by the English soldiery, of smallpox among other things, in the early part of the eighteenth century, added fuel to the flames of political animosity in those days : smallpox was then scarcely ever absent. John Galt in his *Annals of the Parish*, tells how in 1762 at Dreghorn " the smallpox came in among the weans of the Parish, and the smashing that it made of the poor bits o' bairns was indeed woeful."

In 1726 inoculation for the prevention of smallpox was first tried out in Aberdeenshire, but it was not persevered with because of some early fatalities there. About 1733 inoculation was started in Dumfries, and by 1745 was being practised on a fairly large scale there, and in Edinburgh, Glasgow, and some other Scottish towns, though mortality from the practice was high—about 1·5 per cent. In some Highland parishes inoculation was said to be " general." Sometimes the cost of inoculation was borne by the heritors, sometimes by the Kirk Session, sometimes by the chief proprietor. In 1779 Arnott wrote that inoculation was " a remedy so compleat that we hesitate not in the least to pronounce those parents who will not inoculate their children for the smallpox, accessory to their death " ; and the College of Physicians of Edinburgh, in a formal Minute of 1754, pronounced inoculation to be " highly salutary to the human race."

Among the outstanding outbreaks of the eighteenth century was one in Edinburgh in 1740–42, when of a total population estimated at about 40,000, over 2,700 died in the course of two years, and more than half the deaths were among children under five years of age—the age-period of greatest smallpox mortality. In the twenty years from 1744 to 1763, smallpox accounted for about 10 per cent. of all the deaths in Edinburgh, and in Kilmarnock during the period from 1728 to 1763 smallpox epidemics came at intervals of three or four years, and on an average one death in six was due to this disease. During that period there were in the town 622 deaths from smallpox, 563 of them among children under five.

Some Highland parishes suffered greatly. Most of the ministers who mentioned inoculation in the Statistical Account were strong advocates of it, but they usually implied that the common people were, or had been, apathetic towards or prejudiced against it. The practice was sometimes recommended from the pulpit and actually carried out by the ministers : it was even recommended that students of divinity should be instructed in the art.

In the Statistical Account of Scotland—based on the years 1791–98—it was said that in many parts of Scotland disease had been formerly rare, and, with the exception of smallpox, seldom distinguished by violence. It was recorded that smallpox was formerly accustomed to destroy one-fifth of the human race. Sometimes one-half of the children attacked by it died ; and when the chincough was prevalent at the same time, " the ravages committed by the natural smallpox was truly dreadful." But the mortal pock, as it was called, even alone, caused great devastation, especially in the Hebrides and the Orkneys.

The unfortunate patients suffering from the disease were, according to Sinclair, treated badly. Great fires were kept burning in the room where often two or three wretched children in one bed lay gasping under a weight of clothes. All fresh air was excluded with the utmost care ; and " whisky and saffron and everything heated " were administered with an unsparing hand. " From ignorance, also, and the most superstitious prejudices, the parents, regardless or insensible of the consequences, instead of inoculating their own children, crowded into those houses in which the disease was of the most malignant nature, and at a time when it is the most infectious." The minister of Birsay and Harrap, in Orkney, was reported to obtain good results in the treatment of the disease " by frequently washing the sores with lukewarm water, accompanied with clean linen," and it was said that he never failed to prevent death from the disease.

When smallpox made its greatest ravages among the children, it was popularly believed to be especially fatal to those who lived by the sea coast, where the inhabitants fed much upon fish, and from this Sinclair argued " that fish, unless perfectly fresh, is not a wholesome diet, that it has often a tendency to corrupt the blood, and to aggravate the malignity of putrid disorders."

Glasgow suffered heavily from the disease. Mortality from smallpox was high, especially among children, in the latter part of the eighteenth century. Indeed in the last quarter of the century nearly 19 per cent. of all deaths occurring among the inhabitants were due to it, and more than half of all the deaths of children under five years of age.

Commenting on the Glasgow Bills of Mortality, Dr. Cowan pointed out that smallpox was a prevalent disease during the period 1783 to 1812, and that the number of deaths attributed to it was probably fairly accurate, since its symptoms and appearance were well known. He believed that the introduction of inoculation, although it diminished the relative mortality, increased the absolute mortality from the disease, since by the practice of inoculation smallpox, which had formerly occurred in epidemics only at long and uncertain intervals, was kept constantly prevailing at all times and seasons, " and thereby produced a mortality, especially among children, which could now be scarcely credited, but for the attested registers of its ravages." It is certain that inoculation against smallpox did not affect that saving of life so generally attributed to it. Between 1783 and 1802 there were in Glasgow 18,999 deaths of children under ten, and of these 6,360 were attributable to smallpox.

A year or two before the end of the eighteenth century the medical profession in Glasgow had begun in a tentative way to utilize Jenner's discovery of vaccination. By 1801 the value of vaccination was beginning to be generally recognized, and in that year the Faculty of Physicians and Surgeons decided to advertise widely that they would vaccinate all comers at their hall at St. Enoch Square, the operation to be performed every Monday. In the course of a year or two this vaccination station of the Faculty became popular and crowded beyond all expectation, so that the Faculty had to intimate that they expected only the poor to avail themselves of it. In less than five years the Faculty vaccinated gratuitously ten thousand persons. The Cowpox Institution began to offer vaccination in 1831, and the Faculty of Medicine in 1828.

In Glasgow the decline of smallpox deaths at the beginning of the nineteenth century was perhaps more marked than elsewhere, because it was a decline from the excessively high level prevailing at the end of the eighteenth century. The great fall took place in 1805 ; in 1804, 25 per cent. of all deaths under the age of ten were due to smallpox, whereas the following year the figure was only 6 per cent.

The practice of vaccination soon spread in Scotland, though its introduction met with a good deal of popular opposition. Sinclair wrote in 1825 that it would be a good plan to have midwives taught the modern art of vaccination when learning the principles of their profession, and he added that " perhaps it would make the plan of vaccination general were itinerant vaccinators annually sent about at the public expense." The Reverend James Russell, minister of Yarrow, reported that at the beginning of the century vaccination was little practised in his part of the country, and seldom at the hands of a medical man. Mothers who sought it for their children generally kept them till the Rev. Mr. Nicol, minister of Traquair, 1802–19, came over to Yarrow on the Saturday of the Communion. He made a point of arriving a few hours before the service began, bringing lymph and inserting it.

Apparently the practice of vaccination began to fall into neglect, for forty years later, in 1854, the Board of Supervision found it necessary to intimate that all Parochial Medical Officers were required by rule to vaccinate gratis all persons, whether receiving parochial relief or not, who might come or be brought to them at the times and places fixed by the Parochial Board. Three years later the Board reported that it was due to the medical officers to state how assiduous they generally were in promoting vaccination, but added that there was " reason to fear that the population, unless when there is cause for immediate apprehension, are more indifferent on the subject than could be desired." The General Superintendent of Poor in Scotland expressed the view in 1858 that, in the Highlands, vaccination should not be performed during the winter months. " I understand," he wrote, " it is not effective in very cold weather,and parents do not wish to expose their children to cold or snow." The same worthy gentleman also wrote that the dislike to vaccination was on the decline ; but from the Report of the Board of Supervision for 1863 it appears that vaccinations performed by Parochial Medical Officers were in the proportion of only 1 to 4·84 births in 1861, and 1 to 5·40 births in 1862. After observing it was obvious that the proportion of children remaining unvaccinated must have been very large, the Board expressed the view that in this matter the new Vaccination Act passed in 1863 might effect improvement.

There was an epidemic of smallpox at Newton Stewart in the autumn of 1816. In this outbreak were all types of case from the slightest to the most severe, and 12 per cent. of the cases died. There was a major epidemic in Scotland in 1817–18, the cities and Fife being particularly affected. This was the first severe and general epidemic in Scotland since the beginning of the century, though Glasgow had never been entirely free, and Thomson wrote : " It is to the severity of this epidemic, I am convinced, that we ought to attribute the greatness of the number of the vaccinated who have been attacked by it, and not to any deterioration in the qualities of cowpox virus, or to any defects in the manner in which it has been employed." In the five years from 1835 to 1839 the total number of deaths from all causes in Glasgow was 40,366 ; and of these 2,195 were from smallpox ; 93 per cent. of the smallpox deaths occurred among children under ten years of age. Between 1830 and 1840 several Scottish towns were heavily hit by smallpox, among them Stranraer, Ayr, and Edinburgh. Dr. McLellan of Dumfries reported in 1840 that that town was less secure against smallpox than might have been desired : " Either through negligence or prejudice a large proportion of the children of the lower classes in Dumfries are allowed to remain unvaccinated. Smallpox cases of the worst kind have at different times of late occurred in the town and neighbourhood, and if the malady did not widely spread it could scarcely be ascribed to the sanitary check of vaccination." About the same time Dr. Laurie reported that Greenock was frequently visited by epidemics of smallpox. He explained that two years previously, of nine cases which he admitted into the hospital, sailors just arrived from a voyage, seven died. The other two when convalescent were seized with fever, and one of them died. After the admission of these men several patients in the hospital took smallpox, and from the dread of infection, many who had other diseases were removed by their friends : Dr. Laurie added, understandably enough, " Since that time patients hesitate more, and show more reluctance to enter the hospitals than formerly."

There was another period of high smallpox incidence in Glasgow in 1851 and 1852, accounting altogether for 1,202 deaths among the population of 360,000. Yet another scare occurred in 1863, with at the same time a formidable outbreak of smallpox at Greenock, which had by then been brought less than an hour's distance by railway from the city. Greenock was for several months the seat of an epidemic of the disease, " having truly the proportions of a plague ; in the month of August 1863 no less than 48 deaths from smallpox occurred in the town."

During the first ten years after the introduction of registration of the causes of death in Scotland, 1855–64, there were 10,548 deaths from smallpox in the country, almost two-thirds occurring among children in the first five years of life.

6

Typhus fever, too, held a bad record. It is not too much to say that " fever " dominated Scottish life in the first half of the nineteenth century. The term was used to cover several prevalent conditions that were not clearly defined in their clinical features and not always clearly distinguished. Typhus, spotted typhus, common fever, continued fever, relapsing fever, gaol fever, and enteric fever were all liable to be included under the same name, and it was not until near the middle of the century that more precision of diagnosis came to be established. This differentiation was due in large measure to the work of Dr. Robert Perry, physician to Glasgow Royal Infirmary and to the Fever Hospital in Clyde Street. In 1840 Dr. W. H. Forrest, President of the Stirling Medical Association, gave an account of the prevalence of typhus in Stirling, explaining that by the term typhus he understood " the common continued fever of this country and no other fever whatever." Other observers had other definitions. Not until 1865 were deaths from enteric fever separated off in official reports from those attributed to typhus. The fact that there were in all probability several distinct diseases covered by the same name serves to explain in some measure the continued high prevalence of " fever " and its erratic epidemiological behaviour, as well as the wide variations from year to year in the fatality of the condition. During the five years 1835-39 the numbers of cases of fever treated in Aberdeen Infirmary and Dispensary were 616, 684, 1,307, 1,272, and 1,308, and the number of deaths in the same years were 24, 42, 76, 44, and 85. From records kept of cases treated in Aberdeen Infirmary and Dispensary from 1 July 1838 to 1 July 1840 it emerged that case-mortality was higher among males than among females, 10 per cent. as against 7 per cent., and that age played an important part in determining prospect of recovery. Among children under twelve years of age less than 5 per cent. of the patients treated died. Of patients between 30 and 40 years of age, over 10 per cent. died, and of patients over 40 years of age, upwards of 20 per cent. died.

In the seven years 1833-39 there were in Dundee 11,808 cases of fever, responsible for 1,312 deaths. Estimating that half of these deaths were of adults in the prime of life, Mr. McCulloch calculated that the pecuniary loss, by the death of these adults, might be taken as £98,400 :

And, if the remaining 656 under the age of maturity, yet approaching it, be taken as the half of the adults, or £75 each, we have a loss of £49,200 more ; to which, if we add £1 a piece, or £1,312 in all, for attendance and medical expenses, the Fever Bill of Dundee, during the last seven years, will stand as follows :

	£	s.	d.
Loss of labour for six weeks of 5,248 adults at 8s. a week .	12,595	0	0
Attendance, medicine at home or infirmary, at £1 each .	5,248	0	0
Loss of labour for six weeks of 5,248 under age, at 4s. a week	6,297	12	0
Expense of treatment of the above at infirmary or home, at 10s. each	2,624	0	0
Loss by death of 656 adults at £150 each . . .	98,400	0	0
Loss by 656 deaths under age, at £75 a piece . . .	49,200	0	0
Treatment of 1,312 cases, at £1 each	1,312	0	0
Total . .	£175,676	12	0

Or £25,096, 13s. per annum

As was to be expected, there was keen debate among the doctors of those days about the true nature of the disease and about what caused and spread it. Professor Allison of Edinburgh thought that the chief and only certain source of the continued fever then prevalent in Edinburgh was " a specific contagion " arising from the living human body already affected by it, " which putrid effluvia can no more generate than they can generate smallpox or measles." He held that the draining of irrigated meadows in the neighbourhood of the town, though desirable for the health of the people, would not diminish their liability to contagious fever, and he pointed out that though many dunghills had been removed in Edinburgh during the twenty preceding years there had, since their removal, been two great epidemics of fever in Edinburgh, spreading more extensively than ever before.

At a meeting of the British Association held in Glasgow in September 1840 Dr. Neil Arnott made a report on the fevers that had become so prevalent in Edinburgh and Glasgow. He pointed out that four views had been put forward as to the cause and chief remedy of the misery and disease prevailing among the poor of Scotland, " not one of which made particular account of the malaria of filth to which the London reporters had attached so much weight." First there was the view held by " the benevolent and eloquent Dr. Chalmers," that the want of good religious training was the cause and that Church extension was the remedy ; second, " the enlightened Dr. Allison " held that destitution was the cause, and a good Poor Law for Scotland the remedy ; third, another excellent man stated that the abuse of intoxicating drinks was the cause, and a legislative or other suppression of this the remedy ; and fourth, another gave his reasons for believing that want of national education was the cause and the establishment of such schools as he described the remedy. Dr. Arnott's own view was that the faulty sanitation of the times was largely responsible for the condition.

Typhus fever occurred in Scotland before the nineteenth century, though only then did it come to assume great epidemic prevalence. In 1735 Dr. Gilchrist of Dumfries wrote about " our fever," which he thought to be peculiar to that age. Gilchrist was not certain whether the fever he described was to be related to the manner of living—it was a time of heavy drinking—or to a series of warm, wet seasons. Whatever the cause, the disease he described affected chiefly the poor, and was characterized by looseness of the bowels, pains in the belly, local sweating, tickling cough, and " leaping of the tendons." A few years later, in 1741, Gilchrist described another outbreak of fever in Dumfries more malignant than the previous one.

Edinburgh was similarly affected by fever in the winter of 1735. This was apparently true relapsing fever. In 1740, which was a year of famine, fever was superimposed on the other miseries of the people, and in 1741 the deaths from it in the city amounted to nearly one-fifth of all deaths, though they were exceeded in number by deaths from consumption. During the Forty-five, some of the government troops returning from the Low Countries were disembarked at Newcastle-on-Tyne, where many of the men died of gaol fever, as did many of the inhabitants. Pringle describes how in 1746 a brigade that landed at Nairn was seized with fever. Eighty men were left sick there, and during the ten days that the regiment remained at Inverness 120 more were sent to hospital, ill of the same fever, which also attacked the inhabitants of the town. " Though the virulence of the distemper diminished afterwards in their march to Fort Augustus and Fort William, yet the corps continued sickly for some time." From the middle of February 1746, when the army crossed the Forth, to the end of the campaign there were 2,000 sick in hospital, including wounded, " of which number near 300 died, mostly of the contagious fever."

In the latter half of the eighteenth century many outbreaks of fever were reported from different parts of the country, usually associated with periods of severe privation. The disease was prevalent in Highland parishes, and Sinclair, in the Statistical Account, drew attention to the many references to fevers. Sometimes these were reported to be of a " favourable " kind ; at other times they continued long, and carried off many victims. Of the fishing village of Eyemouth it was said that the only complaints proving mortal there were " different kinds of fevers and consumptions," which were for the most part confined to the poorest class of people and ascribed to their scanty diet. There was a general impression that towards the end of the eighteenth century the nature of the prevalent fevers had greatly changed, pleuritic and inflammatory types giving place to low, lingering, and nervous attacks, and it was thought that this alteration had probably arisen from the failing hardiness of the people : " on the whole we have become effeminate, and labour more severely, by which the mind is depressed, from the anxieties of life and the difficulty of procuring a subsistence."

In the last five years of the eighteenth century 317 of the 2,399 patients admitted to the newly opened Glasgow Royal Infirmary suffered from fever. From 1800 to 1814 the proportion of fever cases was little more than 10 per cent., but in 1815 it rose steeply, reaching nearly 60 per cent. in 1818, and rarely falling below 20 per cent. for many years thereafter.

Cleland reported that following a period of acute trade depression in 1817 the lower classes were severely afflicted with typhus fever, and afterwards, when its virulence had been greatly subdued, with Synocha or common fever. He described this nervous fever as being most frequently the consequence of contagion, generally attacking people in a poor state of health. Accommodation in the Royal Infirmary proving quite inadequate, a Society for the Suppression of Fever was formed in March 1818. The Committee were soon satisfied that the contagion was greatest in those quarters of the town in which the poor were huddled together without adequate ventilation ; and that the want of cleanliness retarded their cure. They erected at Spring-garden, an airy situation at the head of the town, a fever hospital containing upwards of 200 beds ; fumigated and whitewashed upwards of 5,000 apartments "which the disease had visited or was likely to visit " ; appointed persons to superintend the cleansing of closes twice a week, and the removal of the soil from ash-pits at least once a month ; made a register of upwards of 600 lodging houses with the dimensions of their apartments, the number of beds and of persons who slept in them ; and, having provided bedding, they caused that which had been used by patients confined in their own houses to be burned.

The new fever hospital was opened for patients on 30 March 1818 and shut on 12 July 1819. Between these dates 1,929 patients were admitted, of whom 171 died. At first patients from the suburbs were admitted without charge : latterly they were charged for at the rate of twenty-five shillings each. The sum subscribed and collected from various sources for the benefit of the institution amounted to £6,627. At first sedan chairs were used for conveying the sick to the hospital ; these were replaced by a low-hung chaise, and latterly a covered litter on springs was provided. "The medical department was conducted by a physician, two surgeons, and an apothecary ; the physician giving his valuable services without pecuniary return." About this time the Committee of the Town's Hospital in Glasgow, an institution financed in part at least from local rates, were considering whether an extension of the hospital was necessary in view of the increasing demand upon it. It was suggested to them that fever wards should be provided in any extension of the hospital, but the Committee expressed the view that a fever ward would not be legitimate use of their funds, " and that such an institution, if necessary, after the

Royal Infirmary received the cases recommended by the magistrates, should be dependent on private benevolence."

There were similar outbreaks in other Scottish towns at this time, and almost everywhere the same great difficulty in finding hospital accommodation for the patients. In Edinburgh, for example, the onus of treatment of infectious fevers fell upon the Royal Infirmary, which in normal times provided at least two wards for that purpose. With the coming of the epidemic in 1817, three additional wards were opened, but these were insufficient to deal with the outbreak, and a number of influential citizens approached the Government for permission to use as a fever hospital Queensberry House Barracks, then unoccupied. Permission was granted, and the managers of the infirmary undertook the administration of the House as a fever hospital. The wooden beds it contained were exchanged for iron bedsteads, and the wards were opened with accommodation for from 60 to 80 patients. A matron, an apothecary, and a nursing staff were appointed, and a young medical graduate became superintendent at a salary of £40 per annum. The epidemic was not of virulent character, and only 4 per cent. of the cases treated died. Although the epidemic abated in 1820–21, Queensberry House continued to be used for fever patients until 1823, and two years later the managers of the infirmary, as a precautionary measure, leased the premises for ten years at a rent of £80 per annum. The buildings were in use again to deal with a second epidemic in 1826–29, and from that time until the end of the lease 150 beds were kept constantly occupied there in addition to those used in the Infirmary for the treatment of fever patients. Later, when Queensberry House was closed, nine wards, containing about 140 beds, were made available in the infirmary for the treatment of cases of fever. Even these were insufficient to deal with the epidemics of 1842–43 and 1846–48, and it was necessary to supplement the available accommodation by tents pitched in the vicinity of the infirmary. During the eight years 1841–48 inclusive, 17,542 patients suffering from infectious fevers were treated in the Royal Infirmary, and the managers expressed the view in 1849 that for the prevention of the disease more stringent measures ought to be adopted to prevent the importation of paupers and vagrants from Ireland.

The position in Glasgow at this time was even worse, and in the Report of the Royal Infirmary for 1824, when cases of " fever " amounted to 24 per cent. of all admissions, it was stated that not only were cases treated at the hospital, but that " measures have at the same time been taken to have the houses the patients left cleaned and fumigated. The directors have thus, they hope, done all in their power for staying the contagion." At the worst period, deaths from typhus fever in one year (1847) numbered in Glasgow no fewer than 4,346.

But for more than half a century from the epidemic of 1818 typhus was always a formidable epidemic disease in the city. Its history during that period has been likened to that of an active volcano, periods of deceptive repose alternating with violent eruptions. For short periods it smouldered in the wynds. Then, when the steady inflow of immigrants, attracted by the prospect of work, had reproduced a susceptible population it burst out into an epidemic.

The same state of affairs prevailed in many other Scottish towns. Aberdeen had three epidemics, in 1817–19, 1831–32, and 1835–39. In Greenock it was noted that the epidemics were chiefly associated with certain parts of the town, where sanitation was worst and overcrowding greatest. Nor did the smaller towns escape. Dr. McLellan of Dumfries wrote in 1840 that there was no disease more justly to be dreaded than typhus fever, a constant foe lurking, sometimes hid, yet ever ready to be roused into action. Within the previous twelve or fifteen months the number of fever patients treated at the Dumfries and Galloway Infirmary had exceeded two hundred, while the average number for many preceding years had ranged from 15 to 30 ; and he added that the number admitted represented only a small fraction of those suffering from the disease. He thought this state of affairs called for the institution of a fever board, of which the principal duties would be : " when the fever case was first reported to it by the medical attendant, to send its appointed visitors and have the patient conveyed in a proper manner to the Infirmary, thereafter to inspect the apartments, and according as they might require to clean, ventilate, and fumigate them and to attend to the washing of clothes to which contagious matter may adhere." About the same time James Cameron, surgeon in Tain, reported that while typhus fever was rarely met with there, synochus in its last stage assumed typhoidal symptoms, and in this state invariably proved fatal among the poorer classes ; continued fever was common among the poor. A surgeon in St. Andrews reported that the fever occurring there was usually the mild form of typhus ; it was not attended with any eruption on the skin, and when death occurred the usual morbid appearance was in the bowels, which were ulcerated on their internal surface.

In his first report to the Glasgow Board of Police, Dr. W. T. Gairdner, the newly appointed Medical Officer of Health, reported in 1863 that almost the only fever then found in Glasgow to which the name typhus could properly be applied was what was called by medical men maculated or eruptive typhus. In that year 1,894 cases of typhus fever were reported in the city and 670 deaths from the disease ; Glasgow was exceeded by Aberdeen, Greenock, and Leith in the proportion of deaths from fever occurring in the population.

7

A severe epidemic of cholera on the continent of Europe, particularly virulent in Hamburg, found its way to England, and towards the end of October 1831 the disease broke out in Sunderland, progressing to Newcastle, Haddington, Musselburgh, Kirkintilloch, Edinburgh, Maryhill, and Glasgow. Everywhere its coming provoked the greatest apprehension. The Cholera Act passed by an agitated Parliament bore testimony to the fear in which this visitation of Providence was held. Save here and there, pestilence was still regarded as a visitation of God, a view that only the failure of the Cholera Acts themselves finally dispelled. It was inevitable that the visitation of cholera should be held to be evidence of divine displeasure at many of the trends of the day ; but in Glasgow a preacher who announced that the epidemic was God's reply to a contemporary attempt to push a Deceased Wife's Sister Bill in Parliament received scant consideration against Lord Ashley's evidence that people with baths and wash-houses had in the main escaped !

Everywhere the most energetic steps were taken to try to shut out the disease. Thomas Guthrie, minister of Arbirlot, near Arbroath, told how, when in 1832 his village was threatened by cholera, " which raged like a fire around us, but never crossed the boundary of the parish," steps were taken to establish a *cordon sanitaire* by appointing a committee of constables to watch over the safety of the parish, not allowing any tramp or beggar to enter. In order that the first appearance of the plague might be promptly met with the most approved remedies, a medicine chest was procured and placed in the manse under the minister's care. But the medicine-chest was never used; "our trust was in God and prevention." The son of the church beadle lived in Dundee, where his wife, if not some children also, had fallen victims to the cholera. "I learned late on a Sunday night that he had arrived in our parish. By dawn of day on Monday morning my servant boy was on horseback galloping to all the farms of the Committee, summoning each to make haste to a meeting at the manse; and before the beadle's son was well out of his bed, we marched him off and beyond the bounds of the parish." The worthy minister does not appear to have been overmuch concerned about the welfare of his neighbour's parish.

At Haddington by January 1832 there had been 47 cases, with 18 deaths. At Tranent a boy died of cholera on 18 January; within a week there had been 61 cases and 26 deaths, and the numbers continued to increase. Musselburgh was the scene of a violent outbreak: in five weeks the disease had attacked one-quarter of the total population and nearly half of the patients died. The disease spread to Edinburgh and the Water of Leith, to Hawick and other border towns, and to the West of Scotland, Lanarkshire, Glasgow, and Paisley. Glasgow at once took precautions. In November 1831 the Lord Provost had called a meeting "of the respectable inhabitants to consider the propriety of forming a Board of Health to guard against the visitation of the calamity . . . and to promote the welfare of this great community by every means which could avert the approach, or effect the extinction of disease." It was decided to set up a Board of Health under the chairmanship of the Lord Provost, and to appoint a Medical Committee to make all necessary arrangements. The Committee proceeded to equip five cholera hospitals, one lazaretto, and a large fever hospital; there were also hospitals in Gorbals, Calton, and Anderston. When fitted up, the fever hospital at Mile End was presented by the Board of Health to the Managers of the Royal Infirmary, who undertook to support it from their funds. A member of the Committee made a present to the Board of a carriage with a spring bed for conveying patients from their houses to the hospital in a reclining posture; and before this carriage was used for the transport of patients it was sent round the town to collect cast-off clothing for the diseased poor. The Cleaning and Fumigating Committee caused the closes, staircases, and lanes where the lower classes resided to be washed, the houses of the poor white-washed, and all infected places fumigated. To promote cleanliness the water-companies supplied water gratis and the Dean of Guild Court caused ill-constructed dunghills to be removed. The Medical Committee, of which the Professor of Chemistry was a member, gave it as their opinion that the disinfecting liquor for clothes should be chloride of lime dissolved in twenty times its weight of water; to be effectual the dry powder should be dissolved immediately before using. Chlorine was used for disinfecting rooms, and the walls were washed with new-slaked lime. The Medical Committee also issued advice on the prevention and treatment of cholera. For prevention, personal cleanliness, adequate ventilation, and the removal of accumulations of filth were recommended. Warm clothing, especially of flannel, was advised, and the use of intoxicating liquors discouraged. A nourishing diet was recommended, but indigestible food was to be avoided, as were raw vegetables, undressed fruits, and watery potatoes : vegetables when used were to be thoroughly boiled. Butcher meat too long kept, and spoiled fish particularly, ought to be shunned as highly prejudicial. It was recommended that medical assistance should be summoned as soon as symptoms appeared. An emetic was advised, a mixture of mustard and common salt in luke-warm water. When the vomiting ceased, forty drops of laudanum were to be given in a little toddy. Every possible means of applying heat to the surface of the body was to be vigorously used : " The patient should be wrapped in hot blankets, hot bricks, bottles full of warm water, flannel or muslin bags, filled with hot sand, bran, or salt should be carefully applied to the trunk and limbs, using, at the same time, continual friction with warm flannel to those parts not covered with the bags. The sand, bran, or salt may be heated on a girdle or in a frying-pan."

On Sunday 12 February the first definite case of cholera made its appearance near the suburbs of the city, and on the following day a series of official reports began to be issued. They showed that the number of cases occurring in Glasgow and suburbs during the week beginning 12 February was 38 ; 19 February, 83 ; 26 February, 82 ; 4 March, 83 ; 11 March, 62 ; 18 March, 122 ; 25 March, 142 ; 1 April, 69 ; 8 April, 72 ; 15 April, 100 ; 22 April, 54 ; 29 April, 46 ; 6 May, 35 ;

13 May, 22. Of the 1,039 cases 553 died, and in addition 107 patients died during the same period in the Barony Parish.

The spread of the pestilence made a deep impression on the community. Resort was had to every known preventive measure. " The theatre and other places of amusement were shut, visiting and dinner parties suspended, and Sunday evening congregations for sermon postponed. Prayer meetings were held in almost every place of worship on the mornings or afternoons of week-days, when fervent supplications were offered up to the Almighty, for mitigating disease, and averting the pestilence." The mortality chiefly affected the intemperate, the dissolute, the ill-fed, and the ill-clothed among the population.

The expense incurred in the prevention and cure of fever and cholera at this time exceeded £10,000, of which £8,000 was raised by voluntary contribution. On 3 June there was only one case of cholera remaining ; according to Cleland, from the commencement of the outbreak on 13 February to its end on 3 June 1832, there were 1,325 cases of cholera and 687 deaths in the whole population district, which contained 202,426 souls.

Even small towns took drastic precautions against the disease. The Burgh Records of Dingwall bear, under date 10 November 1831, that " Intelligence having arrived that the Disease called the Cholera morbus, which has so long afflicted foreign countries, has made its appearance in England and threatens to extend its ravages to Scotland, the Council met for the purpose of devising measures, if not to prevent the approach at least to mitigate the evil of the disease in question." The steps to be taken were very much as elsewhere—cleanliness to be promoted among the inhabitants, dung hills and nuisances to be removed, the interior of houses to be white-washed with quicklime, the local medical practitioners to be invited to form themselves into a Board of Health, and a special Committee to be charged with carrying these resolutions into effect. As the port of Dingwall was much frequented by coal and lime vessels from Sunderland and Newcastle, towns heavily stricken by cholera, it was decreed that no vessel from either of these places should be permitted to approach the town nearer than Ardulie Point or permitted to enter the Canal until examined by the medical men and pronounced to be in a healthy state ; and Mr. Davidson of Tulloch offered the use of his pleasure-boat to carry this rule into effect. A later Minute, of 25 August 1832, bore that a meeting resolved to levy a rate on the inhabitants to defray the cost of measures taken for the control of cholera : for furnishing medicines, medical assistance, nurses, etc., for sick poor who had taken the disease and could not be conveniently removed to cholera hospitals, and for supplying medicines at the dispensary stations, £20 ; for erecting and fitting out a cholera hospital, £30 ; for providing lime for whitewashing houses, ventilating houses, removing nuisances, and fumigation, £25 ; incidental expenses, bedding, etc., which the Board might direct to be destroyed, and burying the bodies of the poor, £25 ; so that the total sum for which it was necessary to levy an assessment in Dingwall was £100.

There have been preserved somewhat similar records of measures taken in Wick, where a Board of Health was set up in April 1832 at the behest of the Privy Council because of " the propriety of medical aid being provided for alleviating distress in the place should the Cholera morbus unfortunately visit the same at the period of the Herring Fishery." The usual resolutions were made to secure cleansing of the town and the removal of nuisances. The Board of Health set up a voluntary soup-kitchen and advocated public prayers by the clergy. On 25 July the disease reached Helmsdale, and on 30 July, Thurso. A medical man familiar with Asiatic cholera was engaged in Edinburgh ; his emoluments were 10s. 6d. *per diem* and the guarantee of a " comporatable bed-chamber." The doctor apparently had his troubles, for he resigned in about six weeks' time. A hospital was provided, with twelve beds in the first instance. The first case of cholera was reported in the burgh on 4 August ; there is no record of current opinion as to how the disease was brought into the town. The epidemic lasted 85 days and there were 411 cases, of which 69 died. The Board of Health was authorized to raise money by assessment. In January 1834 it was decided that " the whole effects in the hospital should be exposed for sale by public roup with the exception of the mattresses which are directed to be burnt, and that all the bedding which had been used shall be boiled before being so disposed of."

During the prevalence of cholera in Inverness a similar Board of Health was organized, and it too took very stringent steps for removing filth and for cleaning, ventilating, and whitewashing the dwellings of the poor, " by which they were much benefited ;

but under ordinary circumstances, such an exercise of authority would be resisted by the people, and the magistrates in fact dare not attempt it."

In the course of the cholera epidemic of 1831–32 there were in Scotland altogether 20,202 cases and 10,650 deaths. Glasgow and its suburbs had about one-third of the deaths, Edinburgh, Leith, Dundee, Greenock, Paisley, and Dumfries together another third, while a large part of the remainder occurred among the inhabitants of mining and fishing villages : among small towns mentioned by Sir J. Y. Simpson as having been heavily affected were Helmsdale, Fort William, Fort George, Port Patrick, Crieff, and Kelso.

The cholera epidemic of 1848–49 was, according to Creighton, first established on British soil at Edinburgh, Leith, and New-haven at the beginning of October. At Newhaven 30 people were affected during the month of October, with 20 deaths ; curiously enough, there were no further cases in the village. The Edinburgh outbreak continued until 8 January 1849 : there were 801 cases and 478 deaths, 196 of males and 282 of females. A cholera hospital was opened in Surgeons' Square, and in the course of three months treated 248 patients. Most cases were from poor districts—the Grassmarket, Cowgate, Canongate. There were severe outbreaks in surrounding districts, and in the area of Carron, Stirlingshire, there were some 400 cases. There was an explosive outbreak in the Springburn district of Glasgow, where the disease lingered long. In early December it attacked the city of Glasgow ; on 30 December alone there were 158 burials from cholera there. The epidemic in Glasgow ceased in March, having been responsible for about 3,800 deaths. Case mortality was highest at the beginning of the epidemic. Many other towns and villages were affected, including Coatbridge, Hamilton, Dumfries, Glengarnock, Selkirk, Kelso, Jedburgh, and Moffat, together with the mining villages of Lanarkshire and Ayrshire. It was noteworthy that all the cases occurred in the south of Scotland, apart from an outbreak in Dundee ; and the disease was at its worst in areas where overcrowding was most serious and sanitation most primitive, as in the mining areas. In August 1846 the General Board of Supervision, stimulated by the threat of cholera, issued to Inspectors of Poor official instructions for the removal of nuisances, the legislature having empowered them, in parishes where there were no magistrates or

Commissioners of Police, to carry out the provisions of the Nuisance Removal Act : " It has been clearly ascertained that the accumulation of filth and other impure matter and the noxious effluvia proceeding therefrom tend greatly to the dissemination of fever and contagious diseases generally in the neighbourhood where such accumulation is permitted to take place."

These instructions were renewed in 1853 when cholera again visited the country. The outbreak of 1853–54 caused about 6,000 deaths in Scotland, of which 3,892 were in Glasgow and a considerable part of the remainder in Edinburgh and Dundee. The course of the disease in Glasgow was similar to that of 1832. The northern and eastern districts of the city were first affected, though a cholera hospital that was opened received comparatively few cases. There was a severe outbreak at Symington, where among a population of 240 there were 110 cases and 30 deaths. Nearly all the cases occurred on the side of the village street which drew its water from a public well ; the houses on the other side had private wells. In Edinburgh the disease caused considerable alarm. A cholera hospital was again opened at Surgeons' Square, but after treating only 45 cases in nine months was closed in early June. The real epidemic came in the autumn of 1854, when the hospital had to be re-opened to treat some two hundred cases.

On 15 October 1853 the Moderator of the Presbytery of Edinburgh wrote to Lord Palmerston, then Home Secretary, relative to the appointment of a national Fast. The Presbytery had considered " the propriety of appointing on ecclesiastical authority a day for prayer and humiliation within the bounds of the Presbytery under the visitation of Asiatic Cholera which has again appeared in this country," but decided instead to ascertain from Lord Palmerston whether a national Fast was likely to be appointed on Royal Authority. Lord Palmerston sent the following reply :

SIR,—I am directed by Viscount Palmerston to acknowledge the receipt of your letter . . . and to state that there can be no doubt that manifestations of humble resignation to the Divine Will and sincere acknowledgements of human unworthiness are never more appropriate than when it has pleased Providence to afflict mankind with some severe visitation ; but it does not appear to Lord Palmerston that a national Fast would be suitable to the circumstances of the present moment.

The Maker of the Universe has established certain laws of nature for the planet in which we live, and the weal or woe of mankind depends upon the observance or neglect of those laws. One of those laws connects health with the absence of those gaseous exhalations which proceed from overcrowded human beings or from decomposing substances, whether animal or vegetable : and those same laws render sickness the almost inevitable consequence of exposure to those noxious influences. But it has at the same time pleased Providence to place it within the power of man to make such arrangements as will prevent or disperse such exhalations as to render them harmless, and it is the duty of man to attend to those laws of nature, and to exert the faculties which Providence has thus given to man for his own welfare.

The recent visitation of cholera, which has for the moment been mercifully checked, is an awful warning given to the people of this realm that they have too much neglected their duty in this respect, and that those persons with whom it rested to purify towns and cities have not been sufficiently active in regard to such matters. Lord Palmerston would, therefore, suggest that the best course which the people of this country can pursue to deserve that the further progress of the Cholera should be stayed, will be to employ the interval that will elapse between the present time and the beginning of next spring in planning and executing measures by which those portions of their towns and cities which are inhabited by the poorest classes, and which, from the nature of things, must most need purification and improvement may be freed from those causes and sources of contagion which, if allowed to remain, will infallibly breed pestilence and be fruitful in death, in spite of the prayers and fastings of a united but inactive nation.

8

The major epidemics so far described dominated Scottish life for many centuries. They were so severe from time to time, so compelling in their urgency and so striking in their effects, that they came to be easily recognized and greatly feared. But they do not by any means exhaust the tale of infectious diseases in Scotland, for it seems clear that for many years past epidemic diseases still prevalent—influenza, measles, whooping-cough, scarlet fever and diphtheria—were well enough known in Scotland, though their importance was dwarfed by that of the major diseases.

As early as 1173, there was a reference in the Chronicle Melrose to a bad kind of cough, unheard of before, which affected almost everyone far and wide, " from which pest " many died. Influenza seems to have been prevalent again in the seventeenth century, and in 1716 it was recorded that an outbreak of the disease occurred among the natives of St. Kilda following the arrival on the island of strangers in their ordinary health. These " strangers' colds " occurred repeatedly, one of the worst on St.

Kilda, which attacked almost the entire population of the island, some two hundred souls, following the visit of H.M.S. *Porcupine* in 1860.

Scotland at the end of the seventeenth century was reputed to be tolerably free from ague, and the severe outbreaks of the condition which occurred in the seventeen-twenties were regarded as something new. These agues were often attributed by the Scots to the Union of 1707 :

The effects and evidences of God's displeasure appearing more and more against us since the incorporation union, mingling ourselves with the people of these abominations, making ourselves liable to their judgments, of which we are deeply sharing ; particularly in that sad stroke and great distress upon many families and persons of the burning agues, fevers never heard of before in Scotland to be universe and mortal.

There was another outbreak of influenza in Scotland in 1733. It was said to follow a similar outbreak in cattle a few months earlier. The total number of burials in Edinburgh, which were fewer than a hundred per month before the outbreak, rose in January 1733 to 214. Yet another outbreak of influenza, that of 1758, first noticed in September following a period of easterly wind, started among young people in the east of Scotland, but soon spread through the country, attacking young and old alike. It was again recorded that in some parts of the country, before human beings were attacked, the horses were " more than usually affected with a cold and a cough." The symptoms as described at the time were of a kind apparently typical enough of influenza ; there might be fever with no cold or a cold with little or no fever. Some had bleeding at the nose, which might continue for several days, and soreness and pains in the bones might be in all parts of the body or confined to the cheek-bones, teeth, and sides of the head. Those who returned to work too soon frequently relapsed, but fatalities were not very numerous except among old people. There were outbreaks of influenza in Aberdeen at the end of 1775, and in several parts of Scotland during the years 1782–84. John Mill, a minister in Shetland, described " a strange distemper called influenza," which raged through Britain in 1782 in the same manner as it did in the Baltic States, though not so fatally here. " People are variously affected with it, with swelled faces, sore throats, dizzy heads, coughs, violent pains and feverishness ; for remedy is prescribed a decoction of 2 oz. lint-seed, 2 do. of Liquorish-stick bruised and boiled over a slow fire in a pint water to half do., then strained and mixed with 4 oz. powdered suggar candy, also some lemon juice, brandy or rum ; take frequently a spoonfull thereoff etc."

Of the thirty-five patients treated in Edinburgh Royal Infirmary during the first year of its existence (1729–30) one, Mary Walker, from the Parish of Congalton, suffered from tertian ague and sore eyes, and another, Robert Brown, a dragoon, from quartan ague. Both were discharged as cured. The parish ministers who prepared the reports for Sinclair's Statistical Account had much to say about the occurrence of the ague in Scotland. Formerly very prevalent, it had by the end of the eighteenth century been " entirely banished from a number of districts," and the change was chiefly attributed to rapid improvements in agriculture, especially drainage.

In 1833 and the immediately following years influenza was more or less prevalent throughout the country, especially in Glasgow and Edinburgh, and many deaths were attributed to the disease and to " catarrh, fever, and decline." The only period of life which escaped this high mortality was that between the ages of five and twenty ; young children, and even more particularly old people, bore the brunt of the attack. Thomas Guthrie, minister of Arbirlot, near Arbroath, told how in 1837 influenza— " ' the influence ' as the Italians originally called the disease "— of a most virulent type spread suddenly over the whole land, slaying its thousands and tens of thousands like a deadly plague. " There was not, indeed, as in Egypt, a dead body in every house, but in every house, or almost every house, there was one or more ill ; and of the eleven parish churches in my Presbytery, the Presbytery of Arbroath, more than the half were shut that Sunday."

9

There were several references to outbreaks of measles in Scotland during the eighteenth century. There was an outbreak in Edinburgh in 1735, and Galt, in *Annals of the Parish*, tells how in Ayrshire the latter part of the year was marked by a great misfortune, in that " there was such a smashery of the poor weans [from measles] as had not been known for an age " ; there were three dead children in the village of Dreghorn in one day. But it was not until the end of the century that measles came to take a really dominant position in the epidemic history of the country.

Watt prepared from the Burial Registers of Glasgow a table from which the following figures have been extracted :

Period	Total Deaths	Percentage of Deaths attributed to			
		Smallpox	Measles	Whooping Cough	" Bowel-Hive "
1783–1788	9,994	19·55	0·93	4·51	6·72
1789–1794	11,103	18·22	1·17	5·13	6·43
1795–1800	9,991	18·70	2·10	5·36	6·47
1801–1806	10,304	8·90	3·92	6·12	7·27
1807–1812	13,354	3·90	10·76	5·57	9·26

There was much comment about the remarkable substitution of deaths from smallpox by deaths from measles in the early years of the nineteenth century, and many were of opinion that little was to be gained by seeking to control one major cause of infant deaths, since it was clear that in any case another disease would come along to carry the children off. Farr, the great English statistician, often referred to Watt's work in Glasgow and propounded what came to be known as " the doctrine of replacement " ; a belief that when one epidemic disease is rooted out it is apt to be replaced by others that ravage the human race wherever the conditions of healthy life are wanting. " They have this propensity in common with weeds and other forms of life : as one species recedes another advances."

The great epidemic of measles of 1807–8 extended throughout the entire length and breadth of the country, affecting particularly the cities of Glasgow, Edinburgh, and Aberdeen. Deaths were usually from such complications of measles as bowel complaints in children and pulmonary conditions in adults. In many cases convalescence was slow. Creighton pointed out that the fact that so many adults were affected suggested that measles had not been for some time previously a universal affection of childhood.

During the five years 1835–39, 2,482 deaths occurred in Glasgow from measles, all but thirty-four of them among children under ten years of age, and during this period the disease commanded much attention in Scotland. Dr. Adamson of St. Andrews reported that measles was prevalent there in 1840, and that it exhibited in its course some remarkable peculiarities. The first children affected were, he pointed out, almost all about five or six years of age, and not from the poorer part of the town. These cases were comparatively mild. After an apparent cessation of the disease for some weeks it suddenly became general among younger children of all classes, and was now in many cases very severe, and even fatal. After attaining its greatest degree of severity and extent in the beginning of November, it had again almost disappeared when all at once it revived among older children of well-off parents, but in these cases it was again very mild. This outbreak of measles in 1840 affected many Scottish towns, and was responsible for the deaths of many children.

10

As is apparent from the table on page 133, whooping cough was for long a consistent contributor to the mortality of Scottish children. So much was this the case that in 1813 Dr. Robert Watt, the distinguished physician who constructed the table, wrote a *Treatise on the History, Nature, and Treatment of Chin-cough*, as the disease was then called. In his treatise Watt recorded that " Next to the Small-pox formerly, and the Measles now, Chincough is the most fatal disease to which children are liable," and that the greatest number of deaths attributed to this disease in Glasgow during the thirty years covered by his survey was in 1809, when they amounted to "something more than $11\frac{1}{2}$ per cent. of the total deaths in the year."

11

It is not easy to obtain reliable information about the occurrence of scarlet fever and diphtheria in Scotland in early days. This is not surprising in view of the frequent indefiniteness of the clinical picture as compared with that of such diseases as whooping cough and smallpox. There was much of what was then called " the putrid sore throat," particularly in the north of Scotland, about the year 1790, without reference to any fever or scarlet rash. New Deer, Crimond, and Fyvie were among parishes specially mentioned as having been visited by these sore throats, which

" proved fatal to several people." One of the physicians in Aberdeen reported about the same time that " the malignant sore throat has been most prevalent and very fatal, no period of life being exempted." There were numerous references in the first half of the nineteenth century to severe scarlet fever in Scotland, widespread in its distribution. In the cities it ranked much below measles and smallpox as a cause of death, but yet gave much trouble ; during the years 1835–39 there were in Glasgow 1,056 deaths from scarlet fever, and it was remarked that mortality from the disease was liable to very great variations in different epidemics, depending on the virulence of the epidemic, the season of the year, and the worldly condition of the family in which it made its attacks. It was estimated that about one in twelve of persons attacked by the disease died from it. This same variation in virulence was noted in other Scottish towns. In St. Andrews it was found that sometimes the disease was as deadly as cholera, at other times so slight that the children affected were not even confined to the house ; but unlike their colleagues in Glasgow, St. Andrews' observers found that " worldly condition " appeared to have little effect on the fatality of the disease.

Somewhat similar considerations make it difficult to estimate the part played by diphtheria as a cause of death in Scotland in bygone days. It may well have been that many of the cases of " putrid sore throat " to which reference has been made were in fact cases of diphtheria. During the period 1791–98, when material was being collected for the Statistical Account, croup, defined as an inflammation of the windpipe, appears to have been common, and was in some districts described as the most fatal disorder to which children were liable. It was said to prevail chiefly in damp situations, in cold and rainy seasons and, more especially, near the sea. Stirling and Cupar-Fife were said to be particularly vulnerable. Croup was recognized to be a serious condition. " It is sometimes so fatal that in a single parish from twelve to twenty young children have been cut off at a time." Croup was doubtless often of diphtheritic origin, but " diphtheria " as such did not figure among the causes of death listed by the Registrar-General for Scotland in his First Annual Report, which dealt with the year 1855, but was not issued until 1861. In this report it was stated that in 1855 the total number of deaths from all causes in Scotland was 62,004, and that 13,582 of these deaths were due to zymotic diseases (table overleaf).

In addition to these deaths from the diseases classified as " zymotic," the report showed that there were 7,129 deaths from phthisis, 2,094 from pneumonia, and 62 from tetanus.

Smallpox 1,309	Purpura 51
Measles 1,180	Worms 47
Scarlatina 2,138	Infantile fever 112
Hooping cough 1,903	Typhus 2,419
Croup 873	Metria 169
Thrush 34	Rheumatic fever 57
Diarrhœa 1,320	Erysipelas 326
Dysentery 602	Syphilis 79
Cholera 238	Noma 23
Influenza 701	Hydrophobia 1

CHAPTER VI

SANITATION, WATER-SUPPLIES, AND DRAINAGE

I

THE poet Dunbar, who knew his Edinburgh, wrote of the city in the early years of the sixteenth century in mingled sorrow and anger—its beggars, its " cruikit, blind and lame," its filth, its " stink of haddockis and of scaitis." " Think ye nocht schame," he asked the City Fathers, and apparently King James echoed his sentiments when, a century later, in 1619, he inspired the Privy Council to order the magistrates to take measures to clean the town. " The burgh is now become so filthy and unclean, and the streets, vennels, wynds, and closes thereof so overlaid and covered with middings and with filth . . . and the shameful uncleanliness and filthiness which is so universal and in such abundance through all parts of the burgh as in the heat of summer it corrupts the air and gives great occasion of sickness, and fardir, this shameful and beastlie filthiness is most detestable and odious in the sight of strangers who, beholding the same, are constrained with reason to give out mony disgraceful speeches about the burgh, calling it a puddle of filth and uncleanness, the like whereof is not to be seen in no part of the world."

It was true that visitors had referred to these matters in un-kindly terms. Sir Anthony Weldon (who said of the Scots that " their beasts be generally small, women only excepted, of which sort there are none greater in the whole world ") wondered that so brave a prince as King James should be born in so stinking a town as Edinburgh in lousy Scotland. Sir William Brereton wrote that the sluttishness and nastiness of the people was such " that I cannot omit the particularizing thereof." Kirke found that the poverty of Edinburgh " so well suits the inhabitants, that one character will serve them both, viz. high and dirty."

To do the town council justice, they did begin to make efforts to cleanse the streets early in the sixteenth century. In 1505 they entered into an agreement with the Bellman to provide a horse and cart for this purpose, " when need is " ; somewhat later instructions were given that the town was to be sufficiently

" dicht " every eight days by a certain Alexander Pennycuik and a dozen servants—not at the cost of the town, for the fulzie was to be sold for the common good. Robertson records that in days of plague individual citizens were required " to purge and cleanse the causeway to myd channel fornent their dwelling place or booths," and the refuse thus accumulated in the middle of the streets was removed by the tacksman. These regulations proving altogether ineffectual, partly because the people knew nothing of sanitation, which they could neither understand nor appreciate, from time to time the town refuse accumulated beyond possibility of removal.

Under the stimulus of the Privy Council Edict of 1619, the citizens were ordered to bring out all refuse from their houses twice each week, on Tuesdays and Fridays, and to deposit it at the close heads or on the streets. The town council agreed to pay six shillings weekly to an agreed person, on the footing that he should furnish a cart, horses, and a servant for the removal of the filth. Following the Great Plague of 1645, cleansing received more attention, and it was ordained that any High Constable " whose boundes sall not be clenzed sall pay twenty pounds for his negligence."

In September 1650 Oliver Cromwell issued a peremptory order requiring the Town Council of Edinburgh to have the streets, wynds, and closes cleaned within fourteen days. Citizens who failed in their duty were punished by having soldiers quartered in their houses. A little later a new tax was imposed on the people to pay for cleansing, but this, according to Nicoll, " grieved the pepell and so much the moir becaus the pepell resavit no satisfaction for their money, but the calsey and closes continued moir filthie and no paynes taken for cleyngin the streetts."

In 1678 a Cleansing Committee was set up in the city, but it was a failure ; and in the following year Lord Provost Dick undertook to clean the streets at his own expense, using the fulzie to improve the fields of his estate at Prestonfield. In 1686 another Act was passed in an attempt to secure the cleansing of the streets of Edinburgh :

Our sovereign Lord, considering the many complaints of the nastiness of the streets, wynds, closes and other places of the city of Edinburgh, which is the Capital City of the nation, where the Chief Judicatories reside, and to which his Majesty's lieges must necessarily resort and attend, as also the great trouble that does arise to his Majesty's lieges and to the inhabitants by the great numbers of clamorous beggars repairing in and about the said City of Edinburgh, therefore his Majesty, with advice and consent of the Estates of

Parliament, decrees and ordains the present Magistrates of Edinburgh and their successors to lay down effectual ways for preserving the said town of Edinburgh, Canongate, and suburbs thereof from the nastiness of the streets, wynds, closes and other places of the said burgh, and for freeing and purging the same of those numerous beggars which repair to and about the said burgh, and that under the pain of a thousand pounds Scots yearly to be paid by the Magistrates who shall be in office to the Lords of Session to be applied by them for the end and use aforesaid.

Under this stimulus new contracts were made, in which it was stipulated that " no muck man should receive his weekly wage without a certificate from the constable of the bounds " ; workmen were to be put in prison if they were negligent. The wide variety of penalties placed on the citizens for infringements of the Act—fining, the pillory, whipping by the hangman, banishment from the city—all proved unavailing. About 1700 the first Inspector of Cleansing was appointed in the city, but it was not until the middle of the eighteenth century that the attitude of the people began to change and complaints to be received from the public about the nuisances of filth. In 1771 an Act, later extended to the whole city, provided for the cleansing, lighting, and watching of the southern suburbs ; but effective cleansing required not merely scavenging but abundant water-supply and the construction of drains and sewers not yet available.

2

Another common source of nuisance in those early days arose from the slaughter of animals. In 1621 Edinburgh fleshers were forbidden to " toom the filth of the slaughtered goods upon the High Streets and in open vennalles and closes," or to keep any slaughter-house within the burgh : they were to provide themselves with slaughter-houses at the Nor' Loch, where they might have the use of water for their business. Slaughter booths were accordingly erected at the Nor' Loch, in proximity to Heriot's Hospital, to which they added but little amenity ; and there they remained until displaced by the construction of the railway in the nineteenth century. In 1781 representations were made by public bodies, including the Colleges of Physicians and Surgeons, that the situation of the shambles, which was low and moist, tended to promote putrefaction : they were " noxious to those in the neighbourhood and to all other citizens." In 1847 it was estimated that there were seventy-eight killing booths in the city, and many fleshers killed in their backyards or shops. In 1850 the corporation obtained the necessary powers to provide public slaughter-houses, and the Fountainbridge Slaughter-house, erected at that time, continued in use for about sixty years.

Before 1800 Edinburgh's only fish-market was in the Fish Market Close, a steep, narrow, stinking ravine. The fish were thrown out on the street at the head of the close, whence they were dragged down by dirty boys or dirtier women, and then sold unwashed—for there was not a drop of water in the place—from old rickety, scaly wooden tables, exposed to all the dust, rain, and filth.

Other towns experienced similar slaughter-house difficulties. A Minute of the Town Council of Glasgow referred in 1666 to ". . . vse and custome of the fleshers of this Burgh heirtofore to slay and bluid the wholl bestiall they kill on the Hie Street in Trongait on both sydes of the Gait . . . lothsome to the beholders, and also raises ane filthie and noysome stink . . ." and the fleshers were commanded " ilk ane of them to pruvyd housis in baksyds for the doeing thereof, as is done in Edinburgh and uthir weill governed cities." But this had little effect, and in the middle of the eighteenth century the magistrates erected a new market in King Street ; about the same time a public slaughter-house was provided at the foot of Saltmarket. A new slaughter-house was erected in 1810 on ground south of the Bridgegate Street, and, according to Cleland, was " without doubt the largest and most commodious in the island." It contained seventy-seven separate killing rooms, two cattle-yards and two alleys, and accommodation for the searchers and scavengers. " Water pipes are placed along the whole of the killing rooms and extensive sewers carry off everything which would become offensive from putrefaction. Dung and blood must be removed every day from the killing rooms and every second day from the slaugher-house."

In nearly all Scottish towns the slaughter-house nuisance persisted far into the nineteenth century. In Stirling there was a dwelling-house on the Castle Hill the greater part of which was inhabited, and the remainder used by a butcher as a slaughter-house ; it was common for the butchers in the town to kill sheep and lambs in their back shops, situated under dwelling-houses. In Greenock there were in Market Street two great dunghills. One contained about a hundred cubic yards of impure filth collected from all parts of the town. " It is never removed ; it is the stock-in-trade of a person who deals in dung ; he retails it by cartfulls : to please his customers he always keeps a nucleus, as the older the filth is the higher is the price." This collection fronted to the public street ; it was enclosed in front of a wall twelve feet high, but the dung overtopped the wall and oozed through it to run over the pavement. "The effluvium all round about this place in summer is horrible ; there is a land of houses adjoining, four storeys in height, and in the summer each house swarms with myriads of flies ; every article of food and drink must be covered, otherwise, if left exposed for a minute, the flies immediately attack it, and it is rendered unfit for use from the strong taste of the dunghill left by the flies." There was another still more extensive dunghill in the same street, not so high, but covering double the extent ; it was attached to the slaughter-house and belonged to the town authorities. In Ayr the slaughter-house and the fish-market were regarded as unquestionable nuisances, and Thomson describes how in Dundee the shambles was in 1746 situated in a narrow street in the centre of the town— " to the peril of the subjects and a rich harvest for surgeons, under-takers and gravediggers " ; by the end of the century a new slaughter-house had been provided.

3

There is no reason to believe that the sanitation of Edinburgh in the seventeenth century was materially worse than that of other Scottish towns. Glasgow had its middings and its obstruction of watercourses by a varied collection of filth and litter. Repeated Minutes of the Council ordered the inhabitants to clean the streets in front of their houses. Especially were such precautions urged when plague threatened, as in 1588, 1625 and 1644, or when the town was to be visited by royalty or by the Judges of the High Court. In 1656, in anticipation of a visit of the Judges on Circuit, there was an Act pointing out the necessity for the streets being cleaned, and appointing thirteen persons " to have the care of everie streit for the cleinging thereof." In 1670 the town council instructed the residents to clean their closes on every Saturday and prohibited the laying of middings on the streets unless the material was carried away within forty-eight hours. In 1685 one Thomas Urie was authorized to remove for his own use such fulzie as lay unduly on the streets. These enactments failed in their object, and the town council found it necessary in 1776 again to require dung and rubbish to be removed from the streets within forty-eight hours. As late as 1696 it was necessary in a statute " against nestines " to prohibit the casting out at windows by day or night of dirt or filth of any kind. Macgregor declared that by the end of the seventeenth century Glasgow was, as regards general cleanliness, " in advance of every other town in Scotland, Edinburgh not excepted." This was the view of a number of English visitors to Scotland, among them Frank Morer, Defoe, and Campbell, though a little later, in 1743, Carlyle took the opposite view and compared Glasgow unfavourably with Edinburgh.

The Town Records of Aberdeen for 1543 bear that the " pynours," or shore porters, were " to help to dycht and clenge the calsais, every pynour his day abowtt."

In the smaller Scottish towns and villages sanitary conditions were very unsatisfactory. Burgh records contain stories of never-ending attempts to remove the grossest nuisances, usually only successful under the imminent threat of great epidemic prevalence. In the *Annals of the Parish* John Galt told how in Dreghorn, the Vennel, which was a narrow and crooked street with many big stones here and there, had " every now and then, both in the spring and the fall, a gathering of middens for the fields ; in so much that the coal-carts from the Douray Moor were often reested in the middle of the causey, and on more than one occasion some of them laired altogether in the middens." Great complaint was made about this state of affairs, and for long improvement was talked about, but nothing happened until the spring of 1767, when Lord Eaglesham, a man of a genteel spirit, came from London to see the new lands that he had bought in the parish. He was obliged to pass through the clachan, " when all the middens were gathered out, reeking and sappy, in the middle of the causay," and just as his lordship was driving in with his prancing steeds at one end of the Vennel a long string of loaded coal-carts came in at the other. There was no room to pass, and neither could turn back. " Everybody was out of doors to see and to help ; when, in trying to get his lordship's carriage over the top of a midden, the horses gave a sudden loup, and couped the coach, and threw my lord head foremost, into the very scent bottle of the whole commodity, which made him go perfect mad, and he swore like a trooper that he would get an Act of Parliament to put down the nuisance " ; and in course of time the building of a trust-road was actually put in hand on account of the Lord Eaglesham's tumbling on the midden in the Vennel.

Boswell, in his *Journal of a Tour to the Hebrides* with Dr. Johnson, described how, to the surprise and entertainment of that great man, they encountered a " necessary " in a remote Highland castle. " There was one small room in one of the towers quite entire. It was a little confined triangular place, vaulted as in the ancient manner. In a corner of it was a square freestone in which was cut an exact circular opening such as is in every temple of Cloacina, and from it there appears a clear communication to the bottom, that is to say, anything will be carried by the outside of the rock to the bottom. They call this room the *nursery* and say the hole was for the children. But I take it to have been the necessary-house of the castle. It was much to find such a convenience in an old tower. I did not imagine that the invention had been introduced into Scotland till in very modern days from our connection with England. But it seems we have forgotten something of civilized life that our ancestors knew. It is strange how rare that convenience is amongst us. Mr. Johnson laughed heartily and said, " You take very good care of one end of a man, but not of the other."

The legal powers to deal with nuisances in the first half of the nineteenth century were generally inadequate, though they varied considerably from place to place with the operation of local Acts. The term " nuisance " was a comparatively recent introduction to Scottish legal nomenclature. It was formerly treated under the head of " Public Police,", and seldom applied to any case other than where one party, by his direct operations or by his negligence, produced something offensive to the sight, smell, or hearing of another ; there was no distinction between public and private nuisances. The movement for the establishment of a sanitary police developed impetus in the early years of the nineteenth century. Dr. John Roberton of Edinburgh directed attention to the subject in his treatise on medical police, published in 1809, and in 1840 Professor Cowan, writing on the vital statistics of Glasgow, urged that " besides the criminal police of the district a sanitary police is also requisite, and for this purpose much more extensive powers should be vested in the police than they at present possess. Powers should be given to remove filth of every description daily . . . and proper conveniences, constructed of durable materials and under the charge of the police, should be erected in the localities occupied by the working classes."

There were in the cities many local Acts aimed at the improvement of sanitation. Police Acts for the city of Glasgow in 1800 and 1807 contained provisions regarding the cleaning of foot-pavements, the cleaning of closes, and the removal of dung, among such other things as the construction of footpaths and the sale of gunpowder. The earliest Acts of George IV contained provisions, " to continue, Amend and Enlarge the powers of Two Acts of His late Majesty for paving, lighting, and cleansing the streets and for regulating the police of the city of Glasgow." Among other things, the new Act made it illegal to allow blood to run from any butcher's shop or shambles into the street, or to throw or cart any dirt or dung upon the pavement. It was laid down that the public streets should be cleansed by scavengers and that the closes or thoroughfares not cleaned by scavengers should be cleaned out at the expense of the proprietors at least once a week. About ten years later, power was given to the Superintendent of Cleansing to remove and dispose of accumulations of filth " on a certificate by any regular medical practitioner and a Commissioner of a ward " that such should be removed " as a nuisance," or " likely to be injurious to health." Local Acts applicable to Calton and Mile-end went further, giving power to the Local Authority to order whitewashing of houses, and to cause dunghills to be walled in, cleaned out and raised, as well as to control rigorously the keeping of lodging houses.

In Edinburgh there were Police Acts passed during the cholera epidemic of 1832, and reinforced shortly afterwards by legislation which ordered removal of dung and fulzie and the cleansing of common stairs and areas, besides prohibiting the keeping of swine in dwelling-houses and compelling dealers in rags to fumigate their buildings. It was provided that if a certificate were presented by any two members of the College of Physicians or Surgeons to the effect that an accumulation of dung or fulzie in a street or lane was prejudicial to health it could be removed ; but while the Act denounced accumulations within dwelling-houses (where means of ascertaining their existence were infrequent) there was an exception excluding, to a great extent, interference with accumulations in the open air, and the police authorities found they had no power to interfere with the nuisance generated by such sources as accumulations of putrid animal matter in the tanyards of the Old Town.

With the end of the cholera scare it became increasingly difficult to operate the clauses of the Police Act, and in 1840 in his review of the position Burton came to the conclusion that drastic tightening of administrative machinery was necessary ; he thought that much good might be done in Scotland by a simple enactment authorizing Public Prosecutors " to pursue for the abatement [or rather the abolition, for the word abatement has no existence in our legal nomenclature] of nuisances." He had no great faith in the willing co-operation of the people in the furtherance of sanitation. " Looking to the habits of the people of Scotland, I would venture to recommend that in whatever measures may be adopted, little confidence should be placed in the self-exercitave effects of prohibitions and penalties, though balanced by corresponding rewards to informers, etc., and that the chief trust should be placed in an efficient preventive and inspective machinery."

Dr. John Inglis Nicol, Provost of Inverness, would probably have agreed with Burton, for in the same year he wrote this note :

Inverness is a nice town situated in a most beautiful country, with every facility for cleanliness and comfort. The people are generally speaking a nice people, but their suffrance of nastiness is past endurance. Contagious fever is seldom if ever absent, but for many years it has seldom been rife in its pestiferous influence. The people owe this more to the kindness of Almighty God than to any means taken or observed for its prevention. There are very few houses in town which can boast of W.C. or privy ; and only two or three public privies in the better part of the place exist for the great bulk of the inhabitants. Hence there is not a street, lane, or approach to it that is not disgustingly defiled at all times, so much as to render the whole place an absolute nuisance. The *midden* is the chief object of the humble, and though enough of water for purposes of cleanliness may be had by little trouble, still the ablutions are seldom—MUCK indoors and out-of-doors *must* be their portion. When cholera prevailed in Inverness it was more fatal than in almost any other town of its population in Britain.

In most other towns the position was similar. In Ayr, though a good covered sewer traversed the principal streets of the new town, the old part of the burgh had merely shallow open gutters along the sides of the causeway. These gutters received all the liquid refuse from the closes and alleys communicating with the street, and the greatest nuisance was the filth collected about the houses of the poor.

In the mining villages conditions were, if anything, worse. It was usual to allow ashes as well as animal and vegetable materials to collect in heaps before doors or windows. In winter, and in wet weather throughout the year, small pools of water gathered and favoured the process of decomposition. A cavity was usually dug in the ground so as to retain the heap and to hold the water, for the better promotion of decomposition. " This heap of putrefying materials is made the source of pecuniary return and is therefore carefully preserved and augmented. The colliers and others sell these materials for sums varying from 1s. 6d. to 4s. the cart load. The mass is sold when it suits the convenience of the seller or when he thinks he has a cart load ; and is removed when it is convenient for the purchaser. In some instances the proprietor cotters this manure : this means that he gives it up to the farmer in return for the use of a small piece of ground for the growth of potatoes."

But probably nowhere was the filth and stench of the dunghills to be met in such overwhelming quantity as in the wynds and closes of the great cities, and particularly Glasgow, where in the first half of the nineteenth century they earned the censure of many medical men, from Professor Graham in 1818, in the course of his observations on Continued Fever in the city, to Dr. Sutherland, of the General Board of Health, in his report in 1849 on the measures adopted for the relief of cholera in Glasgow during the epidemic of 1848–49. The criticism was not exclusively medical ; among laymen who participated in it were J. C. Symons, in his report on the Condition of Hand-loom Weavers ; Captain Miller, the Chief Constable of the City, in his reports on the State of Crime ; and Chadwick, in the Report of the Poor Law Commissioners on the Sanitary Condition of the Labouring Population.

The outbreak of cholera in 1848 led to the passing of the Nuisance Removal Disease Prevention Act of that year. Its object was twofold : the more speedy removal of " certain nuisances " and the prevention of epidemic and contagious diseases, although the provisions for the second of these objects did not take effect till called into action by an Order from the Privy Council. Instructions and regulations under the Act were issued under the authority of the Privy Council by the General Board of Health in London in November 1848. In Scotland the enforcement of these regulations was entrusted to all parochial

boards, and in a circular letter the Board of Supervision in Edinburgh trusted that parochial boards would put the measures
advocated into operation at once, and required them to intimate
immediately to the Board of Supervision as well as to the General
Board of Health in London the appearance in the parish of
malignant cholera.

In 1848 a committee of the Royal College of Physicians of
Edinburgh, appointed to consider any Bills that might be brought
into Parliament for the improvement of the health of towns,
commented upon the Towns Improvement Clauses Act of 1847,
approving in general the measures proposed for creating a Board
of Health, securing water-supplies, improving cleansing, and
registering common lodging-houses. The Committee thought
that the duties of the Officer of Health proposed under the Act
" should be widened to a more general instruction to suggest from
time to time such regulations as he may think fit for improving
the sanitary condition of his district," but not, as had been
suggested, to ascertain the cause of death in every case.

There was apparently at this time an unwillingness to have
Scottish public health controlled from London. The Committee
of the Edinburgh College, reporting on the Public Health (Scotland) Bill, 1848, complained that although the Bill was intended
to be executed in large measure by Local Boards elected by the
inhabitants, " yet all these are to be put under the superintendence
of the General Board of Health already in existence in London,
which is to act by a Secretary to be appointed by that Board."
The Committee felt that this arrangement would not work, and
that harmony was " much more likely to be secured by having
a General Board for Scotland, and having at that Board persons
conversant with the law of Scotland and the habits and character
of the Scottish population. The Committee felt compelled to
remark upon " the disadvantages which, in actual practice, were
found to result from the recent attempt of the English Board of
Health to carry out the provisions of the Nuisance Removal and
Contagious Diseases Prevention Act in Edinburgh." There was
another delicious comment :

The Committee will take the liberty of adding, that although they have a high
respect for the individual members of the General Board of Health in London,
yet the confident expression of opinion which those gentlemen have officially
made on several important questions touching the diffusion of epidemic
diseases, which the Committee regard as very difficult and doubtful—and on

which they know that some of the most experienced practitioners in Scotland hold a very definite opinion—have by no means tended to increase their expectation of the efficacy of measures, applicable to Scotland, for restraining the diffusion of epidemics, which may proceed from that source.

It was about this period that the beginnings of Local Authority efforts to control the sanitation of their districts began to take effective shape. There gradually emerged a recognition of the need for a public health or " sanitary " department, and for some uniformity in administration. In Glasgow the Police and Extension Act of 1846 brought the burghs of Calton, Anderston, and Gorbals under one jurisdiction with Glasgow, and the old parochial approach to administration began to disappear. In 1856 the Nuisances Removal (Scotland) Act was passed, and under its powers in 1857 a special " Committee on Nuisances " of the Town Council was formed. The proposal to set up a new Sanitary Department met with some opposition, but in 1862 a Police Act for the city was obtained, and a special sanitary department created : Dr. W. T. Gairdner took office as Medical Officer of Health in 1863. In Edinburgh Dr. Henry Littlejohn had been appointed to a similar post in the previous year.

In the Annual Report of the Board of Supervision for 1858 the General Superintendent of Poor reported that the town of Stornoway had been in a most filthy and dangerous state. The Board of Supervision remonstrated with the inhabitants in terms of the Nuisance Removal Act, but apparently without success. Again, after these remonstrances, fever and smallpox broke out, and lives were lost. " Notwithstanding what occurred," wrote the Superintendent in the following year, " I understand that this year the inhabitants refuse to place the town under the provisions of the Police Act."

One considerable source of nuisance, even in cities, arose from the insanitary condition of the byres. Dr. Littlejohn reported that in 1863 no fewer than 171 byres had been inspected in the city of Edinburgh. He observed that in the country the odour of a byre might not be unpleasant, tempered as it was by the accessories of country life ; but that to be compelled, in a crowded district of a city, to inhale the effluvia of byres from morning to night was highly disagreeable, and to some constitutions positively harmful. Dr. Littlejohn found that even in 1863 the byres were sometimes placed under human dwellings, and proved a source of discomfort to the inhabitants above. There was a general lack

Waiting at the wells

after George Hay, R.S.A., reproduced from *The Edinburgh and District Water Supply*, by James Colston : Edinburgh 1890

Girl with water-stoups

after George Hay, R.S.A., reproduced from *The Edinburgh and
District Water Supply*, by James Colston : Edinburgh 1890

of cleanliness and an unsuitability of premises. Paving was imperfect and drains were not properly constructed. The manure heaps were a constant source of complaint. The cows were kept in a constant state of damp and filth, and many of the animals were diseased. Dr. Littlejohn soon came to the conclusion that graver questions than those of mere nuisance were involved in his investigation, questions involving directly the soundness of the food of the people.

4

In the course of an article written in 1840 on the protection of the public health in Scotland, John Hill Burton, a leading Edinburgh advocate, indicated grounds for believing that in many parts of Scotland the want of a good supply of water was one of the most material impediments to the furtherance of cleanly habits among the working people. He pointed out that besides the immediate evils of a narrow supply, much time was wasted and many bad habits were acquired by those who had to wait their turn at the wells in time of drought. He instanced Dundee, Stirling, Dunfermline, Lanark and Arbroath as towns imperfectly supplied, referring particularly to the experience of Dundee, where much costly litigation had left the city water-supply still in a precarious position. He thought that in large towns, such as Edinburgh, where there was an abundant supply of water monopolized by a profit-seeking corporation, the police or other municipal body should undoubtedly be entitled to erect a sufficient number of wells for the use of the poorer classes, and in the district where they lived, to be supplied with the corporation water.

There is ample evidence of the justness of Burton's assessment. In cities, water-supplies were often poor in quantity and in quality. In many of the smaller towns they were still poorer, while in most country districts water-supplies were largely fortuitous, and, for many years after Burton's time, often highly polluted.

The Dundee position, to which Burton specifically referred, was a glaring example. Writing of the water-supply of the town in the eighteenth century, Thomson said that in the necessary supply of water, " from a plentuous, well-situated and valuable fountain, there is somehow an unpardonable negligence." The cistern was inadequate, being not more than seven feet square and two feet in depth ; " and in place of an elegant and capacious basin and structure the appearance and entry to it would disgrace the meanest village in Britain." Though the supply was scanty, more water was lost and spilled than would serve another town of the same size. " Our servants are wanderers, and idle half the day, journeying to and fro in quest of water, as if we belonged to a caravan in the desert." It was a common experience in those times for servant girls to spend much of their day in quest of water, and the job of going to the wells came to be regarded as something of a servants' perquisite, affording as it did opportunity for a leisurely exchange of views with fellow-servants from other houses. In Dundee a new cistern was eventually provided, and the *Dundee Courier* of 1 June 1827 was rash enough to venture that the complaints of citizens about the supply of water were likely to be removed at an early date, for the cast metal pipes conveying water from the new cistern in the neighbourhood of Ladywell had been completely laid to Dog Well in Murraygate. Apparently the steps then taken were insufficient, for in the following year a correspondent to the paper referred to the distress of the poorer part of the community from want of water, and their constant struggle to obtain very limited quantities of inpure water " not fit for a cow to drink." In Dundee, as in other large towns at that date, and for a long time afterwards, water was hawked about the streets and sold from casks at a halfpenny or penny per bucket. None of the sources was above suspicion, and one at least, and that the main supply, Lady Well, " was horribly polluted by sewage and by animal matters of the most disgusting origin." The reservoir of Lady Well was divided from the slaughter-house by a not-impervious wall, and the Royal Commission on Water Supply reported that " The water is bright, sparkling, and piquant to the palate, but our analysis shows that this is nothing but a very thorough purified sewage, to the properties of decomposition of which it owes its pleasant flavour."

In 1831 the Town Council of Dundee made their first serious attempt to supply the town with water : the burgh then had a population of 45,000. The plans of a projected scheme came before Parliament in 1835, the Local Authorities intending to supply at prime cost by compulsory rating. They were opposed by a private Joint Stock Company, which sought powers to supply at prices to be agreed, with powers to assess users only. Ultimately the Local Authorities obtained the powers they sought, but in the course of legislation they had become involved in such heavy obligations to supply water by way of compensation, that there was likely to be no water at all for the town, and the Council abandoned the scheme. In the following year the same scheme was revived, this time by a Joint Stock Company, and was opposed by the Town Council, who proposed an alternative scheme. Following this, the Town Council obtained parliamentary powers to tap the Monikie Burn, but legal difficulties arose, and the scheme fell through, and by an Act of 1845 a private company obtained authority to provide a supply. The affairs of the private concern " matured to a 9 per cent. dividend," and when the resources of the watershed were exhausted they were taken over by the community after prolonged negotiations, the terms being a payment to the shareholders, for all time coming, of £14,315 per annum. The works were taken over by the municipality in 1869, and the supply, which had long been inadequate, went dry in the first year after they were purchased.

The other large cities had difficulties of their own in securing adequate water-supplies, though in none did the position become quite so ridiculous as in Dundee. Prior to 1804 the inhabitants of Glasgow were scantily supplied by twenty-nine public and a few private wells. The Town Council had already given thought to improvement of the supply, and there is record of a payment of eight guineas in 1776 to Dr. Irvine, " for his trouble in searching round Glasgow for water to be brought into the town." In 1794 a committee was appointed to secure a gravitation supply, but the scheme was too expensive and was dropped. In 1804 a new supply was made available by a private individual, Mr. William Harley, who erected a reservoir in Upper Nile Street, fed with spring water from Willow Bank. The water was distributed through the streets " from square cisterns on four-wheeled carriages," and sold at the rate of a halfpenny per stoup. In 1806 Glasgow Water Company was formed to supply the city with filtered water from the Clyde " about two miles above the toun," and in 1808 Cranstounhill Water Company was formed, drawing its supply from the river below the town until 1830, when it, too, drew from upstream ; later these two companies were amalgamated. The Gorbals Gravitation Water Company was formed in 1846 with a gathering ground near Mearns, and in 1855 the Corporation Water Works Act authorized new works and the taking over of the undertaking of the Glasgow Water Company. With the introduction of Loch Katrine water in 1859 the Clyde was abandoned as a source of water-supply for the city, though the Gorbals supply was allowed to remain. In 1863 the supply of water per head per day in the city of Glasgow amounted to forty-two gallons, and when about that time inquiry was made as to the propriety of closing the public wells it was found that only one of the twelve—Spring Well, near Kelvingrove Street—could be regarded as really satisfactory.

For hundreds of years Edinburgh was entirely dependent for its water-supply upon public or private pump wells. The public wells were comparatively few in number ; the water was hard, and in dry seasons the supply was liable to fail. The danger of contamination was considerable. This state of affairs continued until 1621 when the magistrates obtained power from the Scottish Parliament to bring a supply from the country into the town. It was not until 1672 that the Town Council resolved to exercise these powers, entering into a contract with a Dutchman named Peter Bruschi, for the sum of £2,900, " to bring the water of Tod's Well at Comiston to Edinburgh, in a leaden pipe of a three-inch bore to be laid one foot deep in the ground." The water secured from Comiston soon proved insufficient for the needs of the citizens and other springs in the same area were purchased. They too proved insufficient, and in 1756 the magistrates obtained powers to acquire certain springs at Swanston. In 1799 new rules were made by the magistrates for regulating the distribution of the water at the public wells and for fixing the quantity that was to be taken into private houses ; that " every person at the public wells should take the water as they came, that is, first come first served ; that no person should be allowed to ply with a cask or vessel that would hold more than twenty pints—bakers' tubs excepted—unless before eight o'clock in the morning or after eight o'clock at night ; and that each person who had a private water pipe should pay a duty of twenty shillings sterling per annum for a quantity of water not less than half a hogshead a day." These regulations were designed partly to keep under control the " water-caddies." When water was expected at the well persons of all ages took up their position in a queue, standing often for hours, with an array of vessels, sometimes extending in a line for hundreds of yards from the wells. The vessels used were of all conceivable sorts, the best being the water stoup, circular and broad at the bottom, twenty-four inches high, getting narrower as it reached the top, with wooden handle, and girded round by four iron hoops placed in regular position upwards. Citizens who were unwilling to take their place in the queue and had no private supply were dependent on the " caddies," men and women who " might be seen trotting, with their short sticks, leather aprons, and their little barrels on their backs, dripping all the way like a thawing icicle, down closes, up stairs, filling other people's barrels and emptying their own," dispensing water at a fee of a penny per barrel. The water-caddies came to be rather a thorn in the side of the magistrates, and in 1718 they were formed into a society the funds of which were to be devoted to " supplying of their poor and the burying of their dead." Apart from entry fees and weekly dues, the funds of the society were to be nourished by fines imposed on the caddies for such offences as swearing or cursing at the wells, or flytting or scolding their neighbours, at the wells or elsewhere. Apparently the fines did not prevent these abuses, and in 1727 the magistrates ordered the society to be dissolved.

The duty of providing water remained in the hands of the Corporation down to the year 1819, and was then by Act of Parliament transferred to the Edinburgh Water Company, a joint-stock undertaking, which continued in existence until the year 1869, when a Public Water Trust was created. The Water Company brought a supply from the Crawley Springs into the town, but the available supplies soon again became insufficient and further springs had to be tapped. There were constantly recurring complaints from the citizens of inadequate supplies of water, though the daily supply rose from 22 gallons per head in 1843 to 25 gallons in 1856 and 31 gallons in 1863. William Chambers, giving evidence in 1840 to the Government Select Committee investigating the health of towns, said that there was plenty of good water in Edinburgh, but that unfortunately it was a monopoly in the hands of the Joint Stock Company, "and, excepting at two or three wells, all the water introduced into the town has to be specially paid for in the form of a tax upon the rental of those who use it." With a reasonably assured supply, the practice was begun of leading water into private houses, whereupon the public wells came to be used chiefly by the poorer classes. As the population increased, powers were obtained from Parliament to introduce fresh supplies, and it was estimated that in 1863 the available supply of water amounted to thirty-one gallons per head of the population per day. In that year there were still a number of public wells in the city. In the various

Acts regulating the supply of water to Edinburgh the rights of the poor were reserved, and these public wells were expressly mentioned as to be maintained and increased in number. Littlejohn pointed out that the importance of this provision could hardly be over-estimated in view of the very dense population of the Old Town. The houses of the poor were totally unprovided with water-supply, and it was not until the General Police and Improvements (Scotland) Act was passed in 1862 that powers were granted to compel proprietors to introduce water into houses ; this Act also referred to the provision of conveniences.

An attempt seems to have been made as early as the fourteenth century to introduce a water-supply into Aberdeen in an open stone-lined channel leading from the Loch of Aberdeen, which has now disappeared. It appears that about 1430 a supply was taken from the Denburn, which passes through the town. In later years various wells were utilized, the water being conveyed in lead pipes or stone channels, but not until 1829 did Aberdeen have its first municipally-controlled supply. This was drawn by a steam pump from the River Dee, west of the Bridge of Dee, and taken up to a point at the west end of Union Street, where there was a cistern in a " water house " ; from there it was dis-tributed by gravitation through pipes to the lower parts of the town. In 1840 when the population of Aberdeen was about 48,000 the quantity of water supplied daily averaged about 569,000 gallons. It was estimated that fewer than 6,000 of the population had water piped into their houses. All the others had to draw supplies from the public wells ; nine courts had a common stand-pipe. It was stated at the time that the police could supply water to any extent and that the poor paid no tax for it ; but the expansion of the city soon rendering the supply inadequate, in 1866 a new system was introduced, whereby the water was taken from the River Dee at Cairnton to storage reservoirs at Inver-cannie, twenty miles west of the city, and from there gravitated to the service reservoir at Mannofield.

Many other Scottish towns found it as difficult as the cities to obtain adequate supplies. Greenock was an exception. Dr. Laurie, a practitioner there, reported in 1841 that there were few towns in the kingdom so well supplied with water as was Greenock. A Joint Stock Company, the Shaws Water Company, distributed an unlimited supply of water through the town in pipes : " there are few good houses not so supplied." In addition the town possessed a reservoir of its own, the water from which was distributed through the streets at intervals of one hundred yards, the poor having unlimited access to these distribution points.

In Ayr there were few good wells. The water was heavily impregnated with lime and the supply was defective, though in 1841 steps were afoot for its improvement. In Stirling the inhabitants during many months of the year did not obtain water sufficient for their domestic wants. Lanark was tolerably supplied with wells, but in seasons of long drought the deficiency of water was serious and many of the inhabitants were obliged to go long distances to procure water from a perennial spring. Tain was indifferently supplied with water, viz. from some draw-wells and a few springs ; water procured from the springs, which were rare, was of excellent quality, but that from the draw-wells was inferior.

The records of many of the smaller Scottish towns are full of references to the difficulty of maintaining adequate supplies of pure water. The experience of Dingwall was typical. In 1765 a petition to the Council by Adam Ross, minister, Colin MacKenzie, writer, and William MacKenzie, schoolmaster of the burgh, represented " how greatly the water running through the town and affording water to the inhabitants is abused and adultered after entering the town by different canals and conveyances from the closes on the south side of the street." Since on investigation it appeared that the complaint was only too well founded, the Council directed that all the heritors and possessors of tenements on the south side of the High Street, " By the first day of May open a canal in each respective close from the Head next the Street to the back end of their tenements." In 1771 the Council, in order to discover the sum required for carrying out a scheme " anent the cleaning the water," employed Thomas Ross to make an estimate " for the expense necessary for the pypes and other necessary articles for the sufficient accommodation of the inhabitants in water," all the inhabitants to be stented for the purpose in proportion to their circumstances. Later in the same year the Council considered reports made by John Boag and Thomas Russell, " with respect the conveying of the Dyke water [a ' dyke ' was a channel for conveying water, generally cobbled and open] through timber pipes into the town and the necessary operations thereanent." The work involved " digging for the pipes and bedding and convening them with clay and of five stone troughs and building with hewn stone a cistern nine feet in length and three

155

feet in breadth and height divided in three," with a house fifteen feet in length and nine feet in breadth for holding the cistern. The total estimate for the work amounted to £58 sterling, and it was specified in the contract that " the size of the boar and the timbers was to be two inches diameter at the least and the size of the timber six inches diameter at the small end." It was found in 1785 that the timber cistern had become rotten, and did not hold the water, " and the inhabitants are most frequently in distress for want of water." Further, the free stones that covered the Dyke water were often broken, with resultant pollution. It was agreed to make a new cistern of stone, or of oak-wood, and to forbid any of the inhabitants or their families or servants " from washing of cloaths, ffish, or other articles upon any part of the Free Stone or any part of the High Street or at the East End of the Dyke waters where the Ffree Stone ends and Eastward to the timber nailling made there." A separate place was to be set aside for watering cattle and cleaning fish and clothes. But progress was slow, and in 1787 the Council authorized a committee to consider again the position with regard to the Dyke water and to " contract with any fit person within the town for supplying free stones for convening the Dyke from one end of the Burgh to the other, in place of such stones as shall be broke." A few months later the Council received from the Laird of Seaforth a present of the sum of £100 sterling to be spent on the proper conveyance of water to the town. The Council were of opinion that the best way of doing this would be " to continue the fir pipes from the West of the Town all along through the same into the water stone at the East, and that such pipes shall be bedded and covered with clay beneath the pavement and that there shall be a proper number of fir trees had for this purpose." It was agreed to purchase the necessary wood in Garmouth, as timber was cheaper there than locally, and when, in June of 1789, the timber arrived at the shore of Dingwall, Alex. Aird, square wright of the burgh, was engaged " to bore the trees two inches and a half in the bore and to cleanse the bore . . . and to lay the pipes . . . for the sum of eight pence per yard." He also agreed to erect four standards from which the inhabitants could draw water at convenient stances as directed by the Council, and to " cleanse all the old pipes that lye without the Town."

In 1810 it was reported that the water pipes had for a considerable time back been getting into disrepair, but the funds of the burgh were inadequate to purchase iron pipes and a subscription list was opened for the purpose. Subscriptions to the amount of £280 were received or promised, and it was decided to go on with the work ; but in 1819 an inadequate supply of water being again reported, the Council came to the conclusion that the existing system had been laid too low and that the trouble could only be remedied by building a new cistern at a place called Bualachs, in a situation formerly advocated by certain members of the Council. The total distance to the new cistern was 220 yards ; for this, 80 yards of old wooden pipe being still serviceable, the Council resolved to purchase the necessary number of trees and to employ the wheelwright to bore and lay them in continuation of this remnant of pipe, any damage caused to private property being settled by arbitration.

In 1823 the inhabitants being again very ill supplied with water " owing, as it is supposed, to the Pipes having contracted Rust, the Council are of Opinion that in case the Obstructions may be occasioned by Sand or Gravel, an experiment should be made in the first instance by means of a forcing Pump, but in case of that not answering the purpose that the pipes should be raised, cleansed, and relaid, previously consulting Mr. Wilson the engineer on the subject."

When, in 1834, the funds of the burgh were again in a parlous state and drastic economies became necessary, the magistrates decided that the need for improving the waterworks of the burgh was so great that the Council should apply to the National Bank of Scotland for an advance to enable the work to proceed. In May of that year it was reported that the magistrates had inspected the site of the intended reservoir, " between the Banks, and across the Burn of Gortain," and there was reason to believe that the proprietrix " would accept the proposal of the Magistrates, which was to grant them a ffeu of the space of ground necessary for building thereupon the reservoir, together with the right of conveying thereform the necessary pipes, for annual payment of ffeu duty of Five shillings Stg."

5

One result of the difficulty of procuring adequate supplies of water was the development of communal washing-houses. Cleland reported in 1840 that in Glasgow the cost of hot and cold water for one day's washing, without the use of tubs and stools, was 4d. ; the use of a washing tub and a washing stool for one day cost three half-pence, and the cost of watching through the night a day's washing of clothes was 3d. About the middle of the century Lord Cockburn, addressing to the Lord Provost of Edinburgh a letter on the most certain means to spoil the beauty of the city, expressed regret that a part of the higher ground of the Calton Hill had been set aside for a public washing-green. Cockburn wrote of " The decorous matrons and timid virgins who watch the habiliments—whose eloquence let no prudent passenger provoke," and asserted that no-one could have a stronger desire than himself for the comfort of the " lower orders," " for whom scientific wash-houses ought to be provided "—but surely not on the Calton Hill.

6

Inadequate water-supplies long interfered with the provision of drainage facilities in Scottish towns and were in large measure the cause of the prevailing nastiness. In their periods of rapid development most Scottish towns of any size faced serious drainage problems, and none more so than Edinburgh, despite the fact that, as Littlejohn pointed out, few cities are more favourably situated for efficient drainage than the capital, with its succession of valleys running parallel to one another and naturally draining the intervening heights. " The Water of Leith receives the drainage of the New Town, while the Jordan Burn performs the same office for the southern suburbs. The intermediate valleys converge into the Foul Burn, which, on its way to the sea, supplies the well-known irrigated Meadows."

This problem of the irrigated meadows was for long a matter of heated controversy in Edinburgh. In 1770 a beginning was made with the drainage of the Nor' Loch for the purpose of collecting and running off the waters of the feeding springs, but not until the nineteenth century did sewers and drains become recognized parts of the sanitary arrangements of the city. Until shortly before 1840 the Cowgate had only surface drains, which in rainy weather became a gigantic sewer. When a committee of private gentlemen arranged for the building there of a spacious sewer 830 yards long, at a cost of two thousand pounds, collected by subscription, the utmost extent to which they received assistance from the police consisted in being vested with the authority of an Act of William IV as a protection from the interruption of private parties. During the construction of the sewer " they were never-

theless harassed by claims of damage for obstructing the causeway, and their minutes show that they experienced a series of
interruptions from neighbouring occupants, likely to discourage
others from following their example." Cockburn complained that
the Cowgate had lost half its character by getting a large sewer
underground, though he admitted that before this innovation,
" The Cowgate Strand," as it was called, when in flood was a
great torrent, " not filling the cellars merely, but almost the whole
of the street." In the drainage of the Old Town, three sewers
were formed delivering their contents into the Foul Burn, which
flowed in open channels towards the sea through the estate of
Craigentinny. The burn was interfered with in two ways—first,
by the digging of pits in its course and the collection of the sludge
for manure, and second, by irrigation, with the formation of the
notorious Craigentinny Meadows, conveying water from the main
stream of the burn into lateral channels, small and numerous and
level, so that the water flowed slowly enough to ensure its gradual
absorption, and the complete and equal saturation of the land.
The foul water was spread over as large an area as possible and
an offensive smell inevitably resulted. The Foul Burn remained
a problem for over a hundred years, and was not finally and completely solved until 1922.

In the early part of 1840 three representative Edinburgh
citizens gave evidence on the irrigation problem to the Government Committee considering the health of towns. One was Dr.
James Simpson, later Sir J. Y. Simpson. In his evidence he said
that he had repeatedly complained of the use of water from
common sewers for irrigation in the immediate vicinity of the
town, and that the majority of medical men in Edinburgh were of
opinion that such use of foul water injured the health of the
inhabitants. The practice of irrigation was extending ; within
three miles of the town, east, west, and north, " every landlord
round the town is taking advantage of it for his own purposes."
Irrigation increased the value of herbage ; some land near Edinburgh, let a few years previously for very few pounds per acre,
" now let as high as thirty to forty pounds a year." It was impossible for the police to interfere without new legislation. Dr.
Simpson thought that the working people had legitimate ground
for complaint, in that while they had the power of going over the
King's domain at the Royal Palace of Holyrood, the stench there
was so dreadful that they could not go except on particular days ;

apparently irrigation was practised within the royal precincts under the direction of the Earl of Haddington, Keeper of the Royal Park. To ascertain the effect on health of the irrigated land, Dr. Simpson studied the state of health of the troops at Piershill, the cavalry barracks in the vicinity. He compared sickness and mortality in all cavalry stations over a period of seven years with mortality and sickness at Piershill, as he found it recorded in the records of the Adjutant-General's office for the same seven years. The illness of the cavalry soldiers stationed at Piershill, as compared with the experience of soldiers in barracks throughout the kingdom, " was greater in the proportion of ten per cent. ; I infer that it was from that cause, because I could find no other." Dr. Simpson informed the committee that there were no open common sewers in the town itself, but that immediately in the suburbs the practice was general, and he believed the same practice prevailed in other Scottish towns—in Crieff, for instance, to which the practice had been imported from Edinburgh, with the same unpleasant effect. About two years previously the Lord Advocate had asked the opinions of the Queen's physicians and surgeons in Scotland about the healthiness of Holyrood in consequence of this practice of irrigation, and they gave it as their opinion that Holyrood would not be a fit habitation for her Majesty on that ground ; but though that report had been obtained two years previously, no steps had been taken to remedy the condition.

John Redde Stodhart, Treasurer of the City of Edinburgh, said in his evidence that the practice of irrigation was very prejudicial to the senses, causing a disgusting stench. The practice had increased tenfold within the previous ten or fifteen years, and there was no legal remedy. Six or seven years previously an attempt was made to suppress the practice by a clause in a Police Act, but the Earl of Moray determined to oppose it with all his power and influence in Parliament, and as it was thought that the clause would lead the city into great expense, it was abandoned. The Treasurer said that the irrigated meadows were within a mile of some of the principal houses in Edinburgh ; there were " dwelling houses of an inferior kind " standing in the neighbourhood which had existed before the nuisance was brought to them.

William Henry Miller, Esq., a Member of Parliament, took the opposite view. He said that the water then forming the Nor' Loch was previously used to irrigate meadows. It had formerly been used as a mill stream for many years, but its use for that purpose had been given up because in summer it interfered with the supply of water for the meadows. Mr. Miller said that about 1805 Mr. Duncan of Restalrig had tried to get irrigation stopped, but it being proved that the inhabitants of the village of Restalrig and its neighbourhood were perfectly healthy and remarkable for their longevity, Mr. Duncan lost his case, with costs. Mr. Miller said this land had been under irrigation beyond all memory, but that there had been no recent expansion of the meadows. The whole of the irrigated area to the east of the city was considerably less than 200 Scotch acres, of which perhaps 130 acres belonged to himself; there were only about 30 acres to the west of the city. He personally found residence beside the meadows healthy; sometimes there was an unpleasant smell, but this was chiefly in consequence of the very improper admission of gas water into the stream. When cholera was in Edinburgh in 1832, anonymous letters were inserted in some Edinburgh newspapers representing the meadows as a source of contagion, but not one case of cholera occurred in Restalrig. There had certainly not been more fever in Edinburgh than in Glasgow, where there were no irrigated meadows; and Mr. Miller had been told that the average cases of sickness and mortality in the cavalry barracks at Glasgow and Hamilton were 25 per cent. more than at Piershill.

Following the issue of the Report of the Select Committee on the Health of Towns, the Commissioners of Police in Edinburgh consulted two eminent lawyers as to the best means of stopping this system of irrigating meadows with the contents of the common sewers. They received this opinion : " We think that an action of law would not be competent at the instance of the Memorialists, in their representative capacity of Commissioners of Police. Such an action, we think, could be maintained at the instance only of those who individually are the sufferers ; and even such parties may be precluded from insisting, if they had either come to the nuisance or had submitted to it so long as to amount to acquiescence." Ultimately, since the irrigation nuisance interfered with the habitability of Holyrood House, an action was raised by the Queen in the capacity of a proprietor and probable occupant, in virtue of an old Act that exempted the Crown from the effect of prescription by acquiescence.

In 1863 Dr. Littlejohn reported that there were in Edinburgh large sewers of the best construction which fulfilled the important sanitary purposes of carrying off the rainfall, and the drainage of more elevated districts ; " but so far as the closes are concerned, these drains, for any sewage they convey from such poor localities, might never have existed. This depends at once upon the manner in which the poor live together, and on the system of cleansing which experience has determined as best adapted for Edinburgh."

The character of the dwelling-houses in the city made it much more difficult than in England to put each house in communication with the common sewer, for the houses were much subdivided and in many cases in a state of decay. Dr. Littlejohn reported that the experiment of introducing conveniences had been tried again and again in the city and always with similar results—the production of much annoyance, and, ultimately, the removal of what was considered a sanitary improvement. His experience was that the poor required preliminary education in keeping their houses and stairs clean, before they could be expected to make a proper use of conveniences. Many tenants, apprehensive of their neighbours, begged their landlord to withhold these benefits. Within the city the cesspool nuisance in time became so clamant as to demand a thorough remedy. Builders and architects upheld the necessity of cesspools, and strongly opposed the introduction of tubular or pipe drains having direct communication with the main sewers ; Sir Henry Littlejohn, as he then was, advocated direct drainage.

Dundee was another city in which there was a " meadows " problem. Thomson reported that in 1746 the meadows were unenclosed, wet and dirty, and that the health of the inhabitants was much affected by the resultant stagnant pools. By the end of the century there had been some improvement and the meadows had been partially drained. They were enclosed with stone walls " and laid out [though yet greatly deficient] for washing and bleaching the linens of the inhabitants " ; but in Dundee, as elsewhere, it was many years before the drainage of the city was placed on a satisfactory footing.

For a long time it was the custom of the inhabitants of old Glasgow, the High Street and Trongate, to throw out their ashes and other refuse on the streets—to have their " middings " in front of their houses, as was the practice of the time in all Scottish towns. In 1589 the magistrates ordered " that na midding be laid vpon the Hiegat," but this exhortation had little effect, a Minute of the Council of 1655 bearing that many inhabitants of the right side of Trongate had to make stepping-stones through the water lying between them and the street " for entrie to thair houssis." Another Minute of Council, dated September 1666, was to the effect that whereas the syve in Trongate used to carry away the water, " now of lait divers persones, yea almost all who has houses and killes narrest the said syve casts in stra ilk ane foiragainst their awin land to mak fulzie of, quilk stops the passage of the water should goe that way, and jorgs up so that filth and myre is made to be sein in the gutters quilk is verie lothsome to the beholders." The magistrates ordered that this practice should stop, but apparently without success, since there were other subsequent minutes prohibiting the accumulation of stones, turf, stakes, and the like " vpon the foirgait," and as late as 1795 there was an unsuccessful petition for removal of all haystacks in the Trongate.

Prior to 1790 there were no common sewers in Glasgow, but in that year the New Town Building Company made the first one in the city ; it was in George's Square and Buchanan Street, and terminated in St. Enoch's Burn, where it crossed Argyle Street. Between 1809 and 1812 sewers were built to serve Stockwell and Jamaica Street, and by 1820 there were common sewers in forty-five streets in the royalty, extending to over five miles in length. By 1861, according to Glaister, the " total length of main sewers within the municipal boundary was sixty miles, and nearly all the streets were provided with them." But the Clyde remained virtually an elongated cesspool.

In 1840 Drs. Kilgour and Galen, Secretaries to the Committee of Magistrates that inquired into the sanitary condition of the poor of Aberdeen, reported that in the city only streets built during the nineteenth century had large common sewers and that there was extensive use of cesspools in an attempt to compensate for this deficiency of sewers. The cesspools were most numerous near recently built houses, in streets and squares off the main line of new streets. There was no power to tax the inhabitants for the making of common sewers, however necessary, nor to compel persons opening these streets, or building in them, to put down sewers. By the Police Act the whole manure, with the exception of that of stables and of a few streets of the suburbs, was the property of the police. The manure was collected by the police at their own expense and the police funds derived a profit from it. The manure was collected by carts every morning from the street doors at heads of closes, where it was deposited in boxes, intimation being given of the passing of the dust-car by a bell attached to it ; but the inhabitants of courts and closes often retained filth in the house " till it has accumulated past endurance," or threw it out in the court to form an open dunghill. The Commissioners of Police had no power to erect public water-closets or privies in those parts of the town where they were required.

The Den Burn was a mill burn that passed through the centre of the town. It was open above, but built with stone in the bottom and at the sides, and it was laid out with cascades in the ornamental style. Sometimes the quantity of water scarcely covered the bottom of the trough, but into this " ornament of the town," which extended to 588 yards, there fell over forty-five drains, channels or open sewers.

The harbour of Aberdeen was a tidal one, with only a very moderate fall. It received two mill-streams, into each of which opened a great number of drains, privies, etc., as well as the refuse of some large manufactories. All the sewers and drains of the town terminated in the basin of the harbour. " The consequence of this is that the harbour is covered with a thick, foetid mud, from which at nearly low water the surface becomes covered with bubbles of a foetid, noxious gas, which, bursting, give forth a most intolerable stench that is perceived at a considerable distance in the town."

In Stirling during many months of the year the inhabitants had no water to spare for their sewers or " sivers," which were all open and sloping. The filth of the gaols, containing on an average sixty-five persons, was floated down the public streets every second or third day, emitting during the whole of its progress down Broad Street, Bow Street, Baker Street, and King Street—the principal streets in the town—the most offensive and disgusting odour. Two drains from the Castle conveyed the whole filth of it into an open field, where it spread itself over the surface and seriously polluted the atmosphere.

This method of sewage disposal was common in Scottish towns, in many of which the streets sloped steeply. In Lanark a large common sewer ran underground through the principal street and carried away the filth from it, but in back courts and narrow lanes there were many dunghills. In Inverness there were but few common sewers, and the drainage from the dwellings of the poor was often purposely obstructed by the people for the purpose of adding to their dunghill heaps or middens, which as manure

Beggars' badges from Dundee, Kirkcaldy, and Dysart

Wooden houses of Old Glasgow

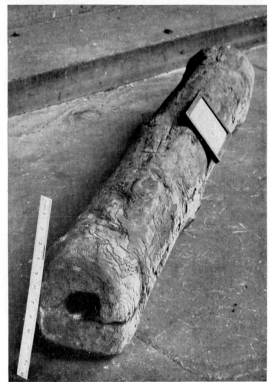

Wooden
water-pipes

Glasgow Art Gallery

the lower specimen
was found in Barrack
Street, Glasgow

for their potato grounds formed the chief treasures of the poorer cottagers and labourers. Water-closets and public privies were both rare. Such was the position in the middle of the nineteenth century in many Scottish towns. In most the magistrates had a constant struggle to keep what drainage facilities there were in a condition to carry away the most offensive filth. The burgh records of Dingwall carried repeated exhortations to heritors and tenants to " keep the drain clear and clean through the haill season of the present years to come." The Council repeatedly authorized the bailies to employ proper persons " to have the back drain cleansed and kept free of filth all through the year," and " to prosecute such persons as shall dare or attempt to break through or fill up the same with any filth." It was reported to the magistrates in 1825 that the common sewer had not been cleaned for several years, " and was now almost either filled up by Gravel and Soil, or obstructed by Hay Stacks or common necessaries built over it," and the Council made a contract for cleaning the sewer at 1½d. per yard. Some nine years later it was decided to spend one-third of the limited resources of the burgh on " the scouring and repairing of the existing sewers and the making of additional ones where necessary for the removal of waste and foul water."

Chapter VII

THE CARE OF THE POOR: EARLY TIMES TO 1845

I

The care and relief of the poor have been major problems in Scotland for many centuries. The seventh enactment of the Statute of Perth (1424) directed that companies of people should not be permitted to traverse the country, " begging and harbouring on kirkmen or husbandmen." It was also ordained that " no thiggars [beggars] be thoiled to beg, either in town or country, between the ages of fourteen and seventy," unless they were unable to " win their living otherways," in which case they were to be furnished with a certain token or badge. Persons having no such badge were to be charged by open proclamation to labour for their living, under pain of burning on the cheek and being banished from the country. If any idle men " that have not of their own to live upon " were found within the land, the Sheriff was to cause them to be arrested and kept in durance until it was known on what they lived ; and the Sheriff was to assign fourteen days to such idle men in which they were to find masters or to apply themselves to lawful crafts. If still idle at the end of fourteen days, they were to be sent to the king's prison to wait and be punished at the king's will.

But these laws did not prove sufficient in their troubled times, and in 1449 there was another attempt at " the away putting of sornares [stout armed vagrants who insisted on taking up their abode for an indefinite period at the houses they visited], overlayers, and masterful beggars." They were to be imprisoned or put in irons as long as they had any goods of their own to live upon ; if they had nothing to live upon " their ears are to be nailed to the trone, or to any other tree, and then cut off, and themselves banished the country." If they came back again they were to be hanged.

This legislation was typical of the times, and of the robust measures taken by the law in the attempt to enforce order. Those were the days in which football and golf were to be " utterly cried down and disused," and attire appropriate for

166

each of the several strata of society was defined. It was apparently easier to make such laws than to enforce them, since in the twenty years between 1455 and 1475 there were seven enactments in much the same strain for the control of beggars. Another Act in 1503 was of milder tone, enacting that none were to be tholed to beg in boroughs " except cruiked folk, blind folk, impotent folk, and weak folk " ; while yet another, passed in 1535 " for the refreyning of the multitude of maisterful and strang beggaris," laid it down that no beggars were to be allowed to practise in any parish unless they had been born there ; every parish thus being made responsible for the support of its own aged and infirm poor.

Heritors and kirk sessions were empowered to grant a badge or token to paupers entitling them to beg within the bounds of the parish, but the paupers seem to have had the option either to avail themselves of this privilege or to require support from parochial funds. " This mode of supporting a part of the poor," as Sinclair wrote in his *Analysis of the Statistical Account*, " besides being not the most respectable, is not the cheapest." But for a long time the legal mode of dealing with the begging poor was to oblige them to wear badges and confine their activities to their home parishes, a procedure so disagreeable to them as effectually to diminish the number of beggars. Towards the end of the eighteenth century the magistrates and kirk session of Montrose gave out badges to forty persons as licensed beggars, permitting them to go through the town the first day of every month ; but they were not allowed to beg at any other time or to go beyond the bounds of the parish. In the town of Irvine there were twenty-four licensed beggars who were supposed to collect at the rate of two shillings and sixpence each per week. About sixty of the permanent poor in Dumfries had for many years been privileged to beg through the town in this way every Saturday, wearing a large badge or brass plate, though many without badges joined in the ranks or took their chance. The beggars had also their set day for working in the country and their set time of calling at every house and shop, receiving from some weekly and from others fortnightly or monthly. At last the beggars became such a nuisance that the town resolved to abandon this system and to suppress all public begging ; instead about four hundred pounds for them was subscribed annually for four years. Each " badger," as he was called, was paid 1s. 6d. per week, and a lodging-house keeper was engaged to whom all beggars and vagrants were referred with tickets for supper and bed, at a total cost of upwards of a hundred pounds per annum. Subscriptions soon began to fail and this system was of necessity abandoned. For one year a voluntary assessment was tried unsuccessfully, and legal assessment had to be instituted in 1834.

There were many statutes excluding from towns all vagabonds and others who had no claim on the burgh. From the frequency with which the statutes were renewed it can be assumed that they did not work. After the Reformation and the destruction of the monasteries, the weight of the support of the poor in towns fell on the town councils ; thus in 1562 the Assembly of the Church petitioned Queen Mary that " some public relief may be provided for the poor within burghs." At first the magistrates adopted temporary measures, such as the licensing of beggars. They also took into their hands the dispensing of alms to needy cases on council days, a time-consuming process. In Edinburgh a poor Italian, who had been a prisoner among the Spaniards, was provided with clothing, and a French boy from Dieppe was given five pounds Scots to " transport him hamewart." Very often the object underlying this giving of alms was to get rid of the liability as soon as possible by encouraging the recipient to move on ; thus the Council granted the sum of ten pounds to George Hay " quha is oute of his right witts for the present " and to his wife, for putting them over the water.

2

The year 1579 saw the opening of a new chapter in poor-law administration in Scotland with the passing of a comprehensive Act " for punishment of the strong and idle beggars and relief of the poore and impotent." The first of its provisions was that all strong and idle beggars between the ages of fourteen and seventy should be apprehended and tried, and, if convicted, scourged and burned through the ear with a hot iron, unless some honest and responsible man would of his charity take and keep the offender in his service for the whole of the year succeeding. The Act defined strong men and vagabonds as " all idle persons going about, using subtle craft sand unlawful plays, as jugleirs, fast and loose, and such others ; the idle people calling themselves *Egyptians* or any feigning themselves to have knowledge of prophecy, charming, or other abused sciences by which they persuade people that they can tell their fortunes, and such other fantastical imaginations . . . and all minstrels, songsters, and tale-tellers, not in the special service of some Lord of Parliament or great Baron ; all common labourers, being persons able in body, living idly, and fleeing labour ; all counterfeiters of licences to beg, or using the same knowing them to be counterfeit ; all vagabond scholars of the Universities of St. Andrews, Glasgow, and Aberdeen, not licensed by the Dean of Faculty to ask alms ; all shipmen and mariners alledging themselves to be shipbroken, without they have sufficient testimonials."

Other provisions made it an offence to give alms to an unlicensed beggar and ordered the appointment in each parish of certain persons for policing the vagabonds. The condition of hospitals for the housing of aged and impotent poor was to be the subject of inquiry. Magistrates were to prepare a register of " aged, pure, impotent, and decayed persons born within the parish or having their most common resort therein, the last seven years, and who of necessity must live by alms." All poor people were to repair to the parish of their birth or settlement, where the magistrates were to assess the needs of the poor and " to tax and stent " the whole inhabitants within the parish according to the estimation of their substance," without exception of persons, to such weekly charge and contribution as shall be thought expedient and sufficient to sustain the said poor people." Obstinate refusers to contribute to the relief of the poor were to be put in prison. Magistrates were ordered to return poor folk to their parish of settlement, " except leprous people and bedridden people who may not be removed." Any aged and impotent poor who refused to work without being so diseased, lame, or impotent that they were totally unable to work were to be treated firmly—" the refuser is first to be scourged and put in the stocks, and for a second fault is to be punished as a vagabond." In substitution for relief the poor might be licensed to beg ; and since it was felt that as a result of the enforcement of this legislation the prisons were likely to be crowded, it was provided that the expenses of maintaining prisoners should be a charge on the parish in which they were apprehended, " allowing to each person dailly one pound of oat-bread and water to drink."

The ensuing years saw many further Acts " for punishment of masterful beggars and relief of the poor," heavily charged with further penalties. An Act of 1617 instructed justices to put the law into due and full execution against wilful beggars and vagabonds, solitary and idle men without calling or trade, lurking in ale-houses, tied to no certain service, reputed and holden as vagabonds, and against those people who are commonly called the Egyptians. A constable might apprehend any suspected person, " who for the most part sleepeth all day and walketh at night," though if the victim were a man of quality a justice had to accompany the constable making the arrest. Other provisions charged the justices with the duty of making orders for the government of the country in time of plague, and for the severe punishment of disobeyers.

3

It was no easy matter to enforce these laws. In Glasgow, following the Act of 1579, the poor between the ages of fourteen and seventy were designated " vagabonds, sturdy and idle beggars." In August 1583 there was appointed for the first time a Collector for the Poor to stand at the Laigh Kirk door " to receive alms of townsfolk that go into the said kirk to hear preaching." In 1595 the kirk session appointed a committee to prepare " a roll of the people who were able in the toun to be stented for helping the poor," and an assessment, termed " buttock mail for poor householders," was first imposed. The session also enacted that no beggars were to be allowed on the streets or at doors, and had constables appointed to see this enforced ; but to little purpose. In 1586 it was ordained that " all poor be marked with the town's mark that they have been within this toune remaining and lodging for five years bypast." In 1613 one Matthew Thomson, a Highland fiddler, was by a judgment of the Bailie Court " put out of the town at the West Port and banist the same forever " as being " ane idyll vagabond." In 1638 the General Assembly, meeting in Glasgow Cathedral, forbade the poor to beg in the streets and provided for their maintenance in their own homes by a special stent or levy for the purpose. This measure enjoyed a transient success ; but a minute of 1667, complaining that " this haill citie is greatlie overburdened with ane number of beggars, all strangers, quhilk ought not to be permitted in any well governed citie," ordered that all these stranger beggars should be removed from the town, only those being allowed to remain who were well known to have been born in the city, " and to the effect that they may be better known, appoints ane badge with the tounis arms thereon to be raised and given to each one who is suffered to beg, and that none be suffered to beg except such as has the said badge." In Glasgow at this time, following an ancient custom, certain favoured gaberlunzies, recognizable by their blue gowns, were accredited as " King's Beggars."

In June 1658 an arrangement was made with William Lightbodie and John Williamsone " to put the sturdie beggars and otheris the lyk off the toune, and to punish delinquents by putting them on the Cock Stool." Not unexpectedly this office seems to have been attended with personal hazard, and in April 1662 another minute increased the payment to Williamsone and Lightbodie, and ordained that each of them was to carry on his perambulations a staff bearing the town's arms.

About this time a great immigration of Irish considerably increased the number of poor, in 1642 special provision having to be made for their support. Soon afterwards the bailies " ordained ane proclamation to be sent throw the toune to desyre all these who will geve or contribute any supplie to the distressed people that cum from Ireland, that they cum upon Wednesday next at the ringing of the Bells." A great influx of Highlanders also taking place about this time, special collections were made for them, but the Highlanders were dealt with much more summarily than the Irish strangers ; a minute on 12 December 1642 ordered them " to be removit off the toune on Monday next," there being charitably added an order, however, " to give everie one of them some meil for their supplie."

The magistrates and council of the city, finding increasing difficulty in collecting contributions for the poor, were driven to authorize the treasurer to spend twenty pounds sterling in monthly payments for their relief, the maximum allowance to each to be 1s. 6d. per week ; " but that the poor of the town should first be inspected, the roll of them revised and purged, and all strangers and unlicensed beggars summarily ejected." In 1663, when the population of Glasgow amounted to about fifteen thousand souls, twenty pounds sterling sufficed for the annual maintenance of such poor—then thought to be very numerous—as could not support themselves by licensed begging ; but by the end of the century the town council was again appointing constables to keep strange beggars out of the city.

In Edinburgh similar difficulty was experienced, so that in 1591 it was resolved to levy a tax, either in money or in promises of house-room, for " decayed burgesses," and street begging was henceforward forbidden, though the prohibition was in fact made effective only on special occasions such as royal visits. Edinburgh was " ane nest of beggars who haunted the markets of meal and other victuals and levied blackmail from honest people " ; the " beggaris " and the " cruikit, blind, and lame " of whom Dunbar had written years previously. In 1626 the town council approved the building of a House of Correction in the Calton district, known as St. Paul's Work, for the training of the indigent poor in the manufacture of woollen goods. In 1632 and again in 1636 they instructed the constables to apprehend masterless persons, and sturdy beggars young and old, and to bring them to the Laigh Tolbooth in order that the magistrates might send them to St. Paul's Work to be " corrected in manner to be appointed by the Magistrates." While in the House they were to be compelled to work at such labour as was given to them by the master, and to receive such " entertainment as he sall think thair work to deserve." The Correction House existed for about a century, and in times of pestilence was utilized as a shelter for vagrant children whose relatives were either dead or confined on the Boroughmuir. In 1631 the town council, at the command of the Privy Council, established experimentally another Correction House, which functioned in turn as the charity workhouse and as a casual ward.

In an Act of 1661 the Scottish Parliament directed Justices of the Peace to draw up in every parish a list of the " poor, aged, sick, lame, and impotent inhabitants of the said parish who [of themselves] have not to maintain them, nor are able to work for their living," as well as orphans and other poor children within the parish left destitute of help. A convenient house was to be provided for their dwelling and collections made for their maintenance. Again there was provision for the punishment of such poor as refused to work. The poor were divided into two classes : the regular or disabled, and the casual or able-bodied, the one to be relieved at the public charge, the other not so ; and this distinction was long maintained in practice throughout the country, though it was a distinction not always easy to draw. " A man," wrote Nicholls, " may be able to do some things and not able to do others—he may be able one day or one week and be unable in the next—he may be able in the morning, but if left without sustenance through the day he may be disabled in the evening." It is interesting to note that in the Act of 1661 neither presbytery nor kirk session was mentioned in relation to the relief of the poor.

Two years later there was another Act concerning beggars and vagabonds. Since previous legislation had proved ineffectual, this new Act gave powers to all persons or societies engaged in manufacture within the kingdom " to seize upon and apprehend the persons of any vagabonds who shall be found begging, or who being masterless and out of service have not wherewith to maintain themselves by their own means or work, and to employ them for their service as they shall see fit, the same being done with the advice of the magistrates of the place where they are to be seized upon." The parishes from which such vagabonds were drawn had to make a payment to the employers (2d. per day per vagabond for the first year and 1d. per day for the next three), and the poor were bound to continue in the service of their employers for a lengthy period of years.

An Act was passed in 1672 requiring the magistrates of the thirty-two principal burghs in Scotland to " provide correction houses for receiving and entertaining of beggars, vagabonds, and idle persons within their Burghs and such as shall be sent to them out of the Shires." It was laid down that each house should have a large close, sufficiently enclosed that the poor people might not be constantly compelled to stay indoors " to the hurt or hazard of their health." The masters of Correction Houses were charged to hold the inmates to such work as they found them most fit for, and were empowered in case of disobedience " to use all manner of severity and correction, by whipping or otherwise (except torture), and to detain them within the said Correction House." It was declared to be lawful for coalmasters, saltmasters, and those who had manufactories to seize upon any vagabonds or beggars and put them to work, and to have the same power of correcting them, and the benefit of their work, as the masters of the Correction Houses.

There were further Acts " anent the poor " before the end of the seventeenth century, taking the same repressive line as the many others that had gone before them and being apparently equally ineffectual. As an offset to these harsh official measures there grew up in Scotland in the sixteenth and seventeenth centuries such hospitals as that of St. Nicholas in Glasgow, with its range of buildings including hall, old men's house, and female servants' cottage, and Trinity Hospital in Edinburgh. The first Trinity Hospital was built in 1462 for the reception of poor and needy persons within the city, and in 1575 the Provost and Prebendaries drew up a code of regulations to be observed by the headsmen and hospitallers. The inmates of the hospital were required to learn the Ten Commandments, the Lord's Prayer, and the Articles of the Creed. They were forbidden to be absent from preaching and prayers in the College Kirk without permission of the master. The hospital aimed at providing reasonable support for honest poor and impotent persons, aged and advanced in years, or sick. In 1611 the number of inmates was thirty-five, and in 1628 it reached fifty, the number varying from year to year according to the state of the funds. At the time of the Great Plague of 1644–45 all the inmates died and the place was left deserted. Later the governors decided that the persons to be admitted were to be " no other than old men and or women, burgesses' wives or children of burgesses, not married nor under the age of fifty years." At the time of admission, each person would require to bring to the hospital a bed and bedclothes, and to sign a disposition of all his or her goods to the master ; thereafter the persons admitted were to be provided with food, clothing, and lodgings for the rest of their lives, to have a weekly allowance for petty expenses, and finally to be decently buried at the expense of the Charity. In 1655, for the first time a temporary pension was granted to a pauper resident out of the hospital. The hospital fell into disrepair, and in soliciting subscriptions for it in 1728 the treasurer said that the slates were tumbling off the house, the flooring and joists were rotten, " the Nor' Loch ran thro the north end of the House, which brought the whole nastiness of the north side of the town and the butchers' booths through the House." It was recorded in 1730 that each of the inmates had a convenient room, his " ark." The men were allowed annually a hat, a pair of breeches, a pair of shoes, two shirts and two neck-cloths, and every second year a coat and waistcoat. The women had yearly a pair of shoes, a pair of stockings and two shifts, and every second year a gown and petticoat. For snuff and tobacco and other odds and ends the men were allowed 8s. 8d. a year, while the women received 6s. 6d. Each inmate received a daily supply of 12 oz. of bread and a pint of ale. For breakfast they had porridge, for dinner broth and boiled or roast beef, with a fish diet on Friday. There were two common tables, one for men, presided over by the chaplain, the other for women by the mistress of the House. Religious services were held every morning and evening on week days, and a third was added on Sundays. Difficulties arising from incompatibility of temperament and dislike of regulations were not uncommon, and Arnott reported that the conduct of the inmates " although they are a class above the vulgar and are so comfortably sustained, support the argument against maintaining the poor in a congregate body and public poorhouse. The quarrels and riots among them are so frequent, the selling of victuals allowed them and applying the price to improper purposes and their nasty way of living has aroused the attention of the Governors endeavouring to correct their abuses." It must be pointed out that this account scarcely squares with that of Lord Cockburn, who found the pensioners to be as happy as age, when combined with final destitution and with the recol- lection of better days, could probably ever be ; but he added, " They are human. They doubtless have their magnates, their disputed principles, their wrongs, intrigues, and factions. The dullness of their day is no doubt relieved by occasional dissension and ingratitude, but there is as little of this, I understand, as generally enlivens hospitals." The hospital was closed in 1845.

4

In the seventeenth and eighteenth centuries provision for the poor proved difficult alike in town and in country. The Privy Council records show that the problem was an acute one in some rural counties, such as Selkirk, where on account of bad times and taxation the people were scarcely able to provide for them- selves, much less to help others, and representations were made to the Government that, though the county would help the truly indigent and impotent within its own bounds, it could not carry the burden of the large number of sturdy folk who would not work, or of the others who were willing to work but unable to find employment, there being no jails to hold the one, or work to employ the other. The petitioners craved that some common work should be appointed in every parish, such as the mending of the highways, " whereby the idle may be forced and the willing employed." Thomas Somerville, minister of Jedburgh, writing of travellers, sorners, and beggars, said it was another proof of the prevailing hospitality of the middle of the eighteenth century that there existed a description of persons called "sorners," persons destitute of a fixed home, and possessing slender means of subsistence, who used to lodge by turns, and for many days, or even weeks at a time, at the houses of their acquaintances, and were treated with as much affection and generosity as if they had been capable of making a return in kind. Before the general establishment of poor rates, the county was overrun with vagrant beggars. They had access to every house, and received their alms in meal and bread, which were deposited in bags or wallets hung over their shoulders. Strolling beggars often travelled in companies, and used to take up their night quarters at the houses of the tenant farmers in the country, who, after entertaining them with a supper of porridge, conducted them to the barns and outhouses for their night's rest.

5

In the cities the problem was a formidable one. In Glasgow during the eighteenth century there were three main sources for the relief of the poor :

1 From the fourteen incorporations. When persons connected with any of the incorporations were so reduced in circumstances as to require relief, they applied to the deacon and master of the incorporation concerned and received money grants ranging up to ten shillings per month. Those who had held office in the incorporation received larger allowances. When any of the members desired to be admitted as pensioners of the town's hospital they were recommended by their incorporation, and readily admitted. Somewhat analogous was the relief to be obtained by members of the friendly societies, of which, under the name of the Bell's Wynd Society, the first in Glasgow was established in 1746. By the end of the century there were many friendly societies in the city, and in 1826 altogether seventy in Scotland with over 85,000 " free " members.

2 From the kirk session. After the Reformation the Assembly of the Church petitioned Queen Mary in 1562 that " some public relief may be provided for the poor within burghs," and at that time, when Glasgow consisted of a single parish, the

charge was devolved on its ecclesiastical rulers. In 1649 the
Great Session, as it was called, was convened monthly, and part
of their duty was prescribed " to regulate an equal provision for
the poor." The funds received by the General Session were derived
principally from collections at church doors, fees for proclamation
of marriages, and donations at funerals, and these funds were
allocated by the General Session in stated proportions to the
several sessions in the city, regular paupers receiving pensions
varying from 1s. 6d. to about 4s. 6d. per month. If the elder after
investigation was satisfied that a petitioner was poor and had
established a domicile of three years' duration, he gave temporary
relief pending the next monthly meeting, when, if accepted, the
applicant was enrolled on the funds of the Session.

3 From the Town's Hospital. As early as 1682 arrangements
had been made to build a large stone lodging at the corner of
Trongate and Saltmarket for the use of the poor, and the Town's
Hospital was finally erected by public subscription and opened in
1733. The site was in the Old Green near the Clyde, a little west
from the Stockwell. It was described as " more like a palace than
a habitation for necessitous old people and children." In some
of its features it anticipated the modern workhouse. Its maintenance was undertaken by representatives of the Town Council,
the Merchant House, the Trades House, and the General Kirk
Session, these bodies contributing in definite proportions. Aid
was also given to it by benefactions from individuals and cor-
porations and by a small tax on the citizens. This tax was levied
by virtue of the Act of 1579 which empowered the magistrates of
burghs to consider what provision would be necessary to enable
aged poor and impotent persons to " live unbeggand " and " to
tax and stent the haill inhabitants within the perochins, according
to the estimation of their substance, without exception of persons."
(In Edinburgh in place of a tax on personal property the rate was
levied on the rents of houses, with the exception of those occupied
by the clergy, the professors of the university, and the members of
the College of Justice.) Of the first year's revenue of the Town's
Hospital, £820 in all, £570 was derived from contributions, and
the balance from the tax for maintaining the poor. In 1780,
when the deficit was £985, the clerk of the hospital, " as use is,"
craved that the magistrates would assess £985, and appoint a
committee of their own nomination, consisting of eleven merchants and four tradesmen, in all fifteen, " to proportion the

assessment on the inhabitants in conformity to the best information obtained by these gentlemen, and from the public appearance, credit, and magnitude of their business."

6

The Town's Hospital seems to have aimed at the gradual extinction of pauperism " by the profitable employment, the virtuous education, and the frugal maintenance of the inmates." In the preamble to the confirmation of the hospital's charter, dated 1744, it is described as contributing " to the advancement of religion, virtue, and goodness, and the public utility, honour, and advantage of the country, that provision be made for the necessities of poor, indigent children, old decayed men and women, and of others rendered unable to provide for themselves ; and that idle, dissolute, irregular and disorderly persons be restrained from begging, wandering and vaguing, while they might be provided for, and usefully and profitably employed for the service of the country towards their own maintenance." One of the very first regulations made after the opening of the hospital sought to control begging in the streets, by giving to the directors powers to incarcerate all vagrant persons—in law a magisterial function solely. Like other attempts to control mendicity this regulation was ineffective, and in 1741 it was agreed that six staffmen should be appointed, one for each parish, " to go through every day and search for and take up all beggars, and bring them before the committee for examination and expel the stranger beggars, or send them to the Correction House." This, too, proved ineffectual, and in 1746 it was determined that those of the poor who were entitled to city charity should be relieved, to prevent begging, and that those who had no title to relief should be "suppressed."

A more than usually determined effort seems to have been made at this time to put down begging : proclamations were published from pulpits that all beggars should be apprehended and brought before magistrates for imprisonment or banishment ; it was decreed that no houses should be let to strangers without testimonials—the magistrates of Edinburgh had already in 1685 ordained that " no person set their houses within the city to any unfree persons, without a special ticket from the Baillie of the quarter, under penalty of ane unlaw of £20 for ilk person, with the escheat of a year's mail to the town's use."—the names of all incomers were taken to ascertain how far they were able to support themselves, and give security that they would not become a burden to the city ; and that the enrolled poor should go to the hospital and receive there a meal each day. Every inducement was given, in Glasgow as in Edinburgh, to encourage the poor to move out of the city of their adoption, and a committee of the directors of the Glasgow Town's Hospital reported with more than a suspicion of envy that in Edinburgh a proclamation by magistrates and sheriff warning all without legal claim to quit the city, and offering assistance to that end, had resulted in the departure from Edinburgh of 237 stranger beggars at the trifling expense of £15, 6s. 10d.

But even these determined efforts did little to reduce begging in Glasgow and it was reported in 1747 that " several of the poor do still continue begging, and refuse to go to the hospital, where they may have both bed and board." In 1773 it was agreed to try another plan to restrain begging, this time by " providing three meals a day to each of the begging poor, who shall receive badges." This, too, was unsuccessful, and in the following year the managers extended the relief to out-pensioners by an allotted allowance in meal, which later was supplemented by money. The recommendation of suitable recipients for these pensions came principally from ministers and elders, and in 1795 it was decided that before a person was recommended to the hospital he should be raised to the highest pension given by his kirk session ; if he was unable to live on that amount, he should then be recommended to the hospital, and when accepted by it should cease to be a pensioner of the session by which he had been referred.

In 1801 the pensioners of the Town's Hospital were receiving in money ten shillings to thirty shillings (occasionally forty shillings) per quarter, or in meal, six to twelve pounds weekly ; and in that year the directors had recourse to the Police Act " with a view to put the law into execution against vagabonds, idle and disorderly persons, public and sturdy beggars, and other persons who follow no lawful employment, and particularly to prevent such from acquiring residence in the city." This line of approach was no more successful than earlier attempts, and in 1805 the whole question was referred to a committee of the hospital. But no report appears to have been forthcoming.

The expenditure for the first year of the hospital's existence (1733–34) was £468 ; in the second year it rose to £820. By 1786 the inmates of the hospital numbered 288, and the children upon nursing wages, 106. There were 136 families receiving meal, so that the total number of persons on the funds of the hospital was 530. The cost of maintenance of each person in the house averaged £4, 16s. per annum.

7

Living conditions in the hospital appear to have been spartan. The diet was simple in the extreme, and there were many regulations, inevitably irksome. The aversion of the Scottish poor to such institutions was strongly marked. In an early account of the hospital published in 1737, complaint is made of the prejudice against it entertained even by persons otherwise dependent on charity. Among other things, the " confinement " was much disliked, and the authorities were at pains to show that there were no just grounds for this criticism. It was pointed out with satisfaction that the poor, " besides their going to church every Lord's Day, by which they are obliged by the rules, have liberty and encouragement to attend the several week day services." Though the hospital was designed to cater for young, the aged and the impotent, and was not a hospital in the modern sense of professing to provide active medical care for all the inmates, there were always a number of sick people in the house. In 1766 on being asked for a donation to extend the hospital the Faculty of Physicians and Surgeons demanded that at least twenty beds should be fitted up in a clean and decent manner, twelve of them for the sick poor from the hospital, the other eight to be occupied by sick poor sent in by the physician or surgeon in attendance, without restriction to persons who had established a legal settlement in the town.

On the death of a pauper the friends of the deceased received from the magistrate or preceptor of the hospital a certificate authorizing the supply of " a gratis coffin, with printed instructions regarding the funeral " ; the use of a mort cloth, hand spokes, etc. was given free, and a grave provided for the sum of one shilling, which was apparently the perquisite of the gravedigger.

The hospital had constant difficulty in making ends meet, and the directors had almost constant mortification at discovering how often they were imposed upon by people seeking assistance. In 1818 they were driven to appoint a committee to review the whole method of conducting the business of the hospital, and to report on the desirability of an extension of its activities. It appeared that in the year ending August 1816 the cost of maintaining each person in the house had risen to £9, 3s. 3¼d., and the total number in hospital to 504 despite the fact that during the three preceding years " many idle, worthless and dissolute characters were thrown out from participation in a fund to which they had never any title, chiefly by the zealous and indefatigable exertions of the superintendent." The committee started from the basis that no person should be maintained by charity in the same manner that he lived by labour : there ought not only to be a descent from station, but an abridgment of comfort and the object ought never to be more than a mere decent subsistence. It was felt to be wrong that the cost of maintaining a pauper in hospital for a year was over £9, while a weaver's earnings for the same period did not exceed £10, on which he had to maintain his whole family. There was considerable difference of opinion in the committee about the best method of providing for the poor ; some believed the English practice of workhouses to be " most economical, comfortable and effectual," others held that the plan was delusive in theory, and still more injurious in practice, and pointed out that while in Aberdeen a workhouse had been established in 1741, it had been discontinued after a few years, since it had been found better to allow the paupers at their own homes what the charitable funds and contributions could afford. Opponents of the poorhouse system pointed out that the system did not promote industry, that it obliterated domestic relationships, that it crowded together persons of low order, that it increased pauperism, and that it was expensive. While the cost of maintaining the inmates of the Town's Hospital in Glasgow had averaged about £4,250 per annum during the years 1814–16, the profit from the manufactures carried on by the inmates had only averaged £268 ; and the experience of other places, both in Scotland and in England, had been similar. In the town of Stirling, perhaps more amply provided with charitable institutions than any other town of comparable size in the country, having in addition to the funds of the Sessions and the Trade Incorporations three richly endowed hospitals, it was estimated in the Statistical Account of 1793 that every twelfth man was a pauper.

Yet despite all these considerations the committee felt constrained to recommend that a new poorhouse should be built, chiefly for the following reasons :

1 because such a place forms a suitable refuge for people in their declining years, in poverty or with incurable disease and without friends :

2 because it is a convenient receptacle for orphan children who can there be fed, clothed, educated, " and rescued from the contagion of vice." It thus makes " a nursery for good servants." This view of the directors about the responsibilities of the hospital in relation to child care is interesting in view of the high mortality that resulted among children entrusted to the hospital : the directors were apparently quite satisfied that the system pursued in the hospital was judicious. They were apparently conscious of criticism directed at the arrangements whereby children could be handed over entirely to the care of the hospital on payment of £25, for they were at pains to explain that this plan could not be considered as an encouragement to vice ; and they obviously regarded with approval the existing practice of putting children out on " nursing wages," " till they be seven or eight years old, when they are brought in for work or education."

3 because a poorhouse is a suitable place for fatuous paupers. On this there was already in 1818 much difference of opinion, since the physician to the recently established Mental Asylum wrote to the directors of the hospital protesting that a receptacle for idiots was of all others the least proper appendage for a workhouse. But what appealed to the directors was obviously the question of cost, for they said frankly that the cost of keep in the lunatic asylum, upwards of £20 per annum per patient, was out of the question as they had in their charge nearly one hundred fatuous paupers.

On one point the members of the committee were emphatic : to the new establishment there must be attached a school of industry, chiefly directed to the suppression of child-begging. The directors had apparently become convinced that confinement in the bridewell was not the solution to this problem. In their report of 1818 the committee analysed the inmates of the hospital according to their working capacity and the nature of the work in which they were engaged. At the time of the survey there were in the hospital 478 inmates, 377 adults and 101 children. Of the male adults, 63 were regarded as " partially able," and were in employment. Of these, 39 were engaged in work for gain —29 in picking oakum and cotton, 7 in weaving, and 3 in knitting ; while 24 were employed in the occupations of the house as labourers, tailors, shoemakers or coopers. Fifty of the males were classified as " totally impotent," of whom 20 were the halt, the blind and the lame, and 30 were diseased in mind. Of the female adults, 129 were graded as " partially able," and were in employment, 48 in work for gain—knitting (24), spinning (14), winding (5), tambouring (4), and weaving (1) ; while 81 were employed in the occupations of the house, 28 as nurses, 23 making and mending clothes, 9 in washing, 3 in cooking, 3 in baking, and 15 in drudgery work. Eighty-eight of the female inmates were regarded as " totally impotent," 40 of them being diseased in mind.

In considering what ought to be the size of the new hospital, the committee took notice of the need for institutional accommodation for the general sick, for patients suffering from infectious fevers and for the insane. They were satisfied that it was not possible to rely for the treatment of their sick patients on the Royal Infirmary " which is a general receptacle for recovery—not of paupers, whose age and ailments admit of no hope of ultimate cure—but of patients to whom relief may be successfully administered for the purpose of restoring them to health and ability for exertion." They concluded therefore that an infirmary should be attached to the new building with 120 sick beds of the total 500.

The committee thought the provision of a fever ward would not be a legitimate use of their funds, and that such an institution, if necessary after the Royal Infirmary was relieved of cases recommended by the magistrates, should be dependent on private benevolence. On the question of provision for lunatics, the committee recommended that where there was " a rational prospect of cure " a fair trial should be made of treatment in the lunatic asylum, but, actuated doubtless by motives of economy, the directors were equally certain that " when this object appears hopeless, they should immediately be brought back to the hospital."

Finally, the committee recognized that what was required was not merely an extension of existing provision, but a change of atmosphere, a softening influence which they thought could best be secured by interesting the ladies of the city in the work of the hospital : " Your committee know the ladies of Glasgow too well to imagine that they would decline a labour of charity."

In February 1832 the hospital contained over 400 persons, though it was not fit for the proper accommodation of more than 320. The patients were for the most part old and infirm, many of them bedridden. There were between sixty and seventy fatuous or insane paupers who occupied chiefly cells on the ground floor of the northern division of the building. " The cells vary in size from seven to eleven feet square, being six feet in height, with a stone arched ceiling. They contain either two or three beds, occasionally with two persons in each . . . the floors are flagged with stones. They are very damp. . . .

At the west end of the front building there is a large dunghill. . . . The hospital being situated so very near the river and surrounded as it is by several common sewers is, *of course*, subject to occasional inundation, generally once and sometimes twice during the winter and spring seasons. Sometimes the accumulation extends to the depth of several feet."

In many other towns this same question of the desirability of making institutional provision for the poor was being discussed, often with considerable heat. In Edinburgh a city workhouse was established in 1740, and in Aberdeen the following year, though this latter did not long continue ; and in the Statistical Account there are many references to workhouses and the lack of enthusiasm for them. They were regarded by the clergymen responsible for the parish records as in many cases " great sources of corruption and expense." It was reported that after thirty years' trial one established at Inveresk was given up. Another was tried at Prestonpans, but after a few years it too was abandoned, the expense being found greater than when pensioners had a stated allowance given to them and were allowed to spend it out-of-doors as they thought fit. It was agreed, however, that workhouses were often of use in dealing with the idle and the dissolute. As late as 1837 workhouses existed only in Edinburgh and in Paisley in addition to the Town's Hospital in Glasgow. The one in Paisley had been built in 1750 and opened the following year. It was three storeys high and had accommodation for 200 people. It was supported by a tax levied on the inhabitants quarterly, and was under the management of fifteen directors, ten of whom were chosen by the magistrates and council, three by the kirk session and two by the Society of Tailors.

All parochial authorities deplored the prevalent attempts at imposition on the poor's funds, and various measures were adopted in an attempt to check improper applications. One common measure was to require six weeks prior intimation before enrolment was granted, so that inquiry could be made by the kirk session before the meeting that was to deal with the case. Another method was to place on every applicant for admission to the poor roll an obligation by which he bequeathed all his effects to the kirk session. If he left a young family, the household utensils were generally exposed for sale and the proceeds laid out in bringing up the children and setting them up in business ; if he left no young children but had other poor relations advanced in life the proceeds were generally given to them according to their needs. The aversion of the poor to a funeral devoid of any part of the usual celebration prevented many from claiming to be put on the roll. The anxiety for what was called a " decent funeral," *i.e.* a funeral to which all the inhabitants of the district were invited and at which every part of the usual entertainment was given, was very strong among even the poorest. It was reported by Chadwick in his Report on the Practice of Interment in Towns (1843) that in Glasgow the expenses of funerals of persons of the middle class appeared to vary from £12 to £50, and that the expense of the decent burial of a labouring man was not less than £5, exclusive of the expense of mourning. In *Reminiscences of Old Scots Folk*, Barnet, after pointing out that all and sundry were welcomed to funerals and that professional beggars usually attended these functions in large numbers, being fed with food specially provided for them after the mourners themselves had been refreshed with ale and shortbread and oatcakes, gave an account of the expenses for a funeral in the year 1795.

	£	s.	d.
For the Coffin.	1	15	0
To Bread	3	10	2
To Wines.	2	9	8¾
To Rum	1	2	0
To Whiskey	0	10	0
To Beer	0	2	6
	9	9	4¾
To Mort Cloth	0	2	6
	£9	11	10¾

Barnet remarks that an observant Englishman once declared that a Scots funeral was merrier than an English wedding.

A curious method of relieving the poor existed for a long time in Shetland, where the parishes were commonly divided into fourteen parts, called " quarters." To each of these a proportional number of poor was allocated. In every family within each quarter the poor belonging to it received their board for as many days as the family occupied merks of land ; and after proceeding in this manner through all the families in that quarter returned to the first again. When any person, unable to support himself, applied " to be put upon the quarters," as it was called, the minister gave notice of the application from the pulpit, and if nothing was urged against the character or circumstances of the applicant as rendering him an improper object of the charity, he immediately obtained his request. The weekly contributions made at the church, together with the more liberal one at the celebration of the Sacrament, were expended on the purchase of clothes and other necessaries for the poor who were maintained upon the quarters. None were suffered to beg. As late as 1861 the Board of Supervision on calling for a report on the administration of the Poor Law in Shetland, found that " the ancient and primitive mode of providing for the poor still maintained in Shetland had become ineffectual or precarious." Relief was in many cases altogether inadequate and the board saw no reason why ordinary procedure prevailing in other parts of Scotland could not be carried into effect in Shetland. They thought this change could not long be postponed, and a few years later " quartering " passed out of use.

9

By the end of the eighteenth century the Church was having almost insurmountable difficulty in affording reasonable relief to the poor. The funds available for the purpose were drawn from several sources :

1   Ordinary church collections—in the eyes of churchmen the most desirable way of raising the money, but often inadequate

2   From an extra collection at the celebration of the Sacrament

3   From dues collected for the use of hearses or the parish pall or mort cloth, the kirk session having acquired

by immemorial usage the privilege of letting these out for hire

4 From mortifications for the benefit of the poor
5 In some parishes, from the rent of seats in the church
6 From the proceeds of fines imposed for various offences : formerly fines for breaches of chastity were a source of income to the poor, certain sums being exacted from the delinquents before they were restored to full communion with the Church

At this time assessments for the relief of the poor prevailed in ninety-two parishes, mainly urban, of the 878 in Scotland. The practice of assessment was increasing slowly but steadily under sheer force of economic pressure, as against the wishes of the Church. Sinclair reported that the opinion of the Church at large on the subject of assessments, as it emerged from the Statistical Account, was " greatly in favour of the primitive mode of providing for the poor, by collections and voluntary subscriptions." The power of levying an assessment belonged in burghs to the magistrates, and in landward parishes to the heritors and kirk sessions. Sinclair shared the opinion that where the Church could relieve the poor out of its voluntary revenues, that was the most effectual and frugal method conceivable ; and he quoted with approval the view of a contemporary writer " that in such cases the administration of the poor is perfect." He pointed out that at each annual meeting the conduct of the paupers was examined in order to praise and reward those that had behaved well and censure and punish those that had acted otherwise. " On the whole," wrote Sinclair in 1825, " the poor in Scotland are, in general, sufficiently, though not luxuriously, provided for under the control of a pure system of administration and at a moderate expense." There was still something to the old " independence," " decent pride," reluctance of the people to accept poor relief, but already times were changing, and always there was complaint that in such parishes as Campsie and Tillicoultry the old outlook had largely disappeared. In 1820 one person in forty of the population was a pauper. The total amount of money raised for the relief of the poor was £114,196, of which £64,477 came from Church collections and other voluntary sources, and £49,719 from assessments. The average outlay on each pauper was £2, 11s. 8d. per annum.

Whatever its merits the voluntary system was being severely

strained. Begging was still common—so common that the second decade of the nineteenth century saw the formulation of new steps for its control. In the parishes of Langholm and Hawick there was tried with some success the plan of referring to a local society for the distribution of alms all beggars who approached individual contributors to the society's funds, while " in Berwickshire a method somewhat similar was found extremely useful." In that county two salaried constables were appointed whose business it was to go through the county attending fairs, markets, and public meetings, and arresting all gipsies, tinkers, beggars, and disorderly persons who could not give a proper account of themselves. They carried their prisoners before the nearest Justice of the Peace, who committed them to the county jail for some days, after which they were conducted to the extremity of the county nearest to their respective parishes. Besides their salary the constables received ninepence per mile for carrying the prisoners to jail, which expense was paid out of the " rogue money." Apparently the ministrations of the two constables sufficed to keep the county fairly free from beggars, and it was reported that as a result very few petty thefts were committed.

Assessments for the poor were still almost unknown in the rural districts of Scotland, particularly in the northern part of the kingdom, where, in addition to the usual sources, funds for the poor were often supplemented by donations handed to kirk sessions by the successful candidates at Parliamentary elections. The parish minister of Resolis in Ross-shire, writing of 1822, said that all the money available for poor relief did not in any year exceed forty pounds, and that after deducting the cost of certain necessary articles, such as coffins, the balance to be divided among the poor persons on the roll (and they numbered fifty-six) never amounted to as much as twenty pounds. The poor were divided into four classes according to their circumstances, and the available money was divided accordingly. Sometimes in periods of great distress the Highland parishes were very severely hit. In the dearth of 1783 when corn and potato harvests were a complete failure on account of the severity of the seasons, a committee of the House of Commons inquired into the circumstances. The sheriff of Caithness and Sutherland informed this committee that the condition of the northern parts of Scotland was truly lamentable : in Sutherland and Ross-shire many people had already perished for want of food. Caithness was not far removed from similar disaster, while Orkney was in still worse plight. Following the report of the committee, Parliament authorized relief and removed restrictions on the importation of corn for a limited time and a limited area of the country.

10

In urban areas distress was more frequently associated with trade depression. In the latter part of 1816 and the beginning of 1817 the distress of the working classes, arising chiefly from want of employment, was so great that in Glasgow £9,079 was subscribed for their relief, and distributed as follows :

	£
Direct relief within the Royalty	3,865
Direct relief in the Barony Parish	2,682
Direct relief in Gorbals Parish	585
Relief available to all three parishes by the employment of labourers in the Green and Quarry, and promiscuous disbursements	1,497

About this time the celebrated Dr. Chalmers asked that his congregation should be allowed to administer its own collections. Having full confidence in the minister of St. John's, the Town Council agreed, to the great annoyance of the General Session. In Chalmers' administration the deserving received consideration, but the idle and profligate were compelled to work for their living ; and Chalmers directed the surplus of his parish collections to the establishment of parochial schools.

At Paisley many applied to the parish for relief in 1819, 1826-27, and again in 1837. The heritors and kirk session refused relief on the grounds that the applicants, being able-bodied, " did not fall within the class of poor for which the law provided." This decision, on appeal, was upheld, though the view was expressed that in time of such severe actual want as was then prevalent in Paisley some measure of relief becomes " almost as essential for the general tranquility, as it is for the distressed areas themselves." There was more acute distress at Paisley in 1840-1-2. It was so severe as to call for Government interference, and eventually for the raising of relief contributions in other parts of Scotland and in England. To investigate the circumstances connected with the distress, the Government sent a commissioner, Mr. Twisleton, who reported in 1842 that the workers in Paisley were nearly all employed in shawl manufacture, that voluntary subscriptions were inadequate to meet the needs, that in January 1842, 12,703 persons (out of a total population of 48,416) depended for subsistence upon what they obtained from relief funds, and that in many houses there was no furniture at all. He described the people as "very wretched," "spiritless and despondent," and his findings largely prompted and hastened the inquiry into the general working of the Scottish Poor Law, instituted in 1843.

Other Scottish towns reported distress almost as great. John Gibson, surgeon in Lanark, wrote that he had often entreated the magistrates to interfere on behalf of the poor, but in vain : " they always seem to consider every shilling spent upon necessaries for the poor as money thrown away ; even money subscribed for the relief of poor families and placed in the hands of the magistrates is dealt out to the afflicted in gills and half-gills of wine, because in this way it affords a greater profit to the bailie than if given in the larger quantity of a bottle at a time. The same conduct is observed in regard to all cordials and necessaries doled out by the bailies to the afflicted poor." A census of thirty-five colliers' families in Tranent showed that in no fewer than ten of these the head of the family was a widow ; and widows were expected to support themselves, though if they had children of tender years a small allowance was made for them, about 1s. 6d. a week for each child. The total number of poor to whom relief was given in Tranent in 1840 was between 100 and 110, chiefly old men and women unable to provide for themselves and helpless children deprived of their parents : the total amount spent on relief was £450 per annum. In the neighbouring districts of Musselburgh and Inveresk, where there were 320 paupers on the roll, the allowances ranged from 6d. to 3s. 6d. per week, the average according to Dr. Stevenson being perhaps 9d., "certainly far from extravagant." In Greenock where no assessment had been levied for the support of the poor since 1816 there were, in 1840, 1,098 paupers on the roll, and the amount distributed among them was £4,600.

It was estimated in 1820, when the population of Glasgow was about 147,000, that the number of poor within the royalty connected with the kirk sessions and Town's Hospital totalled 2,755, after that year the number increasing rapidly. A large proportion of the poor in Glasgow and in Edinburgh were natives of other places. In 1837–39, of 3,072 persons supplied with work by the Relief Committee only 1,253 belonged to the city, while in 1840 only 38 of 178 patients under treatment in the Royal Infirmary were natives of Glasgow and not more than 15 per cent. of the patients admitted into the Albion Street (Fever) Hospital ; in Edinburgh less than a quarter of the patients treated in the Royal Infirmary were natives of the city, and only one-half of the paupers in St. Cuthbert's Workhouse. In both cities something under one-third of the inmates of the night asylums for the homeless were natives.

In 1837 it was found necessary to support in Glasgow, through the agency of the Relief Committee, some 18,500 persons. Most of these were given supplies of meal, a few who could be trusted receiving small sums of money. It was found necessary to provide 230 beds, besides straw, etc., for patients who had, even in the severity of winter, nothing but the damp floors of their dwellings, or perhaps in some few instances a bundle of shavings or a scanty supply of straw to lie upon. The amount of destitution in the city was very great, and in the opinion of the city missionaries its chief causes were, in order : intemperance, want of employment, low rate of wages, ignorance or want of education, and early and improvident marriages. " That regular manufactories of pauperism exist in the damp and unventilated cellars and the ground floor in the lanes and closes of the city is a fact of easy demonstration." The great English reformer, Chadwick, secretary to the Poor Law Commissioners, wrote in 1842 : " It might admit of dispute, but on the whole it appeared to us that both the structural arrangements and the condition of the population in Glasgow was the worst of any we had seen in any part of Great Britain." The level of education in the poorer parts of the town was very low : in Gorbals only 7 per cent. of the children were under instruction, and in St. Mary's Parish, where the total number between the ages of five and fifteen was 1,691, " 382 cannot read and are not learning and 1,291 cannot write and are not learning." Captain Miller, the Superintendent of Police, repeatedly pointed out the close relationship between the poverty of the Glasgow wynds and the conditions under which the people lived. Dr. Robert Perry reported that previous to 1844 " there were at one time forty persons, most of them able-bodied, undergoing voluntary imprisonment, subject to all the rules and restrictions of the prison," presumably because they found conditions inside more tolerable than those they could obtain otherwise. By inability to find employment many more were driven to crime. Dr. Perry found that the prevailing fever epidemic incapacitated labourers, on an average, for five weeks and that little was done for their relief.

One direct outcome of the increased misery of the cities was the growth of pawnbroking. The first pawnbroking office in Scotland was opened in 1806 in the High Street of Glasgow, by an itinerant Englishman who " eloped " at the end of six months, and by 1820, when the working classes were in great distress, 2,043 heads of families in Glasgow pawned 7,380 articles on which they received £739, 5s. 6d. About nine-tenths of the articles pledged were redeemed within the legal period. In 1833 there were fifty-two pawnbroking offices, and within the five years following they increased by 70 per cent. In 1836 Cleland found that in one pawnbroker's shop in Glasgow bed and body clothes were nine times more numerous than all the other articles put together. In Edinburgh there were in 1817 thirty-two licensed pawnbrokers, besides 192 known brokers and a multitude of " wee pawns," of which no accurate return could be obtained. Another evil of the times was the growth of shebeens, unlicensed drinking-houses which were often also brothels.

II

In the early years of the Hungry Forties, when many social reformers had already been urging that relief could not be put on an adequate basis if the voluntary principle were maintained, circumstances threatened the complete breakdown of the existing means for the relief of the poor. Yet from motives not altogether disinterested the Church opposed a compulsory system, and so did many other groups, especially landowners. But the position was aggravated by the Disruption in 1843, since the Established Church was apt to confine the limited resources for relief of the poor to its own members to the exclusion of other religious persuasions. A further aggravating circumstance was the worsening of the employment position and the growth of a body of continuously unemployed poor, which came to form a separate class, a new state. " Of all the new features of modern society," wrote Lord Cockburn, " none is so peculiar or frightful as the hordes of strong poor, always liable to be thrown out of employment by stagnation of trade. There have been above ten thousand of them in Paisley for more than a year ; and a similar cloud darkens every considerable town in Scotland." He doubted not that there were many good people among them, but their position did not tend to improve them—" they have discovered that their number is their force."

Moreover, the development of the railways added to the difficulties by causing wholesale movements of labour (especially Irish), with the consequent mushroom growth of towns and all the evils this brought in its train by the crowding of the people together under conditions grossly insanitary. Epidemics raged. Sickness, especially typhus fever, so prevalent among the railway labourers, spread from west to east, particularly to Edinburgh and to most other sizable towns along the new lines. With a view to obtaining for them free treatment in the infirmaries there, railway contractors moved sick workers to Edinburgh and Glasgow, but the infirmaries being full, the care of the destitute sick fell as a heavy burden on those cities. Also, dread of infection shutting against the poor the houses in which they had usually been lodged, many of them had to put up with huts by the side of the railway, while others lay in outhouses and other places unfavourable to their recovery.

As a general result of these circumstances an increasing number of parishes were driven to levy assessments for poor relief. The arguments brought forward against such assessment were many : that an organized system of relief would take away the earnings of the industrious to support the idle and dissolute, make no distinction between poverty resulting from misfortune and that from vice, destroy the ties of relationship, and lessen both the sympathy of the wealthy and the mutual aid of the poor. Cockburn, seriously concerned about the dilemma, wrote : " The question is whether we shall continue to adhere to our ancient and often-praised poor system, or shall at once abandon it for poor rates, workhouses, overseers, relief as a matter of right to the unemployed and able-bodied, and all the other peculiarities that have hitherto been generally condemned in England. An odd question apparently for Scotland to tolerate, but so it is."

Chapter VIII

RELIEF OF THE POOR 1845 to 1863

I

In 1843 the Commission appointed by the Government to review the administration of Poor Relief in Scotland reported that while conditions varied widely from one part of the country to another, the general standard was low. Thirteen poorhouses had been provided in Scotland, but the Scottish system for relief of the poor was essentially one of outdoor relief. The allowances were very low, sometimes almost negligible. In Glasgow and some other parishes there were two distinct classes of poor, "sessional poor " and " hospital poor," the former coming under the kirk sessions of the several city parishes, who granted relief to the extent of 6s. per month ; but when more was required the applicant was transferred to the class of " hospital poor," who were under the charge of the managers of the Town's Hospital. In some parishes the poor were licensed to beg within the limits of their own parish, in terms of the Act of 1672. In Campbeltown, as late as 1842, beggars' badges had been supplied to some persons struck off the poor roll, and in many towns paupers were allowed to beg on one or more days of the week, as in Dingwall, Inveraray, Kirkcaldy, Perth, and Thurso. In Shetland the poor were still relieved by " quartering," and in Kirkwall, where the people were much divided by sectarianism, each dissenting congregation undertook to support its own poor. Allowances were occasionally granted out of the poor fund for relief on account of sickness, for payment of funeral expenses, and for defraying the costs of removals.

Medical relief in Scotland was left almost entirely to private charity, especially in the rural areas, and medical men were not unnaturally dissatisfied with this state of things.

The general attitude of the Commissioners was that they would " consider that they were activated by a false and ill-directed philanthrophy were they to recommend any measures likely to create an abatement of exertion on the part of the labouring classes, or a less independent feeling than that which now exists, or which would lead them to rely on any other means of support than those derived from the exercise of their own energies—being convinced that such measures, however specious at first sight, would not be calculated ultimately to contribute to the happiness of the poor, or to promote their welfare."

The Commissioners thought that the managers of the poor in each parish should have full discretionary power to afford medical relief in all cases where it might seem to them desirable, medical relief being understood to include " the supply of nutritious diet, wine or cordials, where deemed necessary for the proper treatment of the case : and also the vaccination of children where necessary." The Commissioners found there had been great improvement in the treatment of insanity, but that generally accommodation for pauper lunatics was very inadequate ; and they recommended " that where an insane person is in receipt of parochial relief, it shall be imperative on the managers of the poor to send such insane person forthwith to a lunatic asylum, unless authorised by the central authority to treat him otherwise."

The Commissioners were conscious of the strong feeling of opposition to a legal assessment for the poor, and aware that the clergy had exerted their influence to prevent recourse to any compulsory mode of raising funds for this purpose ; but they realized that the need for such an assessment was coming to be appreciated, especially in the towns, and even in Inverness, where an assessment had long been resisted ; and they felt that the adoption of the method of assessment was inevitable.

The principal recommendations of the Commission were incorporated in an Act, passed in August 1845, for the amendment and better administration of the laws relating to the relief of the poor in Scotland. This Act provided for the creation in Edinburgh of a Central Board of Supervision charged with general responsibility for the relief of the poor. It also provided for the creation of parochial boards whose duties were to make up rolls of the poor, to name an Inspector of Poor, and " to concert and determine as to the methods of raising funds requisite for the relief of the poor." It legalized three modes of assessment and left it to parochial boards to adopt one of them, the most widely adopted being the first, that one-half of the assessment should be imposed on the owners and the other half on the tenants or occupants of all land and heritages according to their annual values. Before the passing of this Act, only 230 of the 878 parishes in Scotland had been legally assessed for the relief of the poor. In 1846, as recorded in the First Annual Report of the Board of Supervision, the number of parishes assessed had risen to 448, and in 1862 to 759.

The new assessments for the relief of the poor were not introduced without a certain amount of opposition. In the parish of Coll, for instance, it was agreed to assess the island under the second mode laid down by the new Act, that half of the assessment should be imposed on the owners of all lands and heritages according to annual value, and the other half on the whole inhabitants " according to their means and substances," but when a meeting was held for the purpose of hearing appeals, " certain riotous proceedings caused an adjournment." The objectors were the officers of the Northern Lights Commissioners stationed at Skerryvore, who were to be charged on their salaries.

2

The salaries paid to the newly appointed Inspectors of Poor were low. In county districts the inspectors were appointed on a part-time basis, and they were drawn from many walks of life— doctors, schoolmasters, farmers, foresters, sheriff officers, post-masters, lawyers, catechists. They were of widely varying intelligence and proficiency. In Highland parishes some spoke little English and others little Gaelic, and both had their difficulties. In 1853 it was decided that in parishes where it was considered necessary to conduct public worship in Gaelic, the inspector should be able to speak the language. In that year a case occurred in which the ability to speak Gaelic of the person appointed was questioned by some of the members of the parochial board and asserted by others. The wretched appointee was required " to repair to Edinburgh for the purpose of being examined as to his fitness for the office, but he preferred tendering his resignation, which was accepted." In the early years comparatively few inspectors kept record books in a form commending itself to the officers of the Board of Supervision. Some had not been provided with any books, and others did not trouble to make entries even when books were available ; one in Snizort, when called to task, naïvely explained that he " did not think he was to be so well looked after," and it is plain from official records that some made a point of being from home when a visit from an inspector from Edinburgh was to be apprehended. Of the work of the unhappy inspector at Barra it was said that in his parish the Poor Law Amendment Act did not meet with common justice, and that the inspector was " unsuited for the important office which he now holds." The inspector at Blair Athole absconded and was dismissed by the Board of Supervision. When an assistant inspector at Falkirk was indicted for culpable homicide before the Circuit Court of Justiciary in Stirling, on the ground that in consequence of negligence in the discharge of his duty he had allowed a pauper to die for want of sufficient relief, the court found the indictment relevant, thereby establishing the liability of inspectors to be indicted criminally for any such neglect. Dr. Mackenzie, the inspector at Gairloch, was invited by the Board of Supervision to resign, " notwithstanding his respectability " ; he lived in Inverness, visiting the parish occasionally and managing for his nephew the principal estate in it, an arrangement which did not appeal to the Board. In some cases the Board of Supervision permitted to resign inspectors " whom we should otherwise have dismissed " ; " and one inspector to whom we should not have offered the alternative anticipated his dismissal by resignation." It was obviously felt that the risk of abuse was so great that it must be checked by the exercise of drastic measures, and the Board thought it expedient to issue an order by which inspectors were prohibited from deriving any profit or emolument directly or indirectly from dealings with paupers ; there was inevitably suspicion when an inspector had invested money in importing into his parish corn or meal that was sold to the poor at market prices, though an officer of the Board who inquired into these matters reported that he had not sufficiently precise information to entitle him to charge anyone with making an improper trade of supplying the poor with provision. In 1858 the General Inspector of Poor, reporting on a visit to the northern counties, wrote that the inspectors he saw were intelligent and of good position, well adapted for the office (" with the exception of one who, I fear, wants energy of character and is not of active habits "). They had one failing ; inspectors were in general too fond of law proceedings, " evincing a great desire to patronize solicitors, and by so doing getting rid of duties they should perform themselves, and they are too fond of technicalities." A year or two earlier the ministrations of the inspectors and their assumptions of powers in dealing with lunatics were severely criticized by the Lunacy Commissioners. In the main, however, the inspectors did their work conscientiously and well, often with little resources and little encouragement ; as one said, an inspector without funds at command must become a refusing officer whereas his duty is that of a relieving officer. The early reports of the Board of Supervision recorded with regret the death of several very efficient inspectors and assistant inspectors and more than one medical officer, from fever caught in the discharge of their duty among the poor.

3

The failure of the potato crop in 1846 and the distress associated with it submitted the new arrangements for the relief of distress to an early and severe test. It is certain that the allowances to the poor did not err on the side of generosity. An inspector of the Board of Supervision wrote that in forming an opinion of the state of the poor he always " kept in view the simple habits and abstemious mode of living of the people generally, conceiving that the same style of living to which they had been hitherto accustomed was the proper standard upon which to judge of their wants when they became a burden upon the public." In some cases the calculation of allowances seem to have been based on elaborate formula. It was estimated that where an old man sat rent-free with a small garden, and fuel (peat or wood) was very cheap, an allowance of 1s. to 1s. 6d. per week was sufficient, 1s. being sufficient to purchase adequate food and 3d. or 6d. being added for his clothing, etc. ; if the man was unable to do any work 3d. more was added. Five pounds of potatoes were taken as equal in nutritive value to one pound of meal, " enough for an aged pauper," and 1s. a week purchased one pound of meal per day. The average amount of potatoes raised by each pauper being taken at one and a half to two bolls, calculated to provide three-twelfths of his necessary sustenance or the equivalent of six and a half stones of meal, it was reckoned that the potatoes reared in a poor man's garden represented a saving of 13s. per annum, which should suffice to buy fish as well as other small items. Where allowances were made in kind, it was usual to supplement the grant at irregular intervals by a little money, ranging from 1s. to £1, to purchase clothes or pay the expenses of a funeral. Where allowances were paid in money they were often determined by a classification of paupers into three groups according to the measure of their necessity. In practice the allowances paid seldom exceeded £2 quarterly, and the practice of dividing paupers into classes came to be regarded with official disapproval on the ground that it was absurd to say that the circumstances of twenty or thirty individuals with families dependent on them, or having children on whom they were partly dependent, could be in every point so similar that the same amount should be allowed to each ; even supposing the number and ages of the children to be the same, the health and abilities of the parties would generally be found to vary. It sometimes happened, as in Barra, that the inspector was not always furnished with either meal or money, and was able to distribute allowances only when he happened to have resources at his command.

The average allowances per annum to paupers on the Roll of Poor in Scotland was £3, 13s. 7¼d. in the year ending February 1846, £4, 10s. 9d. in the year ending May 1847 (when the price of provisions was unusually high), and £3, 19s. 7¼d. in the year ending May 1848.

4

Prices of provisions in the Highlands in 1846 did not differ much from those in other parts of Scotland. Meal cost about 20s. per imperial boll of 10 stone, but by the spring of 1847 the price had risen to 30s. per boll. Early in 1846 the price of potatoes was 15s. to 16s. per boll of 4 cwt. The price had already begun to rise because of increased demand for potatoes for export even before the failure of the crop, which sent it rapidly upwards. In seaside towns fish was cheap. In Tain a common price for haddocks was twelve to sixteen for 6d. In Dingwall or Tobermory a 5-lb. cod could be bought for 3d., and a hundred herrings for 2s. Eggs cost 3d. or 4d. per dozen. In the spring of 1847, tea cost 3d. or 4d. per oz., sugar 6½d. per lb., molasses 4d. per lb., and tobacco 3d. per oz. Braxy mutton cost 3d. per lb.

The price of fuel varied greatly from town to town and from one Highland parish to another, according to the distance from natural resources. In Tiree, fuel was particularly scarce and expensive, the peats being cut in the Ross of Mull, a distance by sea from Tiree of about thirty-five miles.

5

In the second half of 1846 there was a big demand for labour. The building of railways went on apace and absorbed a large number of workers, not merely town-dwellers and immigrants from Ireland, but many men from Highland counties ; the quarrymen of Kilbrandon, for example, emigrated in large numbers, some to teach the art of quarrying, and many to work on the railroads. This migration helped to relieve the weight of destitution in many Highland parishes, Kilbrandon among them. Tiree was grossly over-populated, on three small farms there being dependent 1,760 souls. Of these, 1,000 agreed in 1846 to emigrate, conditional on the receipt of assistance ; their houses were to be pulled down, and the materials applied in fencing and draining. George Douglas Campbell, eighth Duke of Argyll, wrote that between the Union of the Crowns and the first Jacobite Rebellion the population of the Highlands was kept down only by pestilence and famine, but that even with these checks the population did increase beyond the average means of subsistence. He instanced the case of Tiree, where the population " increased more rapidly than that of Glasgow," so that from 1769 to 1802 it had increased from 1670 to 2,776, and in 1846 it had mounted to 5,000. " The people," he wrote, " petitioned my father to help them to emigrate to Canada . . . large sums were spent on emigration for several years, and before the operation had been completed we had helped to settle in the New World, under favourable conditions, very nearly 2,000 souls from the over-burdened island of Tiree." The Eighth Annual Report of the Board of Supervision recorded that applications to the Inclosure Commissioners for advances under the Emigration Advances Act had been transmitted to them in respect of Lord MacDonald's and the Skeabost properties in Skye, and the Glengary property in the parish of Glenelg. In each of these cases, as in several others, the Board certified in terms of the Act that the proposed emigration from the property was expedient.

6

Farm wages were of the order of 1s. to 1s. 3d. a day (without food) in Sutherland, 1s. 6d. to 1s. 10d. in Argyll. Ample harvest work was available at 1s. 3d. to 2s. per day with dinner. In the northern counties labourers employed by contractors on the roads made 1s. 6d. to 1s. 8d. per day, but their employment was not constant, and they had many days on which they were out of work. It was estimated that, allowing for holidays and fast-days and for days on which no work was done, the yearly gains of a day labourer did not work out above 7s. per week. All the families eked out their wages by growing potatoes and generally by keeping a pig or bees or fowls. The money wages of a ploughman ranged from £7 to £9 a year with certain allowances—meal, coals, potatoes, and milk. He also had a house and was sometimes allowed a day's cutting of peat ; and if he kept a pig he might get some of the refuse of the potato crop as food for it. The total value of these allowances in kind was about £15, so that the total remuneration of the highest class of farm servant did not exceed £24 per annum. The ferryman at Kessock received £8 in money in the half-year, with a house and three bolls of meal. The rate of wages for opening moss drains two and a half feet deep, of width at top eighteen inches and at bottom nine inches, was 2½d. per rood.

In Oban, where a large part of the population was engaged on such trades as weaving and shoemaking, there was little employment. A good many of the men fished two or three days a week, sharing a boat. Cod and ling fishing was their general pursuit, and as the catch did not find a ready sale at home it was forwarded by steamer to Glasgow. The fishing industry created a demand for nets ; in Caithness many of the poor earned a pound or two a year in this way. But when it was suggested that there might be similar opportunities for net-making on Loch Fyne-side, inquiry proved that at Tarbert, the principal fishing station, the demand was already being met, while in Lochgilphead, where there was a demand, there were no substantial persons engaging in the fishing, and the fishermen themselves could not be trusted to pay. Many women knitted or carded and spun wool, usually for a few pence per week ; women in agricultural work might be paid sixpence per day.

Not everyone was over-anxious for work—and there was a feeling that recently introduced measures of poor relief had made things worse in this respect. There was an impression that there had been rather a want of ingenuity on the part of some local Boards in devising work for the poor in return for any relief afforded them, and one of the inspectors of the Board of Supervision had occasion to refer to " a most gratuitous piece of philanthropy on the part of the Parochial Board at Duirinish, where it appeared many of the recipients of relief had refused to take work as they liked better to get food without working for it." Another official reported that the poor in the Black Isle appeared to have contracted habits of indolence, and to have little desire to improve their condition ; he had failed to find a certain pauper, whose case was under investigation, because the pauper was away at a roup of cattle, " fond of being where there are cattle and whisky." The Sheriff of Orkney reported that the difficulty was not to get work for the people but to get the people to perform the work required of them. In Knapdale the village storekeeper expressed the opinion that the people were not very willing to work ; they could get work on the laird's property, but they did not know their wages until the work was nearly done, and they did not like such a system ; many would go on a day's wages, but they did not like piece-work. In some parishes poverty was very prevalent, and the great majority were more or less dependent on the few. Much depended on the humanity of the laird. In Kilmartin the liberality of the chief heritor, Malcolm of Poltalloch, was well known : " any comfort which his house can provide is always at the disposal of the necessitous upon the recommenda-tion or suggestion of the clergyman of the parish." Lord Breadal-bane's factor, on the other hand, refused to attend a meeting called in Luing to consider the best means of meeting destitution, on the ground that he was the best judge of the people's wants ; yet in fact at that time many were obliged to part with their clothes for food.

7

With the succeeding years of dearth, poverty in the Highlands increased. In 1851 the chairman of the Board of Supervision conducted a special inquiry in distressed districts of the Highlands (especially in Skye), and reported that although part of the inhabitants in several parishes had suffered great privations and the pressure put on local resources had been severe, yet, with a certain amount of extraneous help and the charitable contributions of individuals, the relief afforded by the Parochial Boards had enabled the poorer classes to surmount the dangers of the year. Only one case in which there was reason to suspect that death might have been caused by want of food had been reported to him. The case was that of an old man named McCrimmon, who was in receipt of parochial relief. The worthy chairman concluded that " it appeared that the relief afforded by the Parochial Board was sufficient for his own sustenance, and that if he really died from want of sufficient food, which did not appear to be ascertained, it must have been in consequence of the other persons residing in his house, amongst whom was a married daughter and her children, having deprived him of the food provided for him by the Parochial Board." There must have been a certain amount of local apprehension about the case, for it was investigated by the Sheriff-Substitute of the district, and reported to the Lord Advocate ; " but the legal advisers of the Crown were of opinion that it did not furnish ground for judicial proceedings against the Inspector."

This was not the first case of the kind, for the Second Annual Report of the Board of Supervision recorded with satisfaction that after careful investigation the Board had been unable to discover any case in which it could be clearly established that want of food was the immediate cause of death, though there had been cases in which there was reason to believe that death had been hastened, if not indirectly caused, by a deficiency of wholesome food—admittedly rather a fine distinction. Widow Christy Morrison, who was said to have died of starvation on the Island of Papa, lived all winter on whelks, dulse, and gruel. Widow Ann Gillies and her four young children lived in South Uist ; she was paralytic and otherwise in bad health. A weaving loom and a horse that she had possessed were sold after her death for £2, 15s. to defray the expenses of her funeral, but she had no other means of support beyond that derived from the parish and from the charity of her neighbours. Her children begged. Between 18 November 1846 and the time of her death—19 February 1847 —she received from the parish altogether ten pecks of meal. Widow Gillies, although in direst need, did not sell the horse, apparently because she considered it necessary to leave at her death an amount of property sufficient to meet her burial expenses.

The Parochial Board of Barra reported in 1851 increasing difficulty in relieving paupers because of long-continued dearth of food, the low price of cattle, unwillingness of the population to migrate (though it appears that upwards of 1,000 of the islanders had petitioned the legislature to afford them the means of emigrating to America, " from whence their relatives are daily sending intelligence calculated to encourage them to follow "), and the unwillingness of individuals to serve on Parochial Boards because of the responsibilities involved. This reluctance was aggravated by a recent legal decision ; most Parochial Boards had been affording relief to the able-bodied destitute, but the Parochial Board of Loch Broom having been interdicted from so doing, other parishes naturally hesitated, for by not opposing interdict they would only lose an obligation they were not unwilling to part with.

The Poor Law Amendment Act of 1845 had laid it down that nothing therein contained should be held to confer relief on able-bodied persons out of employment the right to demand relief. In 1848 the Lord Advocate and Dean of Faculty advised the Board of Supervision that " able-bodied persons accidentally or unavoidably thrown out of employment, and thereby reduced to immediate want, may be regarded as occasional poor, to whom temporary relief may lawfully be given out of the Funds raised by Assessment " ; but that " such persons cannot be admitted to the Roll of Poor entitled to Parochial Relief." A decision given by the Sheriff of Lanarkshire in 1848 raised questions of great importance on the interpretation of the law as to the claims of able-bodied men and their children. William Lindsay, an able-bodied man out of employment, had demanded from the Parish of Gorbals relief for his children, the eldest of whom was ten years of age. The relief was refused on the ground that Lindsay, being able-bodied, was not entitled to relief. The Sheriff found the children legally entitled to relief on the ground that being unable to do anything for their own support because of tender years and being destitute by reason of their father's destitution and inability to find employment, they fell under the class of persons entitled to parochial aid. There was an appeal against this decision of the Sheriff, but it was upheld by the Lord Ordinary.

8

There were inevitably difficulties involved in getting the new mechanism for the relief of the poor to work smoothly. Some of these difficulties turned on the unsuitability of individual inspectors, some on lack of definition of the functions and methods of the new Parochial Boards. In 1848 inquiries by the Board of Supervision brought to light defects in the administration of the Poor Law in Govan and in Gorbals, probably due to the deaths of several inspectors successively rather than to any intentional disregard of the law. Defects were also discovered in St. Cuthbert's Parish (Edinburgh), chiefly resulting in unnecessary delay in disposing of applications for relief, and the Board came to the conclusion that " it will be necessary to extend our inquiries to other parishes similarly situated." The condition of the poor in the Shetland Islands was " not altogether satisfactory." " The intelligent Mr. Peterkin " (a tribute from the Board to one of its zealous officers) was sent to Galloway in 1850 to report on the conditions and management of the poor ; his findings were, on the whole, favourable, though " we have taken measures to remedy some defects." The Report of the Board for the same year told how the late Parochial Board of Glasgow had appointed Mr. William Anderson to carry out certain duties for which the Inspector of Poor was alone responsible. On representations from the Board of Supervision the new Parochial Board disavowed the policy of the old, but Mr. Anderson refused to surrender the functions that had been assigned to him and fought—unsuccessfully—the petition of the Board to have his nomination set aside. Sir John McNeill, Chairman of the Board of Supervision, reporting on a visit of inspection to Caithness in 1853, found little in the administration of poor relief there to which he could take exception, except perhaps that the Parochial Boards seemed to be ignorant of the remedial virtues of poorhouses in the control of applications for relief ; he was struck by the fact that all the Boards were of opinion that the increased facilities afforded by the Act of 1845 " had produced a perceptible relaxation in the exertions of partially disabled persons to maintain themselves, and induced many who had been in the habit of aiding their poor relations, and were still able to do so, to throw the burden of their maintenance wholly upon the parish, and had greatly impaired the disposition formerly manifest to aid parents and descendants, whom persons are by law bound to maintain." A few years later, in its Thirteenth Annual Report (1858), the Board of Supervision returned to the same theme. " In the Highland counties there appears to be a proneness to pauperism, which, combined with and fostered by, laxity of administration, seems to be producing an injurious effect upon the population." In an appendix to the same report, the General Superintendent of Poor spoke freely about the imposition that was commonly practised—" openly and without shame." He had noticed a great number of applicants feigning all sorts of diseases and infirmities, though the parties were evidently perfectly healthy. Inspectors had informed him that as the allowances to lunatics and idiots were of the highest amount, many feigned madness ; and parents often represented that their children were lunatics or idiots when that was not the case. Some inspectors stated that great numbers of their paupers had as good credit with merchants and publicans as farmers had. Parents sometimes stated that they had given up their holdings to sons or sons-in-law ; they then applied for relief, and if that were obtained " their children soon seek payment for lodging them."

There were other administrative problems. The right to demand immediate relief from any parish in which destitution occurred, conferred by the Act of 1845 on all persons legally entitled to parochial relief, increased considerably the cost of relieving casual poor. When the inspector was ignorant of the circumstances of " casual " applicants, as was often the case in such cities as Glasgow, he was bound to provide them with necessary subsistence until he had made his investigations ; and having received a shilling or two in this way, the casuals often failed to make any further contact with the inspector. It became necessary to provide suitable accommodation for the casual poor, and in 1848 the Board of Supervision issued a circular recommending Parochial Boards to make such arrangements. The circular pointed out that poor persons disabled by sickness could not, under any circumstances, be placed in common lodging-houses, where they rarely met with the quiet and attention they required, and that to place paupers suffering from fever in a lodging occupied by the healthy poor, or by independent labourers, was altogether unjustifiable.

9

The Poor Law Amendment Act of 1845 required Parochial Boards to remove all " insane and fatuous " paupers to an asylum or establishment legally authorized to receive lunatic patients, but empowered the Board of Supervision, under special circumstances and in particular cases, to dispense with their removal. The Parochial Board was required to provide for them " in such other manner and under such regulations as to inspection and otherwise as shall be sanctioned by the Board of Supervision." In the autumn of 1845 there were vacancies in public asylums in Scotland for eighty-two patients and in private establishments for fifty-two ; but there were 1,621 pauper lunatics in Scotland who had not been placed in a licensed establishment, so that it was impracticable to enforce removal of even one tenth of the cases at large. At that time the total number of insane or "fatuous" paupers in public or in licensed asylums in Scotland was about 1,400. The Board of Supervision sent medical gentlemen to visit pauper lunatics living with their relatives, to determine whether it was necessary to have them removed to institutions, but in the course of a year removal to an institution was ordered by the Board in only five cases. One reason why removal was seldom enforced was that the Board considered it preferable to keep accommodation for fresh cases arising, " in which it may be hoped that medical treatment and proper discipline may effect a cure," for not only was accommodation in Scotland for lunatics very limited, but the existing asylums were for the most part filled with incurable patients, to the exclusion of more recent cases, many of which were curable.

From the time of the inception of the Board of Supervision in 1845 up to the middle of 1848, the number of cases of lunatic and " fatuous " paupers not in asylums investigated by the Board was 2,003, and removal to an asylum was required in only thirty-eight of these. The Board reported that they had dispensed with removal only in cases where it had been certified by medical gentlemen after personal inspection that the lunatic was harmless, that his disease was unlikely to be aggravated by allowing him to remain in his present residence, and that his existing accommodation and attendance were satisfactory, though it was added that deficiency of institutional accommodation had induced the Board to dispense with removal in certain cases where it would actually have been preferable. There were numbers of " maniacs " wandering about, especially in country districts—as at Tain— dependent solely on charity for a precarious and miserable existence ; " they are generally of a harmless character, but exceptions occur."

With the growth of poorhouses it was found that many lunatic paupers came to be retained in premises not licensed for that purpose, and often unsuitable for it. This matter gave the Board of Supervision some concern, but by 1850 they had come to the conclusion that " for a large class of incurable and harmless pauper lunatics, especially such as have no near relation with whom they can reside, a well-regulated poorhouse affords the place of refuge most conducive to their own happiness and welfare and most advantageous to the community. Not only is the cost of maintaining such persons in poorhouses less than half of what it would be in an asylum, but if it were determined to place in asylums the whole of the pauper lunatics the difficulty in obtaining accommodation for recent and curable cases would continue to be great, even if the present insufficient amount of accommodation in asylums were largely increased." Following the Report of the Lunacy Commissioners in 1855 and the passing of the Lunacy Act, an Act was passed authorizing the Lunacy Board to license, for the reception of lunatics, and for a limited time pending the building of district asylums, certain detached or separate portions of poorhouses ; it had previously been held that a poorhouse could not be licensed as an asylum under the Lunacy Acts, though there were many " fatuous and insane " paupers actually in poorhouses.

Somewhat similar considerations of cost and expediency had weighed with the directors of the Town's Hospital in Glasgow, when, a generation previously, in 1818, they had considered this question of the best means of disposal of " fatuous and lunatic " paupers, and compromised by recommending that where there was a reasonable prospect of cure, a fair trial should be made in the lunatic asylum, but that when it became obvious that cure was hopeless, insane persons should immediately be brought back from the asylum to the poorhouse. The Board of Supervision similarly came to adopt the view that every case in which advantage from curative treatment could reasonably be expected or hoped for ought in the first instance to be sent to an asylum. Sheriff Davidson of Aberdeen helped them to this view by resolving in 1850 that he would not grant a licence for placing in a poorhouse any pauper lunatic or " fatuous " person unless the Board of Supervision certified that this did not conflict with the interests of the patient ; and in subsequent years other sheriffs came to take the same line. In 1851 the Board of Supervision issued a circular reminding parochial boards and inspectors of poor that it was their duty to take care to send to a poorhouse no poor person who was insane or " fatuous " without having previously obtained the sanction of the Board and the licence of the Sheriff.

As from 1 January 1858 jurisdiction in regard to insane or " fatuous " poor was transferred to the General Board of Commissioners in Lunacy for Scotland, and the Board of Supervision felt aggrieved at the change. They pointed out that the total number of insane and " fatuous " paupers returned as chargeable to parishes in Scotland on 1 January 1858 was 4,475, of whom 2,864 were in asylums or poorhouses, and 1,611 residing with relations or other persons. The total number had increased by about one hundred per cent. since 1845, and " During the whole of that time," complained the Board, " we have been left, without any legislative assistance, to contend with an acknowledged deficiency of accommodation, accompanied by a progressive increase in the number of insane or fatuous poor, yet we succeeded, with the aid of the Parochial Boards, in preventing any increase in the number residing in private dwellings, which was somewhat less on 1 January 1858 than it had been in 1846."

One of the interesting features of the change in responsibility for the insane was a difference of opinion between the Board of Supervision and the Commissioners in Lunacy as to the definition of " lunatic " and " fatuity." The Lunacy Commissioners contemplated a more comprehensive definition than the Board of Supervision was prepared to adopt, and having taken the opinion of counsel on the subject, the Board of Supervision intimated that they would leave it to the Commissioners in Lunacy to " ascertain which of the paupers are lunatic in the meaning of the Statute," adding that they would consider all who were so ascertained to be lunatics, and as coming under the jurisdiction of the Lunacy Commissioners. In a letter dated 3 September 1858, towards the end of some coldly polite official correspondence on the subject, the secretary of the Board of Supervision felt constrained to write in these terms to the secretary of the Lunacy Board :

In conclusion I am to state that it appears to the Board very possible that, emanating from so high an Authority on such subjects, the statement of the Board of Lunacy that they consider imperfect development of the faculties and fatuity as synonymous terms might, if unexplained, lead to serious misapprehensions ; and they are glad to have elicited such an explanation of that statement as seems to restrict it to cases in which the development of the faculties is so imperfect as to amount to fatuity.

10

The Act of 1845 declared it to be expedient that poorhouses should be erected in populous parishes for administering more effectively to the wants of aged and other friendless paupers, and of such as were infirm or unable to take charge of their own affairs.

It authorized the Parochial Board of any parish or combination of parishes that contained more than 5,000 inhabitants to erect a poorhouse, as soon as the recommendation to that effect and the plans of the proposed building had been approved by the Board of Supervision. Following the passing of the Act the town's hospitals or poorhouses in Glasgow and Edinburgh were extended ; and when local difficulties vetoed a proposal to provide a combined poorhouse in Aberdeen, the St. Nicholas Parochial Board there proposed to erect a poorhouse of its own—on a site within 400 feet of a powder magazine. In many less populous areas the desirability of poorhouse provision and the need for it were zealously canvassed. The factor of the Earl of Stair wrote to Mr. Thomas Kennedy of Dunure asking his opinion of the poorhouse system as applicable to that part of Scotland, in view of his experience of the system in Ireland, pointing out that the labouring population in the Rhinns of Galloway was almost entirely Irish—"with all the tastes and habits of their poor countrymen—thoughtless of the future—increasing rapidly—and from improvidence and disregard of personal comfort in houses and living, sinking into premature old-age, bad health and poverty." It appeared that the system of outdoor relief had not worked well with such a population, and that most labourers above fifty-five or sixty years of age preferred the poor allowance in idleness (miserable as it was) to double or treble the sum which they might make by persevering in industry. The factor favoured the poorhouse in conjunction with outdoor relief—not to huddle all and sundry into it, as he explained, but leaving discretion to the town's Board. He expected these advantages from the poorhouse system : (1) To secure a comfortable living to the improvident, the weak in mind, the friendless and impotent poor ; (2) To make the poorhouse a stimulus to industry and an efficient school for educating and training the young ; (3) To check begging; and (4) In time, a reduction of the poor rates. He proposed for the Rhinns of Galloway, which contained a population of about 20,000, one poorhouse to accommodate 300 to 500 paupers. In reply, Mr. Kennedy said that he had arrived at the opinion that in parts of Scotland it was expedient and necessary to introduce the workhouse test, and that Wigtownshire was one of them. " Everything, however, must depend on the *correct* and *strict* system of the workhouse. Unless well-managed it will become a fearful nuisance." The poorhouse in the Rhinns of

Galloway was opened in 1853, with accommodation for 362 inmates, some years after the Combination poorhouse in the neighbouring county of Kirkcudbright, which apparently succeeded in securing the much-desired reduction in the cost of poor relief, for in 1852 the Earl of Selkirk wrote that " before the opening of the house, every parish meeting was in a state of siege by the clamorous paupers ; now, not a complaint is heard. The saving of money on the first half year is within a trifle of £450, representing a capital nearly double of what has been expended upon the house."

In Glasgow a case occurred in which a poor person entitled to parochial relief was offered admission into the Town's Hospital or poorhouse but was refused outdoor relief. He brought an action against the Parochial Board for having illegally refused him relief, but the Sheriff was of opinion that the parish had not illegally refused relief, and dismissed the case with expenses. Commenting on this case, the Board of Supervision said that to require a pauper to reside in the poorhouse would frequently inflict a great hardship on the pauper without any benefit to the community. When a poor person was admitted to be destitute, and wholly disabled from contributing to his own support, no test was required ; and if he resided in the house of a relative or friend there might be great cruelty in compelling the pauper to exchange such a home for the poorhouse. In cases of partial disability, where the pauper was willing to contribute all he could towards his own support, there did not appear to be any reason why outdoor relief should be denied ; it was probable that the cost of maintaining him in the poorhouses would considerably exceed the amount of outdoor relief that would be adequate to support him with the aid of his own earnings. On the other hand, many cases occurred in almost every parish in which it was most desirable that the parochial authorities should have it in their power not only to provide in a poorhouse for the various classes of helpless person, but also to test, by an offer of admission to the poorhouse, the destitution of parties whose disability, or the extent of whose disability was doubtful and believed to be pretended or exaggerated. In towns more especially, the Board of Supervision thought, it was desirable that there should be poorhouses for the reception both of the helpless and of those whose destitution or disability was doubtful, and in its First Annual Report the Board regretted that in several of the more considerable towns in Scotland, for example Dundee and Perth, no poorhouses had yet been erected. Prior to the passing of the Act of 1845 there had been thirteen poorhouses in Scotland, but under official stimulus the number soon increased and by 1849 there were no fewer than nineteen in operation (serving the parishes of Abbey [Paisley], Aberdeen, Ayr, Glasgow Barony, Edinburgh Canongate, Dalkeith, Dunfermline, Edinburgh, Glasgow, Govan, Greenock, Inverness, Lanark, Leith, Old Machar [Aberdeen], Maybole, New Monkland, Paisley, and Edinburgh St. Cuthbert's). The nineteen poorhouses could accommodate 4,360 paupers, and the erection of others was in progress in Easter Ross, Falkirk, Kirkcaldy, and Kirkcudbright. By 1863 forty-eight poorhouses were in operation in Scotland, with sixteen more in process of erection. With its Second Annual Report the Board of Supervision issued a set of model plans for poorhouse construction, and in 1853 considered it advisable to require that before inmates were placed in a new poorhouse, or in any addition to an existing poorhouse, the sanction of the Board should be obtained ; and that every application for such sanction should be " accompanied by certificates, in a prescribed form, from a competent medical man and a respectable architect " as to the fitness of the house in every respect for the reception of inmates.

II

It is not surprising that the development of poorhouses gave rise to difficulties and complaints. One large group of difficulties concerned the dietaries in the different poorhouses of Scotland, but many were concerned with general standards of administration. In 1846 a petition was presented to the Board of Supervision on behalf of James Nicholson, a pauper in the Canongate Poorhouse, Edinburgh, representing that house to be unhealthy because of its situation. While this representation was being considered, another complaint reached the Board that Nicholson, a man of seventy-eight years of age, who was suffering from sickness, was neglected by the attendants. Dr. Charles Bell was requested by the Board to visit Nicholson as soon as possible, and from his report it appeared that the complaints of the pauper were not unfounded : " He was in a most miserable state of discomfort and very filthy. All of the beds were very dirty and ill-adapted for such an institution." Dr. Bell concluded that the have Four of them by Turns every Day in the Kitchen.

III. H E fhall be obliged to have the Difhes wafhed Thrice a Day, and the Kitchen wafhed three Times every Week.

Rules *relating* to the Poor.

I. **T**HAT all Perfons on their Admiffion be examined by the *Surgeon* and *Nurfe* whether they have any infectious Diftemper, and fhall be wafhed affoon as they are taken in, if it may be without Prejudice to their Health; fuch as are found to be nafty, or to have any infectious Diftemper, fhall be put into particular Rooms, and not be removed until they are perfectly clean.

II. T H A T new cloathing be given to all the Poor on their Admiffion, and the old Cloaths clean'd and mended for the Ufe of the Owners. The Cloaths of the Children fhall be all of one Colour, *viz.* Blew mounted with Red.

III. A L L who go out of the *Houfe* without Leave, or who bring in ftrong Liquors into the *Houfe*, or who are found Drunk, or who fhall fwear, curfe, or difturb the *Houfe* with Clamour, or who fhall not go Twice every Lord's Day to Church, (when able) or who fhall afk Money from thofe that come to fee the *Houfe*, fhall for the firft Fault lofe their next Meal, for the fecond be denied Victuals

for

continued overleaf

Extract from the Rules of the Town's Hospital of Glasgow
photographed from the original Hospital report

for a whole Day, and locked up in a Room; for the third Fault punifh'd as the *Magiftrates* fhall think fit.

IV. Whoever are found ftealing any Goods belonging to the *Houfe*, or to any other Perfon, care fhall be taken, that they fhall be punifhed as the Law directs.

V. That all who fhall be employed in any Labour, fhall conftantly repair to fuch Rooms in the *Houfe* as are appointed for that Purpofe, where they fhall work orderly at fuch Bufinefs, and fo many Hours as the *Overfeers* fhall appoint to each of them, according to their Age and Ability: whofoever fhall neglect or refufe to do this, fhall be punifhed as the *Magiftrates* think fit.

VI. That all Perfons in Health, both *Young* and *Old* fhall be out of their Bed at the ringing of the Morning-Bell, which fhall be rung in the Months of *January* and *February* at Seven a Clock, in *March* at Six, from the Firft of *April* to the End of *Auguft* at Five, in *September* at Six, in *October* at Seven, in *November* and *December* at Eight; and that all go to Bed, from the Firft of *March* to the End of *September* at Ten a Clock at Night; and from the Firft of *October* to the End of *February* at Nine. And the Doors fhall be locked at Ten a Clock every Night.

Each Perfon fhall change his Linens Once every Week.

In accommodating the *Poor*, Regard is to be had to the different Stations of Life they have formerly been in, which is to be at the Difcretion of the Weekly Committee.   *The* case of Nicholson was one of great hardship, and he added that all that he saw of the Canongate Poorhouse gave him a very bad impression of the establishment which, not only in its internal arrangements but from its locality, seemed a very unfit receptacle for the debilitated and the aged. Drs. Allison and Christison who were investigating Nicholson's earlier complaint reported that while the situation of the poorhouse was not good, they could not say it was necessarily more injurious to health than that of most of the inhabited houses in the parish ; that it would be better were the children of the house boarded in the country, provided they were adequately cared for ; that the building appeared to be in some respects in a dilapidated state, and to require careful inspection and repair, and that in particular " the windows were in a crazy condition." On consideration of these reports the Board of Supervision called upon the parochial authorities to remove the grounds of complaint in the case of Nicholson, but on the wider question of the suitability of the poorhouse took the line that after a full inquiry " the material allegations made as to the unhealthiness of the inmates of the Canongate Poorhouse for the causes alleged or otherwise were ascertained not to be correct."

12

In 1850 the Board of Supervision thought fit to frame model rules and regulations for the management of poorhouses, " which we should be prepared to approve." In introducing these rules the Board said they had reason to hope that poorhouses would be conducted so as to afford an adequate test of alleged destitution or disability in cases where the claim was doubtful, as well as the means of restraining vice and checking the misapplication of allowances, while at the same time affording a secure and suitable refuge to the infirm and friendless poor. " The poorhouses which were in operation previous to 1845 had been regarded almost exclusively as almshouses, which afforded a comfortable retreat for the more respectable of the aged and infirm poor, and were conducted in a manner corresponding with the purposes then contemplated. It was a matter of favour to be admitted into the house, and a severe punishment to be expelled from it."

The Board expected these rules and regulations to be rigorously enforced. So long as relief to the poor was regarded as charitable rather than a legal obligation and poorhouses were regarded merely as almshouses, their inmates were generally of but one class, persons whose destitution and disability was beyond a doubt, and whose character was irreproachable. The whole establishment was managed in a corresponding spirit. The inmates had regular liberty days once a week, when they went to visit their friends or to amuse themselves ; and it was not uncommon to find some of them begging on the streets. Once a week their friends were freely admitted to visit the inmates in the poorhouse, " which, on such occasions, exhibited a promiscuous throng of paupers and their visitors mingled together." The friends of the paupers were permitted to bring to them in the house tobacco and such other articles of luxury (except ardent spirits) as they were able to procure. The inmates were induced to engage in some kind of industrious occupation by a weekly payment of part of the proceeds of their work, to be expended as they might think proper on their liberty days ; and one of the first petitions presented to the newly created Board of Supervision was from the male inmates of a poorhouse, complaining that the weekly sum allowed them as pocket-money was unreasonably small. It had previously been deemed unnecessary to enforce strictly any system of rules or discipline, when flagrant breaches of order were punished by expulsion from the house. But when, with the passing of the Poor Law (Amendment) Act, poorhouses came to deal with a new population, new problems arose. To protect Parochial Boards from spurious claims it came to be recognized that " a well-regulated poorhouse is the best of all tests " ; but it could " only be a test if conducted under rules and regulations as to discipline and restraint so strict as to render it more irksome than labour, without such discipline and restraint, to those who are not truly fit objects of parochial relief."

This was the new situation that the Board of Supervision set out to meet in its code of rules and regulations. The rules laid it down that each parochial board that administered a poorhouse must appoint a house committee, and that the management of the poorhouse was to be under the immediate control of a house governor and a matron, subject to the committee. At least once every year and as often as was necessary for cleanliness, the house committee was to " cause all the rooms, ward offices, and privies belonging to the poorhouse to be limewashed and the cesspools to be emptied."

The poorhouse was to be visited by the house committee once at least in every week and answers were to be recorded to these questions : Is the house clean and well-ventilated ? Do inmates appear to be clean and decent and orderly ? Are the infirm properly attended to ? Are the children making due progress at school ? Are the Medical Officer and the Chaplain regular in their attendance ? Do patients in the sick ward appear to be in as satisfactory a state as their ailments admit of ? Is there any infectious disease in the wards, or are any of the children not vaccinated ? Is the established dietary fully observed, and hours of meals adhered to ? Is separation of the sexes and the various classes of inmates strictly enforced ? Are there any complaints against individuals or against the quality of provisions or accommodation ?

In addition to the governor and matron a porter was to be appointed. His duties were to examine all parcels and goods before they were received into the poorhouse, and to prevent the unlawful admission of any spirituous or fermented liquors or other prohibited articles ; to take care that no inmate entering the poorhouse should take into it any spirits or other prohibited articles, " and for this purpose to search their persons, if he shall think fit " ; and to see that no poor person leaving the house " unduly removes any article from the premises, and to search their persons, if he shall think fit."

The inmates were classified into five groups : males over fifteen years of age, males between the ages of two and fifteen, females over fifteen, females between two and fifteen, and children under two. The rules for the discipline of inmates laid it down that all inmates, except the disabled, those of unsound mind, and children, were to rise, be set to work, leave off work, and go to bed, with such intervals for meals as was notified by the ringing of a bell. The Parochial Board was to be entitled to the whole proceeds of the labour of every inmate. For three or four of the working hours of every day, boy and girl inmates were to be instructed in reading, writing, arithmetic, and the principles of the Christian religion, " and such other instruction shall be imparted to them as shall fit them for service or other employment and train them to habits of usefulness, industry, and virtue." No inmate of the poorhouse was to be allowed to possess or to read in the poorhouse any book or printed paper of an improper tendency, or to play at cards or at any game of chance. "Dice, cards, or other articles relating to games of chance are to be removed." No inmate was to be allowed to smoke within the poorhouse or any building belonging thereto.

Punishment was prescribed for the misconduct of inmates. Among those deemed to be "disorderly" were inmates who infringed the rules and regulations, who made any noise when silence was ordered to be kept, who by word or deed reviled or insulted any person, or who pretended sickness. By way of punishment a disorderly inmate could be required for a time not exceeding two days to perform one or two hours of extra work, or could be deprived for a like time of all milk or butter-milk that he would otherwise receive with his meals, or could be deprived for a period not exceeding three days of such other articles of diet as the house committee might direct after consultation with the medical officer. More drastic punishment was meted out to inmates deemed to be "refractory." This label might be attached to any inmate who, within seven days, repeated any one or committed more than one of the offences regarded as "disorderly." The term was also applied to any inmate who by word or deed reviled or insulted any officer of the poorhouse or any member or officer of the Parochial Board ; to any who attempted to introduce to the poorhouse any prohibited article ; to any who should be drunk, and to any who climbed over any wall or fence or attempted to quit the poorhouse in any irregular way. A "refractory" inmate could be punished by solitary confinement for a period not exceeding twenty-four hours, with or without increase in hours of work or alteration of diet, as in the case of the "disorderly." "Disorderly" and "refractory" inmates might be punished by having to wear for a period not exceeding twenty-four hours a dress distinctive from that of other inmates. It was expressly provided that no child under twelve should be confined in a dark room or during the night, and that the diet of sick, infirm, pregnant and suckling women should not be modified without the consent of the medical officer.

13

One of the inspectors of the Board of Supervision reported in 1851 on the Easter Ross Poorhouse, which had been opened in October of the previous year to serve nine rural parishes. It was built at a cost of £2,820, and could accommodate 174 inmates. In the first ten months of its existence 48 paupers were admitted. The administration of the houses was described as generally good, but as having some objectionable points in management : it had no porter, with the result that the inmates could wander from the house ; the inmates were given too much liberty to leave the poorhouse ; there was no book for recording the observations of the visiting committee ; and the drains for carrying off the foul water caused, from their open state, " a stench along the highway amounting to a public nuisance." There had been in certain quarters a disposition to regard this poorhouse as something of a white elephant. But the inspector was satisfied that the poorhouse was serving its purpose ; there had been a diminution of allowances paid for the relief of the poor, and the paupers who " formerly pressed upon the poor funds with eagerness now find a limit to their demands."

14

A few years later, in 1862, there was more evidence of official zeal to regulate the freedom of poorhouse inmates. A minute of the Board of Supervision dated 14 August of that year dealt with permission to inmates of poorhouses " to leave the house for the purpose of attending Divine Worship or of any other purpose." This minute decreed that religious instruction must be provided in poorhouses and said that the Board of Supervision could not approve of a rule that gave the inmates liberty to leave the poorhouse every Sunday for the real or alleged purpose of attending divine worship. " Such a rule would . . . in many cases, if not in all, be subversive of discipline and proper management." The Board thought it might be competent for a house governor, after due consideration, to authorize an inmate to attend divine worship on any particular Sabbath, either in the forenoon or in the afternoon, at any church or chapel of the religious denomination of such inmate that might be in the vicinity of the poorhouse, but the Board " could not approve of the rule which would secure to inmates of a poorhouse leave of absence from the poorhouse on certain specified days recurring periodically, or what are called ' liberty days.' "

About this time the Board of Supervision was called upon to arbitrate in a case where difference of opinion had arisen in a house committee as to admission to the poorhouse of a pauper suffering from infectious disease. The problem was apparently an awkward one, and the administrative reaction true to type ; it must be left to the discretion of the house committee to deter-mine with reference to the circumstances of each case and the accommodation available at the time whether or not such a person should be received into the house. Another case of similar type called for an official ruling in 1863. Following a case of smallpox in a poorhouse, and difficulty in disposing of it, the Board expressed the view that such a patient ought to be removed to some public hospital if that could be done without injury, " but if not, then the best practicable arrangement should be made in the house for the isolation of the patient, even if that involved the discharge of some of the other inmates."

In 1860 the Board of Supervision published for the first time information about the weekly cost per head of maintaining poor-house inmates. The average cost throughout the country was in that year an inclusive figure of 4s. 5½d. per person per week. Of this sum, " food, fuel, clothing, light and all other necessaries " accounted for 2s. 8¼d. (the lowest individual return being 2s. 1d.) ; " salaries of officials, feu duties, insurance, repairs, etc.," 10d. ; " estimated rent of poorhouse," 8d. ; " medicine and medical attendance," 2d. The cost varied a little from year to year, the average weekly figure in 1861 being 4s. 9d., in 1862 4s. 2¾d., and in 1863 4s. 4½d.

15

There was much violent criticism of the working of the new Poor Law. At a public meeting in Edinburgh some of its faults were recited : it took the earnings of the industrious to support the idle and dissolute, made no distinction between poverty resulting from misfortune and that from vice, tended to diminish industry and frugality, destroyed the ties of relationship, lessened the sympathy of the wealthy and the mutual aid of the poor, tended to destroy Scottish education, and encouraged the working classes to leave rural districts and settle in the towns, thus dis-turbing the labour balance. " The boasted peasantry of Scotland has decreased so that the soil is now to no inconsiderable extent cultivated by the poorest, the most destitute, and too often, I fear, the most degraded class of Irish immigrants." It was pointed out that on the average of the three years 1835–37 the total poor (permanent, occasional, lunatic) numbered 79,429, out of a population of 2,315,926, i.e. 3.42 per cent. of the population, the average sum required for the support of the poor being £155,121. The average allowance to each pauper was only £1, 18s. 6d. per annum in 1835–37 ; it rose to £4, 10s. 9d. in 1847, £4, 17s. 11d. in 1856, and £6, 1s. 5d. in 1866, in which year the total sum spent on the relief of the poor was £783,127. The conclusion, based on this increased cost of poor relief, was simple enough. " In fact, a compulsory system for the relief of the poor, administered chiefly by a salaried agency, is regarded now by all competent and un-biassed authorities as having utterly failed, either as a means of abolishing its misery or of checking its growth."

There was another side to the picture. Dr. Littlejohn, the newly appointed Medical Officer of Health of Edinburgh, re-ported that in 1861 there were 5,908 paupers in the parliamentary area of the city, which had a population of 168,121. There were workhouses in three districts, St. Cuthbert's Workhouse, the Canongate Workhouse, and the City Workhouse. Pauperism gravitated to the poorest districts ; where there was greatest overcrowding and most deficient house accommodation there was also most super-added pauperism and its attendant evils, mental depression, imperfect nourishment, scanty clothing, and, in too many instances, intemperance. So long as there was a population with a high proportion of pauperism scattered through it, it was useless to seek to enforce sanitary regulations. " The pittances that are given to paupers, through the proverbial economy of Boards, representing the ratepayers of our City, are only intended to allow of life being maintained at a legal flicker and by no means at a steady flame." The parties truly responsible were the Parochial Boards who were charged with the support of the poor and who should take care, if they could not afford space to accommodate them within their own premises, that the apart-ments they occupied must be kept decent, clean, and wholesome. Dr. Littlejohn pleaded that the three local boards, laying aside all rivalry and jealousy, should combine to erect one good poor-house in a healthy situation, away from the centre of the city, for as it was, many persons claiming parochial relief would submit to the greatest privations rather than allow themselves to be immured within those barrack-like buildings, where they found themselves in the midst of town life, yet debarred from enjoying it. " The sounds they hear constantly remind them of their bondage, and the confined dismal spaces allowed to the sexes as airing grounds help to deepen the feeling."

The Scotsman criticized the Poor Law system in a vigorous leader of 7 May 1863. Poorhouses, it said, had two objects : to enable local authorities more effectually to administer to the wants of the aged and infirm, and to furnish a test of poverty. But the system was unsatisfactory, for in practice it was as difficult for a poorhouse to serve these two purposes as for a man to serve two masters ; and as was evident from the reports of the Board of Supervision, the guiding impulse had been to test poverty. The average number of paupers in poorhouses in Scotland during the year ended 30 June 1862 was 7,843, and the deaths among them numbered 1,812, *i.e.* 23 per cent. of the average number in residence. About nine of every hundred paupers who entered a poorhouse, whether for a long stay or a short, died within the year. The average weekly cost of maintenance was 2s. 11¼d. (food, fuel, clothing, light and all other necessaries). Could this be reckoned sufficient for the proper sustenance of paupers of exhausted constitutions ? The inmates were deprived of their liberty, exercised in narrow yards, enclosed by high walls, subject to the will of others ; the furniture was " simple," the hours " stated," the sexes completely separated. To any man who looked below the mere surface nothing could be more depressing than a general inspection of Scottish poorhouses. The diet was calculated to sustain life and no more, if indeed it really did so. " Moreover, for proper nutrition mere quantity is not enough. Nature craves for change, but in our poorhouses we greatly fear that both quantity and variety fail. . . . In prisons the diet is much fuller than in these establishments. . . . We express a grave doubt whether aged, sick and brokendown paupers can be sufficiently fed on 3½d. a day." The high mortality that prevailed in Scottish poorhouses must be regarded either as an indication of extensively prevailing disease, or of inappropriate treatment, and *The Scotsman* was led to conclude that in Scotland poorhouses had failed, both as tests of poverty and as the means of more effectually administering to the wants of the aged and infirm poor. It was suggested that two kinds of institution were required, the great majority comfortable, homelike places where the aged and infirm could enjoy a modicum of decency and comfort, with, say, half a dozen more spartan test-houses fulfilling their function throughout the country.

There was at this time much uneasiness and concern about poor relief and a feeling that all was not well, but in the same year 1863, George Falconer, Esq., General Superintendent of the Poor in Scotland, a good civil servant of his day, made this report to the Board of Supervision, who quoted it with obvious approval : " I have to report that the Poor Law in Scotland is in effective operation for the support and care of the destitute. The Parochial Boards look to their duties and responsibilities with increasing attention. As a body, the Inspectors of Poor are careful and intelligent, administering the details of the Poor Law with discretion."

But even Mr. Falconer had to admit that from want of employment there was much privation in industry ; an example in point being the want, bordering on pauperism, resulting from the stoppage of work in the cotton mills. He added that the prospect for the factory operative was " not cheering."

CHAPTER IX

PRISONS AND PRISONERS

I

IN olden times prisons everywhere were scandals to humanity and the condition of those in Scotland was bad enough, though, as Graham pointed out in his *Social Life of Scotland in the Eighteenth Century*, Scottish prison conditions were not then so bad as some. Prisoners were generally few and terms of imprisonment short, with the result that gaols, though miserable hovels, were seldom crowded. Debtors were liable to be put in the stocks, fed on bread and water for a month and then scourged ; in the interests of impatient creditors, who paid three pence per day for their maintenance in gaol, they were rigidly confined, and were in that respect worse off than common felons. In villages prisoners were kept in a " thieves' hole," usually a little hut with damp earthen floor and with hardly a glimmer of light. The prison-house of a small country town was commonly a vile thatched room, miserable, dark, filthy, and fireless, and sometimes loaded with chains.

The gaol at Dingwall must have been typical of its kind. It was erected about 1732 and consisted of three apartments for prisoners, one closet in which maniacs were occasionally confined, and two garrets which were quite unfit for any human use and were used for storing lumber. The apartments had fireplaces but no other means of ventilation, except that windows were without sashes and prisoners occasionally forced a deal out of the ceiling in order to produce a circulation of air. Two apartments on the ground floor had neither joists nor flooring, and were each eighteen feet by sixteen feet by six feet six inches. Originally they did not constitute part of the gaol, one being until 1782 the parish schoolhouse and the other a shop. These rooms were generally used for the confinement of criminals and revenue delinquents. The third apartment on the first floor was eighteen feet by seventeen feet by nine feet ; in it debtors were generally confined. There was no separate accommodation in the prison for females, and as there were sometimes as many as twenty prisoners at one time, the magistrates were more than once compelled to accommodate the females in the council chamber, which was situated under the same roof as the gaol. Prisoners frequently escaped. Of the fifty-nine prisoners who underwent detention during the year ending 25 August 1828, thirty-three were revenue delinquents, ten civil debtors, and sixteen criminals.

There was no airing ground attached to the gaol, and no accommodation for sick or for prisoners under sentence of death. There were two keepers or gaolers, each paid ten pounds per annum. They neither resided within the gaol nor continued there during the night; the duties were performed by the gaolers on alternate weeks, so that only one was in regular and constant attendance.

The magistrates of Dingwall were dissatisfied with the gaol, which they regarded as altogether insufficient for its proper purposes, alike as regards size, accommodation, security, and repair. "For the last two years each of the apartments appropriated to the use of civil and revenue debtors have been so crammed with human beings as more to resemble the celebrated Black Hole of Calcutta than the Prison House of a civilized country." They thought that the gaol should be taken down and wholly rebuilt on such an enlarged scale as would be adequate for the wants of that extensive portion of the county of Ross for which Dingwall formed a centre, and they were anxious that the cost of the new building should be borne by the local authorities concerned on a population basis. Certainly the qualms of the magistrates about the state of the gaol were not unjustified, for it appears from the Burgh Records of 1828 that at a recent Circuit Court held at Inverness the Advocate-Depute had declared that the state of the gaol of the burgh of Dingwall was worse even than a dog kennel in point of accommodation and comfort. The Lord Justice-Clerk thereupon directed that no prisoner should henceforth be confined in it until the gaol should be made more comfortable and secure; but this injunction was ignored. However, in October of the same year the town council received a letter from the Clerk of the Peace of the county of Ross intimating that a committee of the county had been appointed to confer with the town council about the erection of a new gaol.

When describing the Tolbooth of Edinburgh, Hugo Arnot showed its most deplorable condition—without ventilation, without drainage, with unmentionable filth in every corner, with

223

rooms where children were confined in air so pestilential that no visitor could venture in. Such was the state of matters when John Howard visited this and other Scottish prisons to obtain material for his Report on the State of Prisons, published in 1784. He found poor convicts in Edinburgh in " a horrid cage," chained to an iron bar. Aberdeen prison was " almost a loathsome dungeon," containing 15 debtors, 8 delinquents, and a lunatic. In Glasgow there were 18 debtors and only 5 felons.

On 14 February 1814 a new gaol was opened in Glasgow, and, " it being then a time of war," only 35 prisoners of every description were removed from the old to the new gaol. At the end of 1819, when peace had come, there were 190 prisoners in the gaol, 53 debtors, and 137 delinquents. During the year 1819, 1,371 persons were committed to the Glasgow prison and the daily average number of prisoners was 220.

2

There were at that time 87 places of confinement in Scotland —82 common gaols and 5 bridewells or penitentiaries, situated at Edinburgh, Glasgow, Greenock, Roxburgh, and Aberdeen. Of the 1,152 criminals, 217 were under seventeen years of age. In 27 gaols the aliment to criminals was 6d. per day ; in 5, 8d. per day ; in 4, 9d. per day ; in 1 (Inveraray), 10d. per day, and in 1 (Banff), only 3d. per day. In very few gaols was there any allowance for clothes.

The Parliamentary Account of the State of Jails and Bridewells in Scotland for the year 1818 contains this " comparative view " of the 5 bridewells :

Bridewell	Committed in 1818	Greatest No. Prisoners in at one Time	Males	Females	Total Value of Labour, etc.
					£
Aberdeen .	115	56	28	28	182
Edinburgh .	1,490	253	67	186	342
Glasgow . .	1,445	237	86	151	1,708
Greenock .	212	25	19	6	5
Roxburgh .	167	8	3	5	" Trifling "
Total	3,427	579	203	376	

The accounts of the Glasgow bridewell for the year 1818 show total disbursement to have been £1,824—made up of : " victualling for prisoners," who averaged 210 per day, £968 ; " clothing and washing," £79 ; " coal and candle, and oil and tallow for machinery," £134 ; " payment to prisoners for work," £120 ; " superintendent's salary," £200 ; and " servants' wages," £155. The total receipts amounted to £1,728—cash received for weaving, £125 ; for sewing, £104 ; for twisting and twining yarn, £1,179 ; for warping and winding, £60 ; for picking cotton, etc., £110. In addition, certain sums were received in respect of the board of prisoners sentenced to solitary confinement, who performed no work ; viz., from the Government for military prisoners, £19 ; for county prisoners, £58 ; for city prisoners, £31 ; and from the Town's Hospital in respect of beggars, £20. In addition, £25 was received as rent for an unoccupied apartment, leaving a balance of £96 as the net cost of the establishment : " this balance when applied to 210 prisoners amounts to 9s. 2d. per annum for each individual." In 1830 an average of 293 prisoners was maintained in the bridewell of Glasgow at a total expense for the year of £946, equal to a cost of little more than 2d. per prisoner per day. It was pointed out that this cost compared favourably with that in Millbank penitentiary, where the maintenance of 566 prisoners cost £17,983.

In 1839 the population of Glasgow within the city police boundary was 175,000, and the number of offenders in proportion to the population was 1 in 22, a figure which compared with 1 in 24 in London Metropolitan Police District, 1 in 16 in Liverpool, and 1 in 7 in Dublin, though it was remarked that the geography of Glasgow lent itself to crime. The chief offences were " drunk and disorderly," and " drunk on the streets." The Chief of Police reported in 1840 that crime was on the decrease in the city, and that cases were of a much less serious nature than formerly.

Captain Miller, the Chief of Police, recognized very clearly the relationship between the health of the community and the incidence of crime : " it is of great moment, as affecting the state of crime, that the health of the lower classes of the community be strictly attended to." After describing the wretchedness of the centre of the city—" the houses are unfit even for styes " and " every apartment is filled with a promiscuous crowd of men, women, and children, all in the most revolting state of filth and squalor "—he went on to say : " Much might be done to relieve the misery and to repress the crime of this destitute population, by compelling attention to personal cleanliness, so as to remove and prevent disease, by placing the lodging-houses for the destitute under proper regulations ; by preventing the assemblage of a large number of persons in one apartment ; by opening up and widening the thoroughfares, and forming new streets wherever practicable ; by causing the houses to be properly ventilated, and all external nuisances removed ; and by an improved plan of sewerage for carrying away all impurities."

3

In the eighth report of the Inspector of Prisons in Scotland it was shown that in 1842 more than 200 persons in Glasgow were driven to crime by inability to find employment, and that in addition there were 40 persons, mostly able-bodied, " voluntarily undergoing imprisonment in Glasgow in order to get food and shelter." Since the law did not recognize such indulgence, these voluntary prisoners were discharged, only to qualify for re-admission by the committal of a "crime." The lowest rate of diet in the Glasgow prison was equivalent to 24 oz. of wheaten bread in the day (as compared with from 16 to 20 oz. in the poorhouse), the second rate was 30 oz., and the third rate 36 oz. per day ; and the Inspector of Prisons recommended that at one meal each day the prisoners should have as much plain food, as porridge or potatoes, as they wished. Of the 1,558 prisoners dealt with in the prison during the period from 1 July 1842 to 30 June 1844, 1,039 had been convicted more than once, and 26 more than twenty times. In 1844 there were 596 prisoners for 470 cells. Commenting on these facts, Dr. Robert Perry wrote that " either the prison has been made too comfortable, or there is a large class of persons in a state of serious distress."

In a report on the condition of the poorer classes of Edinburgh in the sixties of the nineteenth century it was stated that the number of prisoners in Edinburgh Prison was 344, 134 males and 210 females. Of these prisoners, 124 belonged to Edinburgh and 79 to other towns ; 141 were from the country. The chief crimes for which the prisoners had been committed were theft, 89 ; loitering, 46 ; interruption, 34 ; breach of peace, 31 ; disorderly in drink, 25 ; and selling drink without a licence, 31.

It was estimated that during the years from 1852 to 1866, from 40 to 50 per cent. of all the persons apprehended for crimes and offences in the city were drunk when they committed them, and that the evil of the " shebeens," unlicensed drinking-houses which were generally also brothels, continued. When this investigation was made, 107 of the prisoners were found to have a " liberal education," 92 to be able to read and write, 90 to be able to read but not to write, and the remaining 46 to be able to do neither. Of the 134 male prisoners, 108 had been in employment immediately before committal, earning average weekly wages of 15s. 2d., while 26 had been idle ; and of the 210 female prisoners, 121 had been in employment, earning average weekly wages of 5s. 7d., and 89 had been unemployed.

Chapter X

MEDICAL CARE

I

In Scotland, as in other countries, the healing art was for many centuries associated with the mysteries of magic. The early teachers of Christianity added greatly to the mass of medical superstition. They maintained the efficiency, for instance, of a visit to the cross of King Edwin of Northumberland for the cure of agues ; the marvellous recoveries to be expected from visiting the grave of St. Ninian at Whithorn, or the cross of St. Mary's in the cathedral churchyard at Glasgow ; the curative power of holy robes, bells, bones, and other relics, and the sovereign virtues of the waters of wells (often dedicated to saints) throughout the country. Taylor, the Water Poet (1618), " took a passage boat (from Leith) to see the new wondrous well (at Kinghorn), to which many a one that is not well comes farre and neere in hope to be made well : indeed, I did heare that it had done much good, and that it hath a rare operation to expel or kill divers maladies ; as to provoke appetite, to helpe much for the avoiding of the gravell in the bladder, to cure sore eyes, and old ulcers, with many other virtues which it hath." As late as the nineteenth century, at Biggar in Lanarkshire and at Torphichen in West Lothian, living cows were sacrificed for curative purposes, or under the hope of arresting the progress of the murrain in other members of the flock ; and the sacrifice of other living animals for the cure of disease, especially epileptic fits and insanity, persisted far into the century. Amber beads were used for the cure of blindness, " Barbreck's bone "—a slice or tablet of ivory—had great reputation for the cure of insanity, while the Stone of the Standard found at Bannockburn was said to have virtues not purely martial : " it cures all manner of diseases in cattle and horses, and formerly in human beings also, if they drink the water in which this charmed stone has been dipped by the hands of Struan."

Many ancient families of note affected the possession of a curing stone. One of the most famous of these was the Lee Penny,

The Town's House, Clyde Street, Glasgow

reproduced from " Notes on some old Glasgow Institutions with Medical Associations," *Glasgow Medical Journal* 1910

Suggested design for poorhouse to serve a town parish
from Board of Supervision's Second Annual Report, 1847

St Nicholas Hospital Buildings, Glasgow, in 1740

described by Sir Walter Scott in his introduction to *The Talisman*. The water in which it was dipped operated as a styptic and a febrifuge, as well as exercising some favourable influence over the destinies of man. About the middle of the seventeenth century the Reformed Protestant Church of Scotland tried hard " to extinguish every heathenism and forbid well-worshipings . . . enchantments . . . and the vain practices which are carried on with various spells . . . and with stones." The Synod of the Presbyterian Church of Glasgow made inquiry into the alleged curative gifts of the Lee Penny, but found no ground for drastic action against its use, though they admonished the Laird of Lee " in the using of the said stone to tak heed that it be used hereafter with the least scandal that possiblie may be."

A stone, called the " Deil's Needle," in the bed of the Aberdeenshire Dee, was said to be efficaceous as a cure for sterility in women : if a barren woman crawled through a hole in the stone she was held to have increased her chances of pregnancy. There was on the island of Rona a stone " for providing speedy delivery to a woman in travail." Gregor, in his folk-lore of the north-east of Scotland, mentioned a large granite rock on a hill on the east side of Glenavon, which, if scaled, promised a speedy and successful birth. The *lapis hecticus* for consumption in man and beast was in use until comparatively recent years in Skye : it was made red-hot, cooled in water or milk, and the liquid given to the patient to drink.

As early as the thirteenth century the ordinances of the Provincial Councils of the Church forbade anyone ignorant of medicine to administer, under the guise of medicine, potions of poisonous herbs to a sick person, or to practise any divination.

In the early days medical practice was very largely in the hands of the priesthood, and the most learned physicians were those who had studied their subject in continental countries. One such was Michael Scott, whose memory was immortalized in the *Lay of the Last Minstrel*, and who attained to such skill that he was regarded as a wizard capable of performing miracles outside the scope of medicine or any other science. His vademecum, a pill compounded of aloes, rhubarb, and other fruits and flowers, was said to relieve headache, purge the humours wonderfully, produce joyfulness, brighten the intellect, improve the vision, sharpen hearing, preserve youth, and retard baldness.

For a long time the clergy continued to take an active part in the practice of medicine, especially in outlying districts of Scotland. There was, as already mentioned, the minister of Birsay and Harrap, in Orkney, who obtained good results in his treatment of smallpox. There were " the ministers of the parish " who " performed the operation of inoculation (against smallpox) to a considerable extent and with the greatest success." Sinclair was at great pains to point out the virtues of inoculation and to meet the common objections to it. He felt that in many cases these objections were occasioned by the expense attending it, and he thought that " it would be a good plan to have midwives taught the modern art of vaccination, when learning the principles of their profession ; and perhaps it would make the plan of vaccination general were itinerant vaccinators annually sent about at the public expense." By the end of the eighteenth century the condition of the Scottish people from the medical point of view had in several respects greatly improved. Means of escaping the ravages of smallpox had become available, and in the cure of new diseases the advantage of able medical assistance was coming to be more generally spread over the country ; but it was realized that medical skill was not by any means fully available in outlying districts, and Sinclair thought there was something to be said for imparting to divinity students some knowledge of the elements of medicine. As late as the early years of the nineteenth century the minister of Yarrow reported that in his part of the country vaccination was little practised, and seldom at the hands of a medical man. Mothers who sought it for their children generally kept them till the Reverend Mr. Nicol of Traquair came over on the Saturday of the Communion. He made a point of arriving a few hours before the service began, bringing lymph and inserting it. It was long believed that phlebotomy twice a year was conducive to health, and in spring and autumn in Yarrow Mr. Ballantyne of Dryhope came an hour earlier to church with his lancet. He was followed in the parish by other great " bleeders," Robert Hogg of Yarrow Feus and Mr. Morton from Ettrick Bridgend, " who continued the practice even after their hands had got shakey." The amateur doctor lingered long, and as late as 1858 the General Superintendent of Poor wrote that as medical attendance is so very essential a part of relief, the medical officer should know the state of health of all poor on the roll, and not limit his visits to when he is called upon. " This," he said, " is the more necessary, in consequence of the want of confidence in medical men that prevails almost with the entire rural population," and he went on to counsel that in remote districts the common medicines should be deposited with the clergy and intelligent farmers for the use of the poorer classes.

The kings of Scotland from James II onwards appear to have had apothecaries attached to their courts. The Scottish apothecary was a pharmacist, but he might also visit his patients and prescribe for them, as well as carry out certain minor surgical operations, the scope of which varied with the times and was chiefly dependent on the sufferance of the surgeons. These court associations were not without financial advantage to the apothecaries concerned, as is suggested by the fact that the payments made to William Foular for " potinchary taen by him to the King at divers times " between 25 April 1500 and 27 March 1501 totalled £59, 18s. 6d. Foular appears to have been a man of wide interests, for in 1501 he sold to the king, for a consideration of £3, 17s., " ane buke callit Ortus Sanitatus, twa gret psalteris, and ane matin buke of the use of Rome." King James IV was himself a great patron of the arts and sciences of his time, and he had extensive medical interests. He dabbled in leech-craft, and was said to be " weill learned in the airt of medicine, and was ane singular guid chirurgiana." From the High Treasurer's accounts it appears that the king paid his patients instead of being paid by them—to one, XVII shillings, " to gif the King leve to lat him blud," to another, XVIII shillings, " because the King pullit furth his twyth," and to another XIII shillings, to " ye blind wif yat hed her eyne schorne." There were also several records of sums given to patients suffering from the " grant gore."

About this time syphilis invaded Scotland. When the disease broke out in Edinburgh, in 1497, those suffering from it were ordered off to Inchkeith, and with them all other persons who undertook to cure the infirmity, in order that they might not use the same cure within the burgh. A minute in the records of the Privy Seal of Scotland records the punishment (already noted) of the medical man in whose hands a dignitary of the Church had died while under treatment for syphilis :

January 18*th*, 1509. Respitt made to Thomas Lyn, burges of Edinburgh, for ye slauchtir of umquhile Schir Lancelote Patonsoun, Chappelain, quhilk happinit be negligent cure and medicine yat ye said Thomas tuk one him to cure and hele ye said umquhile Schir Lancelote of ye infirmitie of ye Grantgor yat he was infekkit with. To endure for XIX yeeris. (Subscripsit per dominum regem apud Edinburghe.)

The provision of medical care for the inhabitants began to exercise the magistrates of Scottish towns early in the sixteenth century. Master James Cumyne went to Aberdeen about 1503 as medical officer of the burgh, receiving a retaining fee of ten merks annually and part of the proceeds of the fishings on the Dee as an inducement to settle in the town. Similarly, the Town Council of Glasgow offered salaries to doctors whom they invited to settle in the town. James Abernethie was apparently so invited about the middle of the sixteenth century, and there are records of others in the latter part of the century. In Edinburgh, under the stimulus of the plague, the bailies in 1585 appointed James Henrysoun, surgeon, " to take care of the sick, to visit all the hospitals of the burgh, and the poor who were sick or hurt whatever their sickness might be."

3

About the middle of the sixteenth century Scotland had only a handful of regular practitioners in medicine. The kirk session of Glasgow was apparently concerned at this state of affairs, for there is this curious entry in their records under date 14 September 1598 : " The session thinks good that the University, ministers, and presbytery take cognisance who are within the toun that pretend to have skill in medicine and hath not the same, that they who have skill may be retained and the others rejected," and a message was sent to the town council " to see what course to take with such." At the end of the sixteenth century there were in Glasgow probably not more than six surgeons and one physician. There were at least two midwives. Where the Glasgow midwives got their training at that time does not emerge, but there is evidence to prove that their morals were looked after by the Kirk ; one, Kate Freland, was summoned before the Presbytery in 1589 to undergo censure. The session was anxious to use the midwives as sources of information about the extent of immorality in the town ; there is an entry in the session records dated 8 February 1599 : " The two Midwives in the Town are discharged to go to any unmarried women, within, while first they signify the matter to some of the Ministers or Magistrates in the day-light, and if it be in the night-time that they take the oaths of the said women before they bare the bairn who is the father of it as they will be answerable to God and his Kirk." Courses on midwifery were held in Glasgow in the latter part of the eighteenth century, though the Chair of Midwifery was not founded until 1815. " Man-midwifery " was steadily gaining ground with the advance of time. James Muir, surgeon, advertised in the *Glasgow Journal* in 1759 that he would conduct a course of lectures on midwifery, to which, however, no woman would be admitted " unless her character for sobriety and prudence is attested by some person of reputation in the place she lives in." Mr. Muir stated in his advertisement that he continued as usual to deliver gratis all such women as applied in that way for his assistance ; and he added that he intended to begin a course in midwifery for students at a later date. A similar advertisement by Mr. James Monteith appeared in 1778 :

Midwifery : James Monteith, Surgeon (having provided the necessary apparatus) proposes, on Thursday the 26th of March, to begin a course of lectures on the theory and practice of Midwifery, to which will be added a set of lectures on the diseases of women and children, observations on inoculation, etc. Inquire at his shop, middle of Stockwell Street, or at his lodgings, Miss Semple's, New Street. At a separate hour attendance will be given for the instruction of women in the practice of Midwifery.

Cleland reports that at the end of 1829 there were 175 practitioners in the city and suburbs of Glasgow.

In Glasgow the Faculty of Physicians and Surgeons was established in 1599, mainly through the efforts of Peter Lowe. Henceforward the Faculty regulated the practice of medicine, surgery, and pharmacy in the west of Scotland, and the barbers were conjoined with the Faculty from 1602 till 1708. In terms of its Charter, the Faculty gave gratuitous advice to the sick poor at its monthly meetings, and in 1654 it offered the services of some of its members " for the weel of the poore diseased," without any payment or reward for their pains ; but nothing came of the offer.

An attempt was early made by the civic authorities in Glasgow to meet the need for providing medical care for the poor by subsidizing a physician or a surgeon (occasionally both), an apothecary, and a stone-cutter, whose services would be available for the treatment of the poor. In 1608 Mr. Peter Lowe received £4, 8s. 10d. sterling as retained surgeon. Subsequently a physician also was retained, but this practice was discontinued in 1684 when the town finances were at a low ebb.

27 *October*. The said day the Magistrats and Counsell, considering the sad condition the toun is in throw the great debt they are resting, it is theirfoir concludit that the toun shall make use of no persone as the toun's physitian or chirurgian in time coming, and if any person who is unwell, and *deserves to be cured*, upon their application to any of the Magistrats they are empowered to recommend them to any physitian they shall think fit.

Apparently the magistrates were not very particular about whom they employed, for in the same year a payment of £5 sterling was made " to the mountebank for cutting off umquill Archibald Boyle's leg." The patient died.

This reduction of professional staff did not apply to the stone-cutter. Lithotomy was in the seventeenth century apparently a specialty too dangerous to be ranked as ordinary surgery, and perhaps it was this consideration that obliged the Town Council of Glasgow to appoint a stone-cutter for the city in 1661 : " to pay yearlie to Evir McNeill that cutis the stone ane hundreth markis Scottis, and he to cut all the poor for that freilie." This salary was paid to him for a great many years. From the accounts for 1682 it appears that he was paid the same salary, £66, 13s. 4d. Scots, as the town's physician and the town's surgeon, and even after the appointments of the latter were sacrificed on the altar of economy the stone-cutter continued to draw his annual salary. McNeill was an uneducated man. He could not write, but he was in 1656 admitted to the membership of the Faculty qua Lithotomist. He retired from office in 1688, and in the same year the town council appointed as his successor Duncan Campbell, having considered a testificate in his favour. " Sub-scrybit be the haill doctors and most of the chirurgens in toune, of his dexteritie in cutting the stone, as also in sounding with great facilitie." It is interesting that both McNeill and Campbell were Highlanders ; special attention seems to have been paid to calculus in the West Highlands. According to Professor Mac-Kinnon, the eminent authority on Gaelic manuscripts, there was a tradition that, as early as 1386, an Islay doctor cured the king of gravel, after the court physician had failed. On 16 August

1656 the magistrates of Glasgow granted a Seal of Cause or local charter in favour of the " CHIRURGEOUNIS and Barbouris," these two professions being at that time united in one incorporation. The charter provides :

That no free mane presume to taik ane uzr frea man's cuir of his hand untill he be honestlie payit for his bygaine paines, and that at the sight of the Baillies with the udvyce of thair visitour, in caice the patient find himself grived by the chirurgiane, under the payne of ane new upsett ; excepting always libertie to the visitour and qrter maisters to tak patients from ane free man not fund qualified for the cuiring of them, and to put them to ane more qualified persoune as shall be thought expedient after exact tryall.

Later, the finances came to be able to afford a surgeon again, for from an account of the expenditure of the city of Glasgow in 1795, it appears that the salary of the town surgeon in that year was £20. He was doubtless a part-time employee ; the stipends of seven clergymen amounted to £1,377, 16s. in the same year (with, in addition, " Wine to the clergy, two dozen per annum to each of the six, is twelve dozen, £12, 12s.") ; of four grammar schoolmasters, £115 ; of the " player on music bells," £30 ; and of the " Superintendent of the Clocks," £20.

The course of events in Edinburgh was somewhat similar. As early as 1505 the chirurgeons and barber-chirurgeons of the city had been formed into a deaconry by the town council, with the liberty of distilling aqua-vitae, a right which they retained for the next hundred years ; and regulations were made that no apprentice was to be taken unless he could read and write, and that when the apprenticeship was successfully completed the student must give a dinner to the master of the trade. There were many struggles between the surgeons and the apothecaries, and in 1641 the Scottish Parliament passed an Act ratifying all the privileges of the surgeons and barbers of Edinburgh, and giving power to apprehend all persons practising surgery who were not freemen of the craft, and to fine them twenty pounds Scots for contravention. There was a temporary peace between the surgeons and apothecaries in 1657, but about 1680 war again broke out in Edinburgh between them, the surgeons considering that the apothecaries were taking too many liberties ; one of the offenders, Patrick Cunningham, was charged with " opening a vein of the Earl of Carnwath and with letting the blood of the Lady Lee."

In 1681 the Royal College of Physicians was erected by a

patent from King Charles II. The patent included a list of those duties to which the then surgeon-apothecaries were to be restricted. They were to have " the liberty of curing all Wounds, Bruises, Fractures, Dislocations, Contusions and sick like, being the subject of Chirurgical Operations and accidents arising thereupon," but they were debarred from practising as physicians. After 1682 the apothecaries struggled on in an endeavour to get the Town Council of Edinburgh to recognize their fraternity, but without success, and in 1695 they were further disheartened by an Act of the Scottish Parliament which reunited the arts of surgery and pharmacy and decreed that " none shall be allowed to practice in chirurgery or pharmacy upon human bodies dead or alive within the City of Edinburgh, the three Lothians, the Shires of Fife, Peebles, Selkirk, Roxburgh, and Berwick, but such as shall be tried and approven by the Chirurgeon-Apothecaries of Edinburgh."

In 1707 a druggist's widow left money to the Royal College of Physicians for the benefit of the sick poor, who had long received free advice from the Fellows of the College, and in 1708 a repository was set up for furnishing cheap medicine to the poor in Edinburgh.

When, in 1729, the Royal Infirmary of Edinburgh was established, the surgeons were inclined to look askance at it, but soon six surgeon-apothecaries came forward and not only attended the hospital without fee, but even furnished necessary medicines free of cost from their own shops. In 1748 the Infirmary managers decided to fit up an apothecary's shop in the institution, from which both in-patients and out-patients could be served.

Meanwhile there was a growing appreciation of the value of the help that surgeons could give in war, and in 1644 four surgeons were appointed to the army, " presently sent from this kingdom into England, each to have charge of two regiments, £15 sterling to be paid to each of them for furnishing of their chest, and five shillings of daily allowance to each surgeon and four shillings to his two mates . . . and that there be a month's pay advanced for their outrig and furnishing their horses." In the preparation of these chests much ingenuity was expended in packing the maximum number of articles in a minimum of space, as is well illustrated in the elaborate travelling pharmacy used by Prince Charles Edward, and preserved in the Royal College of Physicians of Edinburgh (see illustration at page 277).

The physicians of the middle of the eighteenth century may not have been very highly esteemed by the civil community—it is said of the doctors in Dundee in 1746 that they " wore large muffs, dangled gold-headed canes, hemm'd loud, and looked wise : and according to the strength or weakness of the natural constitution, the patient survived or expired " ; but by the end of the century a better type of doctor was in existence, and there was evidence of a new approach to medicine alike by its practitioners and by the people. In an early issue of the *Edinburgh Medical and Surgical Journal* (1 October 1805), " The Inquirer " asked, " Is there any certainty in medical science? Can it be wondered at that people, who, from ignorance and imprudence, exchange health for sickness, are unable or unwilling to calculate the superior advantages of the temporary inconvenience of medical treatment over the perilous chance of violent and unbridled actions or the wretchedness arising from an habitual disordered state of the body." He instanced phthisis pulmonalis, " one of the most common and destructive diseases of the age," as a disease the cure of which was rendered difficult and sometimes impossible by causes susceptible of being explained, but not removed ; and he concluded, " our present dietetic and medical means are inadequate in phthisis to fulfil the indications of cure : communication of the lungs with atmospheric air is necessary for the support of life : rest for the damaged lung is out of the question."

But though a more scientific approach to medicine was becoming evident, the latter part of the eighteenth century was not without its medical impostors. One such was "Doctor" Graham, sole proprietor and principal director of the Temple of Health in Pall Mall, London, who made his appearance in Glasgow in 1787, with the assertion that " he was able by his never-failing medicine, and by his scientific treatment of his patients not only to prevent them from dying, but also that through his wonderful discoveries he had absolutely brought a new generation of beings into life, who would never have made their appearance in this busy world unless through his marvellous skill and all-potent agency." His treatment lay in the use, with appropriate and elaborate ritual, of an earth bath. The " doctor " met with little success in Glasgow, but fared better in Edinburgh, until in time he came to grief there, and was fined for printing and publishing

" a scandalous and malicious libel against the Lord Provost and Magistrates."

" Doctor " Graham was followed after a little in Glasgow by Mr. Newham, who cured the afflicted by touching them with a rag dipped in a little spirits, using faculties bestowed on him " in a bye-way where doctors never knew to walk." Mr. Newham was succeeded by Dr. Katterfelto and his wonderful black cat, and he in turn by the Hon. Mr. Nicholson, " a man possessed of an exclusive and peculiar power over the most irrational part of human nature."

In 1802 it was announced that Mr. James Scott, surgeon-dentist, Edinburgh, intended to visit Glasgow annually and would be found at Mrs. Patterson's in Garthland Street. Mr. Scott was apparently the first bona-fide dentist in the city and he did so well in Glasgow that he took up his abode permanently there. " He was a most illiterate man and grew prodigiously stout," but it was stated on good authority that he often drew by way of fees as much as twenty guineas in a single morning, and he certainly conveyed an impression of grandeur as he rode through the city on a small grey pony, attended by a mounted page in gorgeous livery.

5

It was coming to be realized that, with advances in medical science, treatment in hospital often offered to the patient the best prospect of recovery. In his final commentary on his Analysis of the Statistical Account, Sinclair wrote that at each dispensary, skilled midwives ought to be provided, and that " in large towns there should also be an infirmary . . . for not only the health of individuals is thereby promoted, and their lives in many cases preserved, but improvements may be made in the art of medicine and the progress of contagious disorder checked." He added that wherever the population is sufficiently numerous to require an infirmary, a lunatic asylum should likewise be established. By this time infirmaries were springing up in Scottish towns, but there was often difficulty in persuading the people to use them, partly because of a natural reluctance to enter places which were still too often regarded the last resorts of hopeless cases, partly because there was a widespread belief that the nurses in the hospitals were unkind to their patients. As late as 1840, Dr. Alison of Tranent reported that in that parish there existed with most poor people an unwillingness to go to hospital—" this disinclination arises from the distance, the nearest hospital being ten miles distant, the expense and fatigue of travelling, and a feeling of distrust in respect to good usage from the nurses, who bear a very bad character among the poor classes." It appears that there had been great objections among the populace to entering a hospital formerly established at Tranent for the reception of cholera patients, but Dr. Alison wrote that he had heard enough of the management of that institution, both by nurses and others, to account for that reluctance, and he had " no doubt whatever, if incompetent medical men and unqualified nurses are placed in charge of any hospital which may be established that like objections will again arise and interfere with its beneficial operation." He thought that a small hospital might be provided in Tranent at very little expense, and he had no doubt that if it were properly conducted persons afflicted with fevers and smallpox would readily avail themselves of it. Dr. Alison's neighbour in Musselburgh reported in the same year that there was no doubt that the establishment of hospitals for the reception of those afflicted with fever and other contagious diseases would materially improve the sanitary condition of the poor. He thought that at least one hospital should be provided for every three or four parishes, that medical men should be appointed to attend the poor, and that if hospitals were established, it would be a good plan to associate a dispensary with the hospital, which could be attended by two or three medical gentlemen according to the size of the town. He thought that these dispensaries might be supported partly by government grants and partly by private contributions : he understood that such an arrangement existed in Montrose, and he added that in his experience the prejudice against hospitals among the poor was not so great as many supposed.

Under the threat of epidemics of cholera and typhus fever, many Boards of Health were set up in Scottish cities and towns during the nineteenth century, and it is not surprising that in the work of these boards prominent doctors took an active part. It is recorded that before cholera reached Edinburgh in 1832, some rags sent from the diseased districts to a dealer in Edinburgh were intercepted by the police on their approach to the town. They were then conveyed to a neighbouring parish and deposited with a paper manufacturer. The local Board of Health sent a deputation to investigate the conduct of the depository, who consented to the removal of the rags. By the direction of this board, which was self-constituted and acted without the warrant of a magistrate, the rags were deposited in a field, and an intimation was sent to the proprietor that he might remove the rags to any place he might choose " out of the parish." The rags were damaged and the proprietor raised an action for damages. He obtained a decision in his favour, both from the Sheriff and from the Lord Ordinary, the former taking the view that the circumstances were insufficient to justify the interference of the board, the latter holding that the board, though entitled to interfere, should have had the property removed to a place of safe keeping. The Inner House of the Court of Session, however, decided in favour of the board, on the ground " that in the circumstances of the case, and in consideration of the state of alarm for cholera then prevailing in the country, it was the duty of the pursuer to have given the required consent or to have taken other measures for the removal of the rags, reserving his claim against the Board of Health, or its officers, for any damage he might then have sustained, and which must have been inconsiderable."

6

The importance of preventive medicine was beginning to be appreciated. In 1809 Dr. John Roberton of Edinburgh published a treatise on medical police, which was the first notable treatise in English on the subject of public health. In Glasgow, Dr. Cowan, Professor of Medical Jurisprudence and Police in the University, drew attention to the importance of insanitary conditions in the diffusion of epidemic disease and urged the establishment of sanitary police as well as criminal police. John Hill Burton, an advocate of Edinburgh, giving evidence in 1840 to a Government commission on the Protection of the Public Health in Scotland, said that in any proposal to legislate for sanitary reform, it was necessary to keep in view a material obstacle to improvement—the absence of any medical police. "But there is another, and perhaps still more important point of view," he went on, " in which the utility of a medical establishment devoting its attention to the condition of the poor may be entertained, but one so extensive, and opening up such a variety of detail, that I shall only here glance at it ; it is the admitted want in Scotland of hospitals or other stipendiary establishments for the cure of the diseased. Many considerable towns, such as Arbroeth, Dunfermline, Aloa, Renfrew, etc., are destitute of any such institution." He complained that there was no hospital in the populous and affluent county of Fife, and that many other counties were in the same position. People who could get the removal accomplished were sometimes conveyed from places fifty or sixty miles distant to the Infirmary of Edinburgh, an institution which had recently been compelled to intimate to the public that, unless some considerable effort were made to increase its funds, it would be compelled to restrict its services. A multitude of the poor were wholly dependent on the gratuitous services of the medical profession. Burton envisaged a combined preventive and curative service " where the supervisance of the operation of sanitary regulations, and medical attendance on the sick poor are entrusted to the same set of medical officers, the one duty might be expected naturally to aid the other, as the labours of attendance would be diminished or increased with the greater or less efficiency of the preventive measures. With regard to the form in which such an establishment should exist—whether it should be connected with boards of health or should form, either separately or along with such boards, a feature in the general reform of the Poor Law, must depend on matters of legislation, as to which it is not within my province to make suggestions." In 1841 Mr. Baird of Glasgow, secretary of the Glasgow Relief Fund and a member of the acting committee of the Board of Health of 1838–39, giving evidence to the same Government commission, recommended that for sanitary purposes the city of Glasgow and the suburban districts within the parliamentary boundary should be declared one district and jurisdiction, and that a sanitary commission, or Board of Health, should be appointed, consisting of the Lord Provost of Glasgow, the Provost of Calton, the Chief Magistrate of Gorbals, the Provost of Anderston, the President of the Faculty of Physicians and Surgeons in Glasgow, the Professor of Medicine, and the Professor of Medical Jurisprudence and Police in the University of Glasgow, three Commissioners to be appointed by the police board of Glasgow, one by that of Calton, two by that of Gorbals, and one by that of Anderston, with power to appoint a medical or other officer, inspectors or inspector, clerks and servants, " and to adopt and carry into effect all measures necessary, salutary, or prudent, for preventing and removing nuisances or other things injuriously affecting the public health, for the prevention or diminution of contagious or infectious diseases, and for promoting the health, cleanliness and comfort of the inhabitants of Glasgow and suburbs "—and with power to impose an assessment. But over twenty years were yet to elapse before Glasgow appointed its first Medical Officer of Health, Dr. W. T. Gairdner.

7

The immediate problem concerned the medical care of the sick poor. Medical relief in Scotland was left almost entirely to private charity. There were in most of the large, and in many of the smaller towns, dispensaries supported by voluntary contributions, which supplied the poor with medicines, and the officers of which gave their attendance gratis. Baird, giving a list of the medical charities available in Glasgow in 1840, wrote that the city was not surpassed by any other in Great Britain or Ireland, excepting Dublin, for the extent of its hospital accommodation or the freedom with which the people were allowed to avail themselves of it, and he added that no such list could include the mass of charitable aid and advice given by physicians and surgeons : " I do not know any class of the community who are so constant and unweary in their exertions on behalf of the poor."

Dr. James Sym of Ayr, who had previously practised in Kilmarnock, wrote in 1841 that relative to size Ayr had fully double the dispensary population of Kilmarnock, though consumption was less prevalent in Ayr than in Kilmarnock. He estimated that 2·7 per cent. of the population in Ayr received attention from dispensary surgeons, of whom there were five, dividing the town into districts. The surgeons visited the patients in their own homes and prescribed medicines, which were supplied by the dispensary apothecary. The expenses of the dispensary were defrayed by annual subscription, and the surgeons received a trifling sum, " not as a remuneration for their services, but as a token of gratitude for the sacrifices they make for the good of the community " ; the apothecary had a salary of £30. The entire expenditure of the Ayr dispensary in the year 1840 was £106, 5s. 2d., and, as it treated 659 patients, the average cost worked out at about 3s. each. The colliers in the area were attended by Mr. Gibson, who received a salary which the colliery clerk retained from the colliers' wages. " As there is by a gross omission no fund for supplying them with medicines, Mr. Gibson is often obliged to procure medicines for them, and for these he is seldom repaid." Johnston states that in the mining areas the colliery doctor was often " trucked," [1] and his services—like the services of the schoolmaster and the supply of whisky—could not be obtained in time of idleness.

In Stirling there was in 1841 no hospital, but there was a dispensary, which had been founded ten years previously. Its object was to furnish gratuitously medical attendance and medicine to the poor. It was supported entirely by voluntary subscriptions, and no patient was admitted to its benefits unless recommended by a subscriber, who certified that the applicant was a poor person and unable to pay for medical attendance and medicine.

There was at that time no public medical charity in St. Andrews, the poor being attended gratuitously by any of the practitioners for whom they chose to send. Sometimes they managed to pay for necessary medicine themselves, sometimes it was given for nothing by the druggist, while occasionally, and under protest, the kirk session paid for medicine ordered in extreme cases.

Similarly there was no institution in Tain affording medical aid to the sick poor. James Cameron, surgeon there, wrote in 1841 that the mortality rate among the poor was high, and that many died without having the benefit of medical advice. " This district is considered to be well supplied with medical men ; but it is also unfortunately infested by a set of empirics or quacks, and of ignorant midwives, who, though they have never received any medical education, nor indeed any education whatever, yet practice largely and lucratively among the country people, pretending to understand the most difficult and complicated cases." He deplored particularly the want of provision for lying-in women, " this important duty being in general intrusted to a set of inexperienced old quacks who call themselves midwives. Death is a frequent consequence of their mode of treatment ; and the wives of the district have to thank their constitution and hardy habits that it is not more frequent . . . It is seldom indeed that medical

---

[1] " The collier had everything trucked to him—except his coffin ; if he went on strike his children ceased to be educated, for the schoolmaster was trucked, supplied by the employer but paid by the worker, out of levies on their wages. Similarly the doctor was trucked. . . . Under [the Truck System] not only were miners and iron-workers compelled to go to their masters' ' stores ' to buy their provisions, their clothing, whisky, and even bibles, at ruinous prices . . ."—Thomas Johnston, *History of the Working Classes in Scotland.*

skill is called in till the manifest symptoms of death have frightened them to try the last resource."

The Dumfries and Galloway Infirmary treated 404 in-patients and 750 out-patients in 1840. There was also in Dumfries at that time a dispensary, which was not well supported, and was unable to give any remuneration to the doctors caring for its patients, though the number of those applying at the dispensary for advice was about 1,000 annually. One of the dispensary physicians reported that the population of the district to which he attended might amount to 1,700, and that the number of cases he was called upon to visit in their own homes during 1840 was no less than 300. It is not surprising that he wrote, " There is great need of medical attendants being appointed for the poor, as in England." He thought that these officially-appointed doctors for the poor would have the earliest opportunities of discovering contagious disease, for it often happened, under the existing system, that the poor were ill for days of fever or other distemper before making their case known or being able to procure any medical relief.

Of 790 cases admitted to Greenock Infirmary during the year ending 1 May 1841, 588 were cases of fever and 74 were injuries, many the result of accidents in the shipbuilding yards, of which there were eight in Greenock, each employing 60 to 120 apprentices, and each proprietor paying a medical man for attending his apprentices during illness. In addition, the hospital treated 484 out-patients, who received medicine and advice. In 1839 when fever was very prevalent in the town, three district surgeons were appointed in Greenock by the united sessions for attending the paupers in their own houses. They were " of great benefit," but their attendance was too much restricted, " as there is a more numerous class a step removed above actual paupers who are quite unable to procure medical care."

But while in many towns and cities some provision had been made for the medical care of the sick poor by the provision of hospitals and dispensaries, or, as in Glasgow, by making available the services of district surgeons, there were many parts of the country in which there was no such provision. In rural districts, particularly, was this so, and the sick poor in them were generally attended without charge by the medical practitioners, who also in the great majority of cases furnished medicine—" extra diet and wine, if needed, must be obtained from the charity of wealthier

neighbours of the poor." The doctors were naturally dissatisfied
with this state of things : many were not unwilling to give their
attendance gratuitously, but complained of being called upon to
furnish medicine as well ; and they also complained of the difficulty so frequently experienced in procuring necessary diet and
stimulants for the sick. The commission set up by the Government to consider the whole question of the relief of the poor,
reporting in 1843, considered it necessary that " the managers
of the poor in each parish should have full discretionary power
by law, to afford medical relief in all cases where it may seem
to them desirable." They understood medical relief to comprise
" the supply of nutritious diet, wine or cordials, where deemed
necessary for the proper treatment of the case ; and also the
vaccination of children where necessary." They contemplated
a more extensive provision of medical relief, and the provision of
dispensaries for the poor in connection with poorhouses. One
of the more active of the commissioners, Mr. Twisleton, refused to
sign the report on the broad grounds that the remedies proposed
to meet admitted defects were insufficient, and because, among
other things, it was not proposed to make it compulsory for
managers of the poor to provide medical attendance for paupers.
He complained that the arrangements for medical relief and the
power of fixing the scale of remuneration to medical practitioners
were to be left exclusively to the local authorities, who might
deem that they had a direct pecuniary interest in fixing the scale
of remuneration as low as possible, or in continuing to throw
altogether upon medical practitioners the burden of attending the
sick poor gratuitously.

Mr. Twisleton's protest produced results, for in the Act (1845),
for the Amendment and Better Administration of the Laws
Relating to the Relief of the Poor in Scotland, statutory provision
was made for medical relief. It was decreed that in all poorhouses
there should be proper and sufficient arrangements for dispensing
and supplying medicines for the sick poor, as well as proper
medical attendance for the inmates, " provided always, that if
it shall appear to the Board of Supervision that such medical man
is unfit or incompetent or neglects his duty, it shall be lawful
for the Board of Supervision to suspend or remove such medical
man from his appointment and attendance." Parochial boards
were authorized to make such subscriptions from funds raised for
the relief of the poor as seemed to them reasonable and expedient

" to any public infirmary, dispensary or lying-in hospital or to any lunatic asylum, or asylum for the blind or deaf and dumb." Further, it was laid down that, " in every parish or combination it shall and may be lawful for the parochial board, and they are hereby required, out of the funds raised for the relief of the poor, to provide for medicines, medical attendance, nutritious diet, cordials and clothing for such poor in such manner and to such extent as many seem equitable and expedient."

This new medical provision was not introduced without difficulty. Many of the more rural parts of the country had no resident medical man. Early in 1846, Dr. Coll Macdonald wrote to the secretary of the Board of Supervision from Loch Shiel, calling attention to the lamentable conditions of people in western Inverness and Ross from the want of medicines and medical attendance. He complained that there were no doctors in the parishes of Small Isles or Glenelg or Barra, though some half-educated medical men—poor, of bad habits and without means to keep medicines or instruments, practised among the people, prescribing simples where active treatment was necessary. The people suffered acute or chronic disease without any attempt at relief : he had taught several in the district to cup and bleed, and they were of much service to the people, but more was needed. " What is required would be a dispensary in certain places, where medicines and instruments would be kept and a few perambulating, intelligent, well-behaved medical men to attend and prescribe for the people." Dr. Macdonald gave instances of faulty treatment by " inefficient medical men." In some parishes, as in South Uist, tenants subsidized a doctor to stay in the parish, but for the most part there was little inducement for a medical man to settle in these sparsely populated areas. In only a small minority of parishes had a surgeon been appointed by the parochial board at an annual fee to attend the poor and furnish them with medicines. Even where such arrangement existed, the remuneration was almost invariably inadequate, and the Board of Supervision was not satisfied that the medical relief afforded to the poor in Scotland generally, more especially in the rural and remote parishes, was on a satisfactory footing. The board realized that the remuneration of a parochial medical officer must have reference not only to the number of persons he might be called upon to attend, but also to the distances he had to travel.

At a meeting of medical practitioners held in Edinburgh in

November 1845, Professor J. Y. Simpson in the chair, a committee of inquiry was appointed to gather information about the arrangements for the care of the sick poor in Scotland. The first report of this medical association dealt with rural areas. From a questionnaire it was ascertained that of 305 doctors practising in Scottish country districts, 94 had received some remuneration for the care of the sick poor, 39 receiving annually sums ranging from a few shillings for drugs and outlays, up to £20 as payment for drugs, medical advice and attendance. Of these, 13 received upwards of £5 annually, and 26 sums below that amount; 9 received £1 or less annually. Over 60 per cent. of practitioners had never received any remuneration of any kind. Many had in addition to give from their own limited store wine and clothes or other necessaries to sick paupers. Their journeys to the poor often involved the payment of tolls, and sometimes the expense of lodging themselves and their horse at an inn. In most cases in which remuneration had been sought for medical attendance from the parochial authorities it had been absolutely refused. (One doctor stated that he had known the " session " sell the effects of a dead pauper and appropriate the proceeds, without listening to the unrequited claims of the doctor.) Only five doctors reported that midwifery cases, vaccinations and surgery cases were paid for separately, as in England.

Two hundred and forty-six doctors replied to the query, " How far may any patient reside from the house of their medical attendant ? " In 103 instances the maximum distance was less than five miles, in 93 from five to ten miles, in 43 from ten to twenty miles, in 8 from twenty to thirty miles, and in 3 instances it extended to forty miles. In the small, badly ventilated houses of their poorer patients they encountered far more than elsewhere the personal danger of infection ; and several reported that they had lain off work for long intervals, with severe and dangerous attacks of fever, etc., caught while attending upon pauper patients afflicted with the same diseases.

The second report dealt with information from forty towns, exclusive of Glasgow and Edinburgh. In sixteen of these, including Ayr, Leith, Kirkcaldy, Stirling, Perth, Kirkintilloch, Montrose, and Elgin, there had been no payment to medical men for the care of the poor. Few of these towns had a dispensary. In a few towns occasional payments were made, as during the prevalence of epidemics. Thus, the sum of £10 was allowed during an epidemic of typhus fever in Kirkintilloch in the year 1844 by a private individual, while in Dundee, during a similar epidemic, £5 was allowed to each of six dispensary surgeons. In a few places some remuneration had been allowed by the parish authorities to medical practitioners within the immediately preceding years. In Alloa, for instance, a total sum of £10 was allowed for professional attendance, the poor being permitted to select their own attendant. In Dundee 3s. 6d. per week was paid by the parish for such paupers as were received into the infirmary as patients. In Dunfermline £20 per annum had been paid since 1841, together with the cost of drugs. In Dumfries £10 had been allowed to one medical man for the preceding ten years for professional attendance on the sick poor. In Greenock three district surgeons had each received £25 per annum for five years, while in Kilmarnock for three years past £10 each had been paid to three medical officers for visiting the sick poor ; and in Wick, since 1844, £15 had been divided between two medical officers, " and drugs moreover supplied." These recent payments had been made chiefly in anticipation of the new Poor Law Act. It appeared that upwards of 90 per cent. of medical men in their attendance on paupers were in the habit of contributing to them of their substance, as well as giving gratuitous professional services. To the question whether paupers should be allowed to select a particular medical adviser, 82 answers were received, 66 recommending a selection, and 16 being opposed to it.

In presenting their report upon the conditions under which doctors worked in their care of the sick poor, the secretaries of the Edinburgh Medical Association pointed out that in estimating the services of medical officers employed under the new Act it ought not to be forgotten that the practitioner would be required to keep account of his patients visits and to make regular returns to the Board of Supervision, all of which would increase his labour and should enhance his remuneration. The Association suggested to the Board of Supervision that parochial authorities should not be allowed to fill up the appointments of medical attendants upon the poor " by tenders " ; that, though in large towns it might be necessary to have regular and fixed medical attendants for paupers, there were advantages in allowing paupers in other districts choice of medical attendant, " provided it be understood that the remuneration of such attendant is to be so much per head annually for each pauper or family of whom he takes charge—the sum liable to alteration by the distance he has to go, but not by the number of his visits " ; and that while dispensaries for the working classes were of great use in large towns, it was generally advisable to have the treatment of sick paupers kept separate from the operations of dispensaries.

The Association submitted three resolutions drawn up by their committee of inquiry on the subject of the sick poor : (1) that the doctors were anxious to help to carry into effect the new legislation for the care of the poor ; (2) that while they felt obliged to make certain sacrifices in the service of the poor, they thought that the calls upon them had hitherto been unjust and excessive, and that in future their attendance on this class " should meet with moderate remuneration and that they should not be required to supply medicine to paupers at their own expense " ; and (3) " that on account of the peculiar circumstances in which country practitioners are usually placed as regards any official arrangements for remunerating their attendance on the poor of their district, it has appeared expedient that the members of the profession who have better opportunities of acting in concert should in the first instance take up the subject with a view both to the relief of their brethren and the benefit of the sick poor."

One of the early acts of the Board of Supervision was to prepare rules governing medical relief. In a circular issued in October 1848 it was laid down :

I   That all poor persons who stand in need of medical relief shall be duly and punctually attended by a *competent* medical practitioner and supplied with medicines and medical and surgical appliances of such quality, and to such extent, as may be necessary for the proper medical and surgical treatment of such poor persons.

II   A medical practitioner is not duly qualified unless he has a degree or diploma of physician or surgeon from a university or other body in Great Britain or Ireland legally entitled to confer or grant such degree or diploma. A medical practitioner not thus qualified, who has not held the office of parochial medical officer for at least one year prior to the 20th August, 1848, will not be held to be *competent*.

III   In addition to medical relief, parochial boards shall furnish the sick and convalescent poor with nutritious diet, cordials, clothing, suitable lodging, and sick-bed attendance to such an extent as may be necessary, according to the circumstances of each case.

IV A medical practitioner appointed by the parochial board to attend any poor person shall intimate in writing to the inspector the description and extent of the relief which he may consider necessary for the proper treatment of such poor person ; and on receipt of such intimation the inspector, on his own responsibility, shall forthwith furnish or refuse the relief so intimated to be necessary, until he shall have brought the case before the parochial board and received their instructions regarding it. But if the inspector refuses or fails to furnish that relief, or any part of it, he will be held accountable for such refusal or failure.

V Medical attendance and appliances which are furnished by the medical officer, or procured from a laboratory on his prescription, are chargeable under the head of medical relief ; but nutritious diet, cordials, clothing, suitable lodging, sick-bed attendance, and such appliances and means as are not furnished by the medical attendant, nor procured from a laboratory on his prescription, are not chargeable as medical relief ; and inspectors of poor are required to prepare the annual returns in conformity with this rule.

VI A medical practitioner who has undertaken to attend the whole or any part of the poor in a parish must attend personally, and at their homes, if necessary, the poor entrusted to his care, and is responsible that such visits and attendance are duly and punctually given. If he employs an assistant to aid him in performance of his duties, no sub-division of the duty of personal attendance or diminution of personal responsibility will, on that account, be recognized.

VII A medical officer is bound to afford every reasonable facility for sending or conveying the medicines and appliances furnished from his own laboratory to paupers, who are unable to go or to send for them ; but when it is necessary to send a messenger expressly for that purpose he may call upon the inspector in writing to provide such messenger, and the inspector when so called upon will be held responsible that the medicines, etc., are duly and punctually delivered.

VIII A medical officer appointed to attend the poor must, within twenty-one days of appointment, or as soon thereafter as required by the parochial board, if practicable, name to the parochial board a duly qualified medical practitioner, for whose diligence he will be held responsible and whose nomination is not objected to by the parochial board, who will perform the duties of medical officer in case of his absence from home or other unavoidable hindrance to his personal attendance.

With the passing of the new Act there was a rapid extension of the supply of medical relief to the poor. Thus, in the year ending February 1846 the sum expended for this purpose was £4,055 ; in 1847, £12,879 ; and in 1848, £30,339. But medical relief in Scotland was still generally inadequate : e.g. in New Monkland, with a population of 20,511, the sum expended on medical relief in the year ending May 1847 was £21, 13s. 7d., and in Old Monkland (population 19,709) it was only £14, 12s. 2d. The rate per head of population spent on medical relief ranged from 0·09 pence in Orkney to 2·33 pence in Selkirk : the average was 1·14 pence. In an attempt to improve the standard of medical care, Parliament made available a grant in aid of medical relief in Scotland, and in administering the grant the Board of Supervision took the line that it was reasonable that each parish desiring to participate should be required to expend from its own funds a sum equal to the share of the grant apportioned to it ; the distribution was also related to density of population. In the first year of the grant 494 of the 880 parishes in Scotland resolved to comply with the conditions, 240 did not intimate their attitude, and 146 declined to comply. One parish, Aberdour (Aberdeen), declined to participate on the express ground that to provide medical relief would be injurious to the health of the poor, and several populous parishes declined, apparently from the fear that to accept a grant might subject their arrangements more directly to the authority of the Board of Supervision. The number of parishes accepting the conditions increased year by year : in 1854 claims were established by 560 parishes, and in 1863 by 672.

The method of appointment of parochial medical officers was apparently not always above reproach. The Board of Supervision complained that some of the parochial boards had been in the practice of electing the parochial medical officer annually, and they had reason to believe that habit to have been prejudicial both to the harmony of the parochial board and to the interests of the poor. " The annual election is apt to degenerate into an annual contest between rival practitioners, in which the most respectable and worthy are unwilling to engage. Each candidate is supported by partisans in whose estimation professional skill or fitness for the office is not always the primary consideration ; and the fact that the election is only for one year apparently tends to produce recklessness in the choice."

In the report of the Board of Supervision for 1859 a matter is described that had caused great excitement in the parish of Fordoun, viz. the post-mortem examination of the body of Mary Laing, a pauper who had died at an advanced age. Dr. Joseph Henderson, the parochial medical officer, dismissed by the parochial board, appealed to the Board of Supervision. In his letter he said that Mary Laing, lately an inmate of the poorhouse, Fordoun, had been seized with pain and vomiting during the night of 18 June. He saw her on the morning of the 19th and three further times during that day, and she died the same night. Dr. Henderson was anxious about the case, " and not being satisfied as to the real cause of the sudden termination, I proposed to the inspector and matron how desirable it would be to open the body (the abdomen only) ; they readily assented. We were only afraid of it becoming known to the other inmates, and therefore had it done on the 21st in the most private and expeditious way possible. The matter, however, became known, and my conduct has given certain influential individuals great offence. I was summoned to the parochial board, and there experienced treatment I had never anticipated." Dr. Henderson expressed regret in his letter to the Board of Supervision, and a sense of injustice. The Board pointed out that the affair had occasioned great excitement among the inhabitants of all classes and much alarm among the paupers, and while they did not dismiss him from his office they considered themselves called upon to record " unequivocal disapproval of his proceedings in this instance." There the matter might have ended, since clearly the Board had no intention of interfering with the decision of the parochial board, but the Royal College of Physicians of Edinburgh and the Medical and Chirurgical Society of Glasgow both addressed to the Secretary of State for the Home Department memorials commenting in strong language on the case. The Home Secretary asked for observations from the Board of Supervision, and they, while again insisting on the repugnance of the poor, especially in remote rural parishes, to the idea of anatomical examination, took refuge in the circumstance that the Medical Officer had no security of tenure, and that in any case this was not a poorhouse but a lodging-house for the poor. The grateful conclusion of the

Board of Supervision was that " as the re-election by the parochial board of the officer whom they had dismissed accomplished the immediate object of the memorialists, it became unnecessary to prosecute the discussion any further."

The passing of the Medical Act in 1858 placed the practice of medicine on a better footing and simplified many administrative problems, among them the appointment of medical officers for the care of the poor ; thereafter the appointment of no parochial medical officer was recognized unless he had been duly registered under that Act. The number of registered medical practitioners in Scotland in 1863 was just over fifteen hundred.

Long ere this the trek of Scottish doctors to the south had commenced. Alexander Carlyle, a well-known Scottish divine, described how in the second half of the eighteenth century there was a club in London which met once a week in the British Coffee-house at eight o'clock in the evening. The members were Scottish physicians from the City and Court and of the town. William Hunter, the famous anatomist, was one of them, and his was the toast, " May no English nobleman venture out of the world without a Scottish physician, as I am sure there are none who venture in." Some of these Scottish graduates were interested in public health, and one, Dr. William Duncan, was the first Medical Officer of Health to be appointed in Britain ; he became Medical Officer of Health for the city of Liverpool in 1847.

8

In some of the Scottish cities it was coming to be recognized that the appointment of a medical officer of health was desirable if real progress was to be made in improving sanitary conditions and promoting the health of the community. A committee of the Royal College of Physicians of Edinburgh, appointed to consider any bills that might be brought into Parliament for the improvement of the health of towns, referred in 1848, and again the following year, to the need for such an appointment. In commenting on the Town Improvement Clauses Act of 1847 the committee approved in general the measures proposed for creating a board of health, and thought that the duties of the officer of health should be widened to include the drafting of such regulations as he might think fit for improving the sanitary condition of his district, but not, as had been suggested, to ascertain the cause of death in every case. In 1849 the committee regretted that in the proposed Edinburgh Police Consolidation and Sanitary Improvement Bill there was no provision at all for the appointment of an officer of health. But no definite step was taken towards the appointment of a medical officer of health in Edinburgh until the collapse of a house in the High Street, involving the death of thirty-five people, awakened public concern. Advantage was taken of this awakened interest to draw attention again to the need for the appointment of a health officer. A public meeting of the inhabitants was held in February 1862, and one of the results of that meeting was that a deputation was appointed to wait on the town council to urge on that body the making of such an appointment. The deputation was successful in its object and soon afterwards Dr. Littlejohn was appointed.

In 1858 Mr. John Ure had submitted a scheme for the sanitary improvement of the city of Glasgow, and for the creation of a special health department. The purpose of this department was to regulate the cleansing of the city, to prevent the occupation of unhealthy habitations and the overcrowding of small dwellings, to inspect and control lodging-houses, to procure the abatement of nuisances arising from works and from smoke, and generally to supervise closely the sanitary conditions of the city : under the scheme the sanitary department would receive help from other departments, especially from that of the police. The limited sanitary services of the city had previously functioned under police superintendence, and some councillors were sceptical of any good coming of a change, but in 1862 a special sanitary department was set up, and the following year Dr. William T. Gairdner was appointed Medical Officer of Health.

CHAPTER XI

THE GROWTH OF HOSPITAL CARE

I

IN pre-Reformation days the care of the sick and of the impotent lay very largely in the hands of the Church. Most monasteries possessed hospitia, situated either at the monastery or on a route much frequented by pilgrims and travellers. Monks specially skilled in medicine cared for the sick and wounded, and for persons of the district who required medical attention. One of the best known of these hospitia in Scotland was Soutra Aisle, some sixteen miles south of Edinburgh, on the road from the capital to Kelso and Dryburgh abbeys. It was built in 1164. There were many such hospitals scattered throughout Scotland, most of them dating from the thirteenth century. In Aberdeen, for instance, monastic hospitals were founded from 1211 onwards —Trinity, Dominican, Carmelite, Franciscan, St. Peter's, St. Thomas's, and, in Glasgow, St. Nicholas Hospital was endowed in 1456. Already before the Reformation some were falling into disuse, and others were having increasing difficulty in finding funds to continue their work ; but at the time of the Reformation there were still six or seven in or near Edinburgh, and others in Glasgow, Aberdeen, Stirling, Brechin, and small country places such as Lauder in Berwickshire, Ednam in Roxburgh, and Suggeden in Perthshire. In addition, there must have been hospitals in connection with settlements of the Knights Hospitallers, as at Torphichen, Glasgow, and Linlithgow. These early hospitals did not cater so much for acute sickness as do the hospitals of modern times. They were more concerned with chronic invalidity and with the impotence of advancing years, usually working on the plan of admitting sick and decayed persons for the remainder of their lives.

With the Reformation monastic benevolence came to an end, and as there was no agency with resources for the purpose the care of the sick and aged presented a problem of increasing importance. Cowane's Hospital, founded in Stirling in 1637, for the care of twelve decayed members of Stirling guildry, was an isolated attempt to continue after the pre-Reformation tradition, and though, thanks to its rich endowment, it continued to exist for a couple of centuries, it was closed in 1852, the trustees preferring the principle of giving grants to the beneficiaries in their own homes. Some of the pre-Reformation hospitals did exist in a reorganized form for a long time, such as Trinity Hospital in Edinburgh, of which a minute of the town council in 1578 refers to twelve furnished beds then made ready for " pepill seiklie and vnabill to laubour for thair leving." These people, who were called " bedesmen," were given an allowance for food and clothing. Trinity Hospital continued its work until 1845, since when its revenues have been employed in giving grants to aged and sick persons of the city. At the time of the Reformation an hospital in connection with the Dominican convent of nuns reverted to the Town Council of Edinburgh, and was used in 1575 as an isolation hospital for patients suffering from plague.

2

At a much earlier date there are records of the hospitalization of patients suffering from other infectious diseases, notably leprosy, regarding which a fund of valuable information was made available by the researches of Sir J. Y. Simpson. Among the earliest leper hospitals in Scotland were those at Aldcambus in Berwickshire, dating back to the time of William the Lion ; at Aldnestun in Lauderdale, under the control of the Abbey of Melrose ; and at Kingcase, on a bleak moor near Prestwick, in Ayrshire, probably dating back to before the time of King Robert Bruce. In those early days the proximity of this hospital proved a constant source of anxiety to the inhabitants of Prestwick, and many regulations were made to prevent contact between the townspeople and the lepers. In course of time the hospital grants were perverted and were ultimately acquired for £300 by the burgh of Ayr, the revenue from the endowments being made over to the poorhouse at Ayr.

There was a leper house in Glasgow, said to have been founded in 1350 by Lady Lochow, who is reputed to have feued out the ground on which the east side of Gorbals is built and appropriated the feu-duties to founding and supporting St. Ninian's Hospital for the reception of lepers. There seems to be some doubt about the precise date at which this hospital was founded, as there is about the date at which the hospital ceased to function ; though it is recorded that " the disease wearing out of fashion before the Reformation, the rental became a pension to the indigent who chose to be inrolled under that description." It is certain that to this leper hospital patients were regularly sent by the magistrates, and that there were similar leper hospitals in other Scottish cities. That in Stirling dated back to the fifteenth century, while that in Aberdeen seems to have been founded about 1519, and remained in use until the early eighteenth century, when its resources were appropriated to establish a fund for a proposed lunatic asylum. In Edinburgh a leper-house was established in 1591 in Greenside, but was demolished in the following century, the stones being used for other public purposes. There were other leper-houses at Rothfan, near Elgin, one of the earliest, and at several points in Shetland, where the leper-houses were not so much hospitals as small huts hastily thrown up in the fields to secure the isolation of infected persons.

Nearly all leper hospitals in Scotland were small, accommodating only some eight or twelve patients, and they served as receptacles for the isolation of infected persons, not as medical institutions aiming at cure. Lepers were required to withdraw from society, and were almost necessarily compelled to seek the shelter of the lazar-houses. The extent of the endowment of these places varied considerably ; a few, like that at Kingcase, were comparatively well off, but in most the lepers had to eke out a precarious existence by begging. In the early forest laws of Scotland it was laid down that when wild beasts were found dead or wounded, the flesh was to be sent to the house of the leper men, if any such happened to be situated near-by. Another old Act provided that flesh of pork or salmon found to be corrupt in the market, and accordingly seized, was to be sent to the lepers.

There were drastic regulations governing the conduct of leper-houses, and sometimes, as at the Greenside Hospital, Edinburgh, where the inmates were bound to observe these rules under penalty of death, to encourage their compliance " a gallows was erected at the gavel of the hospital for the immediate execution of offenders." It was ordained that none of the inmates should leave the hospital night or day, workday or holiday, and that no-one should be allowed to enter the hospital unless to remain in it, " and that they kaip the dure of the said hospitall fast and clois, fra the dounpassing of the sone to the rysing thairoff, under the payne of hanging." One of the inmates, and only one, was specifically authorized to go to market to purchase provisions for the colony. One of the statutes of the hospital was that none of the lepers should " cry or ask for alms, uther ways then be thair clapper ; and that every ane of thame, his day about sitt at the dore of the said hospitall to that effect, the rest allwayes remaining within the samyn, and that they distribute equallie amongs thame quhat soever money they purches be thair said begging." The rules established for the domestic and religious duties of the inmates belonging to the hospital were few and simple.

" That the said persons, and ilk ane of thame, leif quetlie, and gif na sclander, be banning, sweyring, flyting, skalding, filthie speaking, or vitious leving, or any oyder way, under the paynes to be enjoynit by the counsall."

" That thair be appoyntit ane ordinair reider to reid the prayeris evrie Sabboth to the said lepperis, and ane commodious place appoyntit to the said reider for that effect."

Much more extensive provision had to be made for dealing with the outbreaks of plague that swept over the country in the Middle Ages. Only occasionally was it possible to accommodate sufferers in hospital, and so great was the panic with which epidemics were viewed that, according to Chambers, the families that proved to be infected were compelled to remove with all their goods and furniture out to the Burgh Muir, where they lodged in wretched huts hastily erected. Their clothes were meanwhile purified by boiling in a large cauldron erected in the open air, and their houses were cleansed by specially appointed officers. The enforcement of these regulations was under the care of two citizens selected for the purpose and called " Bailies of the Muir " ; for each of whom, as for the cleansers and bearers of the dead, a gown of grey was made with a white St. Andrew's cross before and behind. Since in a single year an outbreak of plague carried off 2,500 citizens in Edinburgh alone, it can well be understood that the condition of these plague-camps in the sixteenth century was very terrible. The position in Glasgow was similar. When an outbreak of plague occurred there in 1646, wooden huts were erected on the Town's Muir, at a considerable distance from the town. To these huts the infected were transported and there they received medical attendance at the charge of the burgh funds. A superintendent was appointed, with special instructions to " take notice of the graves." Councillors were appointed in rotation, whose business it was to visit and inspect the huts on the Muir twice or thrice a week, and every Saturday to prepare a list of the inmates and of those who had died. It appears that at the height of the epidemic rich and poor alike were isolated and assisted, free of charge, at the cost of the common funds, as, at the end of the following year, the bailies determined to exact payment for the services of the " cleangers " from those householders who were in a position to pay.

3

The Town's Hospital of Glasgow, opened in 1733, contained some beds for the treatment of sick, as distinct from aged and infirm paupers. In 1766 the Faculty of Physicians and Surgeons had insisted that at least twenty beds should be fitted up " in a clean and decent manner, twelve of them for the sick poor from the hospital, the other eight to be occupied by the sick poor put in by the physician or surgeon, without any restriction to persons who belonged to the town, or had resided in it for any particular time." But this provision of sick-beds in the Town's Hospital was unsatisfactory and inadequate, and in time led to the movement which culminated, in December 1794, in the opening of Glasgow Royal Infirmary.

Already there had been sown in other centres the first seeds of the great voluntary hospital movement. The Royal Infirmary of Edinburgh made a humble start in 1729 with accommodation for six patients in a " small hired house " at the head of Robertson's Close. In 1739 the Town Council of Aberdeen convened a public meeting to consider the erection of an infirmary and workhouse within the burgh. It was decided to build, and the infirmary had fifty-four beds for occupation in 1742, Dr. James Gordon being appointed physician and surgeon at a salary of ten guineas per annum, he to supply all necessary drugs.

Meanwhile there was gaining ground in Scottish towns and cities a movement for the establishment of dispensaries for the medical care of the poor in their own homes. These dispensaries in some cases preceded the establishment of hospitals and were in others developed along with them. The earliest to be founded in Edinburgh was the Old Town Dispensary, founded by Dr. Andrew Duncan in 1776 and incorporated in 1818 as the Royal

Public Dispensary. The New Town Dispensary was established in 1815 despite opposition led by Duncan, the Old Dispensary, and the Lying-in Hospital. The opposition was doubtless based on jealousy, but the criticism was directed chiefly at two points in the constitution of the new venture—one that medicine and medical advice, including obstetric aid, was to be given to the poor where necessary " at their own homes," a new departure, and the other that office-bearers were to be elected by subscribers, which was regarded as dangerously democratic. Some of these early dispensaries had a severe struggle to make ends meet. Thus, early in 1846, the directors of the Glasgow Celtic Dispensary were driven to present a memorial to the Board of Supervision " in the earnest hope that you may be pleased to take the subject under your consideration, and in so far as it may be within your province, secure from the public funds an annual grant in aid of an institution so loudly called for by the peculiar circumstances and wants of a most numerous and most interesting class of our population." The directors explained that the dispensary had been instituted in the year 1837, with the object of providing medical advice and medicine, and in urgent cases medical attendance at their own houses, for poor strangers coming from the Highlands in quest of employment but who had not yet acquired a settlement in Glasgow, and who therefore had no legal claim on the various charitable institutions in the city. These labourers, who flocked to Glasgow in quest of work, had been found to be peculiarly liable to infectious diseases, " from being employed in occupations so different from that to which they had been accustomed in the open and pure air of their own native land." Many of them worked under conditions of great privation, and many were unable to make their wants known from their ignorance of the English language. There were in 1836 upwards of 22,000 persons, natives of the Highlands and Islands, in Glasgow, mostly working as labourers in public works and manufactures. These were the facts that led to the establishment of the Celtic Dispensary, and Robert McGregor, a member of the Faculty of Physicians and a native Highlander, acted as its surgeon. In their memorial to the Board of Supervision the directors stated that from failure of subscriptions " they feel themselves under the cruel necessity of closing this most popular institution." The expenditure during 1845 had amounted to £30, besides the surgeon's salary, while the income from annual

The old Lunatic Asylum in Parliamentary Road, Glasgow ; erected in 1810

Robertson's Close from the Cowgate : site of the old Infirmary
of Edinburgh

from a drawing by James Drummond, 1854

subscription amounted to only £10. To the petitioners the Board replied that while they had no power to grant assistance, they would bring the work and needs of the dispensary to the notice of the parochial boards in Glasgow.

These dispensaries did a great deal of valuable work for the relief of the sick poor. Sinclair reported that in the short period of ten years 85,327 patients enjoyed the benefits of the Edinburgh Dispensary, and added, " Such is the state of improvement to which these institutions are brought in Edinburgh that better provision for the indigent sick cannot be found in any other town in Europe. . . . Flannel also is given to infants when in want of clothing ; steel bandages presented to ruptured patients who would otherwise be unable to earn their bread ; and not only drugs but nourishing food, and even wine, when such articles are urgently necessary for the preservation of life, and when a highly dangerous disease is combined with great poverty." It is interesting to note this reference to the importance of ensuring that the patient should be treated until fit to return to work, the same point being made later (1840) by Cowan in Glasgow : " Relief must be extended after recovery until work is found."

In 1845 there were dispensaries not only in Glasgow and in Edinburgh but in such other Scottish towns as Aberdeen, Ayr, Coldstream, Dumfries, Dundee, Eccles, Elgin, Fochabers, Jedburgh, Kelso, Kilmarnock, Leith, Montrose, Paisley, Perth, and Stirling. These dispensaries dealt with up to 4,000 patients per annum, the remuneration of the doctors in charge ranging from £5, 5s. per annum in Kelso to £40 in Jedburgh. The report of the Montrose Dispensary for the year ending 1 June 1840 prided itself, with some justification, on the statistical presentation of its results. Altogether 418 patients were treated, 162 males and 256 females, many of these coming from the surrounding countryside. Ninety-six of the patients were under ten years of age, 135 between ten and thirty, and 58 over sixty. The patients were classified by broad occupational groups as well as by the disease from which they suffered. Sixty were returned as cases of skin disease (itch, etc., 25) ; 45 from common or typhus fever ; 40 from catarrh or influenza ; 30 from dyspepsia ; 27 from abscesses, boils, etc. ; 25 from injuries (2 fractures) ; 20 from diarrhœa, dysentery, etc. ; 18 from apoplexy or palsy ; 17 from female complaints, and 17 from dropsy ; 15 from consumption or debility, and 9 from each of rheumatism, inflammation of the lungs, diseases of the eyes, and "teething and worms." Of the patients treated, 286 were "cured," 34 "relieved," 11 "transferred to Infirmary," 22 died, and the remainder were under treatment.

There was no lack of work for the new voluntary hospitals. In the first year of its existence Edinburgh Royal Infirmary treated 35 patients, and in *An Account of the Rise and Establishment of the Infirmary*, published in 1730, a list is given of the patients treated, the parish from which they came, the duration of their stay, and the diseases from which they suffered. They came from Caithness, Mull, and Peterhead, as well as places nearer Edinburgh ; and among the conditions from which they suffered were some apparently more prevalent then than in later years. There were, for instance, 3 patients diagnosed as suffering from scorbutic conditions, 3 from " bloody flux," and 2, one of them a soldier, from ague. The length of stay ranged up to three months ; of the 35 patients, 19 were discharged as cured, and 5 as " recovered so as to go about their ordinary Affairs and requiring only some Time to confirm their Health, and to restore their Strength fully." Five were dismissed either as incurable or because of misbehaviour, 1 died (from consumption), and at the end of the year 5 remained in the infirmary. To this early report there was an appended note : " Besides those patients in the above list, who were all maintained in bed, board and medicines in the hospital, several out-patients were attended by the physicians and surgeons, who also gave advice daily to all sick who came to the Infirmary at the hours of visiting."

The original infirmary, opened with six beds in 1729, was situated in Robertson's Close, " one of several steep, narrow alleys on the southern slope of the Cowgate gorge." The rent of the premises was £4, 3s. 4d. sterling. The bedsteads were of wood, the mattresses of straw, the sheets of cotton covered with quilts. Lighting was by candle. A matron and one servant constituted the entire domestic staff. A new hospital designed for 228 sick people, " each in a distinct bed," was opened in 1741. On the ground floor were twelve cells for mad people. The rebellion of 1745 threw much additional work on the infirmary, and many sick and wounded soldiers were treated there. On the upper floor a ward was established for " lying-in women, sufficiently separated from the rest of the house," and under the direction of the Professor of Midwifery. In 1748 an apothecary's shop was fitted up in the hospital for supplying drugs to in-patients and out-patients. By 1776 there were in the hospital baths—hot and cold—intended for the use of people in the city, as well as patients in the infirmary ; there the inhabitants of Edinburgh apparently carried out their ablutions, the baths serving as a source of revenue to the institution. Comrie reports that another source of revenue had been tapped in 1746, when the managers of the infirmary and of the town's workhouse took a joint lease of an assembly hall and organized weekly dances on behalf of the hospital, under the patronage of ladies of quality, the profit to the infirmary being £100 per annum. In 1751 the managers decided to pay each of the physicians to the infirmary a salary of £30 per annum, though this practice lapsed later. For a time paying patients were admitted at the rate of sixpence per day, but this also lapsed. It is reported that after the peace of 1763 many sick and wounded soldiers were admitted to the hospital, and the Commander-in-Chief appointed a medical man " to visit the military wards regularly and to report thereon," apparently the prototype of the " Military Registrar " of later years. The nursing establishment about the end of the eighteenth century comprised " ordinary " and " supernumerary " nurses. " Each ward was in charge of an ordinary nurse, whose duties were to clean the ward before nine o'clock in the morning, make the beds, attend generally to the patients, and carry the medicine bottles to and from the apothecary's shop." Nurses' salaries were £5 per annum. There were no ordinary nurses on night duty.

In 1828 the infirmary moved into buildings vacated by the High School of Edinburgh, and about that time Sinclair wrote that it was not to be equalled by any similar institution in any other country, pointing out that in the Edinburgh Infirmary the average mortality was 1:25, which was lower than the figure for other European hospitals.

In May 1856, 144 beds were closed as a precautionary measure, the state of annual contributions rendering this neces-sary. The managers gave consideration to various possible ways of supplementing their resources, including application for govern-ment grant and the adoption of compulsory local assessment, but decided against these. About this time nursing arrangements were recognized to be bad, and the managers accepted an offer whereby an Association for the Training of Nurses provided the nurses (and their salaries), the managers providing rations and accommodation. The Association proposed to provide each nurse with two quart bottles of ale daily, if the managers were not prepared to do so. After a conference it was decided " that in future every nurse should have an imperial pint of good table beer daily, to be drawn off from the cask at the time of its being consumed, a slightly milder Prestonpans beer being ordered."

The Royal Infirmary in Glasgow was opened in December 1794, the foundation-stone having been laid with due ceremony two years before. The hospital, designed by Robert Adam, was planned in the form of a triple cross, and built at a cost of £8,494. It originally contained 150 beds. The patients admitted in the course of the year 1795 numbered 276, of whom 18 suffered from fever ; of these admissions 142 were discharged as " cured," 66 dismissed as incurable, and 18 died. The expenditure of the hospital during the year was £1,779 and its income £3,089. At first the posts of resident medical officer and apothecary were combined, but in 1799 they were separated, the Rev. James Allan, the Chaplain, being appointed apothecary. The number of patients admitted rose steadily until in 1815 it numbered 1,360, of whom 247 suffered from fever. In that year 779 of the patients were discharged as " cured," and 465 as " incurable," while 96 died. The total expenditure of the hospital was £3,459 and the income £4,271. Up to 1815 the hospital had no great difficulty in balancing its accounts. Eighty beds were added in 1816, but the accommodation was severely taxed two years later, when, of 2,336 patients admitted, 1,371 suffered from fever. The expenditure of the hospital in that year rose to £5,689 but was counterbalanced by a very considerable increase in income (to £8,619), the increase in revenue being probably stimulated by alarm of the populace at the prevalence of fever. It was decided to build a fever hospital in association with the infirmary, 100 of the fever beds being opened in 1829 and the remaining 120 in 1832. The total accommodation of the hospital was now 450 beds, of which 220 were for fevers ; " and besides this permanent fever accommodation it was on various occasions found necessary to provide temporary hospital accommodation, and to appropriate within the Infirmary rooms never intended for fever patients." These " fever " demands were almost entirely due to the prevalence of typhus fever, apart from the great cholera epidemic of 1832.

From the opening of the hospital in 1794 to the end of 1831

altogether 50,452 patients were treated, no fewer than 14,089 suffering from fever. Of the patients treated, 36,659 were discharged as "cured," and 10,382 as "incurable," while 4,967 died. Cleland, in presenting this statistical information, wrote that it had been fully expected that a note of the diseases from which the patients died would have been available, but that on examining the infirmary journals "it was found that the dismissals were kept in such a manner, as to render an article of that kind unworthy of credence." Prior to 1827 no official report was issued by the medical officers, but in that year the first report was issued ; it contained not only a full list of diseases treated, but particulars about operations performed : if amputation, whether circular or flap ; if lithotomy, mode preferred and instruments used. In the same year it was decided that a rain-gauge, thermometer, and barometer be set up, and readings recorded each day by the apothecary.

The infirmary at Aberdeen opened in 1742 with six beds and was soon involved in treating casualties of the Forty-five ; by 1749 the infirmary had nineteen beds, and a few years later extensions brought the number to eighty. A new building was completed in 1840, with accommodation for 230 patients and with separate wards for the treatment of medical, surgical, and ophthalmic cases. In Aberdeen, as in Glasgow, the infirmary had to undertake the treatment of fever cases. At the time of the epidemic of 1817–19, when there was accommodation for fever patients only, this was found to be altogether insufficient, and two other buildings had to be opened as fever hospitals. During the epidemic of 1831–32 two additional fever wards were opened in the infirmary, and its fever accommodation raised to 52 patients. In the big epidemic of 1837–40 over 1,900 fever patients were admitted, necessarily at great interference with the other work of the hospital, and in 1844 a fever house was established.

A dispensary was established in Dundee in the year 1782 to provide medical assistance for the necessitous poor. The town was divided into districts, of which the several medical practitioners took charge gratuitously, prescribing for patients who called, and visiting the poor at their own homes. The need for a house for the reception of patients soon became apparent, and a hospital was provided in the spring of 1798. It was capable of accommodating 56 patients, but beds for only 20 were provided in the first instance. By fitting up additional beds from time to time sufficient accommodation was afforded up to 1825, when it was found necessary to erect and furnish one of the wings for which provision had been made in the original plan. By further extension in the following year the available accommodation was raised to 104 beds. Soon after the opening of the hospital three medical attendants were elected to treat the patients, each for one year, with a fixed salary for the year. The hospital at Dundee, like those in other Scottish cities, was called upon to treat the prevalent (typhus) fever, and Thomson, in his *History of Dundee*, reported that while many patients were at first unwilling to enter a public hospital, " the typhus fever, which made such dreadful ravages in 1818, had the effect of removing this feeling, when the patients who were placed in the infirmary felt by experience the benefits arising from such an excellent institution."

At Paisley, too, the infirmary had its origins in a dispensary, instituted in 1786. A House of Recovery was subsequently opened and patients admitted in 1805. After several enlargements the house adopted the name of Paisley Infirmary, which later, when new premises were acquired, became the Royal Alexandra Infirmary.

The Northern Infirmary at Inverness, opened in 1804, combined the care of both physical and mental disease, accommodation of a kind for psychiatric cases being provided in basement " cells " (see page 280). Earlier, in 1782, there had been a somewhat similar combined provision for mental and physical illness at Montrose, where an asylum was opened, together with an infirmary and dispensary for the sick poor. In 1811 this institution was incorporated by Royal Charter under the title of the Royal Lunatic Asylum, Infirmary, and Dispensary of Montrose. The Montrose venture was primarily an asylum, and the association does not seem to have been a very happy one, for in 1839 a new Royal Montrose Infirmary was opened. The new infirmary was capable of containing over sixty beds, though not at first completely furnished. It had a laboratory annexed. The managers were apparently looking to the future, for in their report for the year ending 1 June 1840 they said : " The Infirmary, it is presumed, might now become, in no small degree, available to the instruction of a few youths destined for the Practice of Medicine." During that year 130 new cases were admitted and these were classified :

Abscesses, boils, tumours, etc.	39	Inflammation, etc.	5
Apoplexy, palsy, etc.	7	Injuries	19
Catarrh, etc.	9	Nervous affections	3
Consumption, etc.	4	Rheumatism	3
Dropsy, etc.	4	Skin, diseases of	11
Female complaints	7	Urinary organs, diseases of	7
Fever, etc.	12		

" Various operations (not of the higher kinds) had to be performed, and succeeded without exception." Ninety-seven of the patients treated were reported to be " cured and convalescent." There were 13 deaths—6 from exhaustion, usually soon after admission, 2 from dropsy, 2 from consumption, 1 from apoplexy, 1 from typhus, and 1 from intemperance.

At Greenock the infirmary developed from a previously existing dispensary ; a " House of Recovery " was opened in 1809 and subsequently extended, and a new hospital was opened in 1868.

At Elgin, Dr. Gray's Hospital was built from the estate of Alexander Gray, Surgeon on the Bengal Establishment of the Honourable East India Company, and a native of Elgin, who had bequeathed the sum of twenty thousand pounds sterling for the establishment of a hospital for the benefit of the sick poor of that town and of the county of Moray. He also bequeathed to it the residue of his fortune after deduction had been made of other benefactions and of provision for his family. Dr. Gray's will is an interesting one. He was apparently not disposed to benefit unduly " the most abandoned and deliberately infamous wife that ever distinguished the annals of turpitude," and the hospital benefited accordingly. Dr. Gray invested the Provost and Town Council of Elgin, " who ought to have the interest of such an Institution much at heart," with a power to inspect the hospital. He directed that in order to prevent abuses " no person who has any charge or control on the Institution be employed, either directly or indirectly, on supplies for the sick ; that no expense be incurred under pretence of meeting to consult for the benefit of the Hospital." Dr. Gray also bequeathed the annual interest of two thousand pounds sterling " for the use of the Reputed Old Maids in the Town of Elgin," the money to be paid " into the hands of the Two Clergymen and Physicians of the Town of Elgin, to be distributed by them to the proper objects, as these Gentlemen, from their superior education and domestic knowledge, must be the best judges of this charity." Gray's

Hospital was opened for the accommodation of patients on 1 January 1819.

Perth Royal Infirmary was opened in 1838, and by 1845, in addition to those named, there were infirmaries at Ayr, Elgin, and Kelso. In that year the infirmary at Aberdeen had 270 beds, that at Dundee 120, at Greenock 100, at Perth 84, at Dumfries 80, at Elgin and at Montrose each 60, and at Ayr 40. Most of the infirmaries gave some remuneration to their medical staffs, the honoraria ranging from £20 to £60 ; but some of them, like that of Greenock, gave no remuneration, and in others payment was subsequently abandoned.

4

Meanwhile a beginning had been made with the provision of hospital accommodation for special cases. As early as 1831 there was in Glasgow, in addition to the Royal Infirmary, special provision in the Lock Hospital for males and in the Magdalen Hospital for females, the two having between them 60 patients. There were 37 pupils in the Deaf and Dumb Institution, 40 blind persons in the Blind Asylum and in the Town's Hospital, and 4 patients in the Eye Infirmary. By 1840 there were also 14 beds in the University Lying-in Hospital and 18 in Glasgow Lying-in Hospital, both of these having associated dispensaries. Indeed there were in Glasgow at that time many dispensaries, for in addition to the twelve district " surgeoncies " of the city there were similar " surgeoncies " in Barony and Gorbals, as well as the Celtic Dispensary and that associated with the Royal Infirmary. In Edinburgh there was similar expansion : a Lying-in Hospital was opened in 1793, and the Royal Hospital for Sick Children, the first hospital in Scotland devoted to this special type of sickness, in 1860, with 24 cots.

One feature of the institutional provision in Edinburgh that provoked considerable interest in the early part of the nineteenth century was an activity of the House of Correction (" for offenders against society "), for which, in the envious words of the Committee of the Town's Hospital of Glasgow, " Mr. Stirling, the Superintendent, deserves a statue for a scheme he contrived to reform prostitutes." Mr. Stirling's scheme consisted in removing the women to a clean house, and giving each not money but a pound of oatmeal daily with salt, water, and fire. This he regarded as sufficient to hold body and soul together, and when the women sought more comfort he told them that work would procure them plenty. He provided wool and " they gradually began to spin," and, later, " some of them appeared to be thoroughly reformed."

Sir Henry Littlejohn in his list of the public institutions in Edinburgh in 1861 grouped together the Royal Infirmary, the Maternity Hospital, the Hospital for Sick Children, the Deaf and Dumb Institution, and the Lunatic Asylum. There was also some provision for the sick poor, mostly those suffering from the more chronic types of illness, in the poorhouses serving the three parishes—City, St. Cuthbert's, and Canongate. Sir Henry also mentioned, as being in a special category, Gillespie's Hospital, " for, although it is a charitable institution, it is strictly limited to the aliment and maintenance of old men and women from the age of fifty-five years." The House of Refuge in the Canongate accommodated about 400 persons, many of them suffering from incurable diseases, and nightly afforded shelter to numbers of the wandering poor. The Magdalen Hospital, with accommodation for 66 persons, had by 1861 been removed to an admirable site beyond the city.

Sir Henry was a leading advocate of the transfer of the Royal Infirmary to a new and more open site. He felt strongly that the grounds of the infirmary ought not to be encroached upon by buildings, whether temporary or permanent in character. He recalled that during epidemics of fever, in which the house accommodation proved too limited for the enormous number of cases, temporary provision had been made by erecting wooden sheds. There was necessarily great overcrowding, and heavy demands for nursing and superintendence were made on the resources of the institution. Sir Henry obviously welcomed the resolution of the managers never again to allow the grounds of the hospital to be occupied by such temporary erections, or to admit more cases of infectious disease than the hospital could reasonably accommodate. This decision had been intimated " to the parties on whom the onus lies of providing for the sick poor during the prevalence of epidemic disease, viz. the various Parochial Boards." During an outbreak of smallpox a short time previously two of the city parishes had provided small hospitals, but when the danger passed away these hospitals were applied to other uses, and Sir Henry thought it was time " that a suitable building should be set apart in some central locality as an hospital, which might be useful in an epidemic."

In nearly all Scottish towns and hospitals in the nineteenth century this problem of how to deal with major epidemic prevalence was a dominant one. Nowhere was it more compelling than in Glasgow. The Royal Infirmary had been opened in 1794 and enlarged in 1816, serving not only the city and its suburbs but also villages and country parishes for many miles around. In times of epidemic more and more of the accommodation was absorbed by cases of fever ; in 1818, at the height of an epidemic of typhus, the figure actually reached 60 per cent., and that although the managers were compelled for a time to shut their doors. " The same tragic drama," wrote Russell in the second half of the nineteenth century, " was now enacted as was witnessed on the occasion of every subsequent epidemic up to quite recent times." A fever committee of citizens was appointed, public subscriptions were collected, and while the epidemic was still raging efforts were made to obtain sites for setting up fever hospitals. But these efforts were thwarted by the opposition of the neighbourhood. However, the infirmary itself admitted cases of infectious disease, and also for a long time undertook the cleansing and fumigation of the houses from which the patients came.

In course of time the " injustice and inefficiency of this method of using the charitable organization of the Infirmary as an instrument for the suppression of epidemics as a matter of public policy " came to be recognized. The system was full of abuses. One of the physicians to the infirmary wrote of the difficulty of securing admission for fever patients : " There must be no patronage of individuals ; there must be no roundabout application necessary to the Magistrates, Governors, clergymen, or alders." With the evolution of the new poor law organization, the parochial boards tended to meet their obligations to provide medical treatment for the sick poor by erecting temporary wooden sheds when the need was greatest, only to abandon these as a threatened epidemic passed. These local temporary provisions, as Sir Henry Littlejohn pointed out in Edinburgh, afforded no real solution to the problem of epidemic control, or any assurance that the general hospitals would be allowed to carry on in time of epidemic prevalence with their real job of treating the general sickness of the community. Some years were yet to elapse before specially built fever hospitals of permanent structure began to be erected.

The Twelfth Annual Report (1857) of the General Board of Supervision mentioned complaints of poor persons suffering from disease or accident having been sent from parishes in the country to hospitals in towns without prior arrangement for their admission, with the result that many poor people had become chargeable to the parish in which the hospital was situated.

At the time of the Census of 1861 it was found that the number of patients in hospitals for the sick in Scotland was 1,518, and commenting on this figure the Registrar-General wrote that these hospitals were almost confined to the large towns, " so that but a small proportion of the population can avail themselves of them."

There were few private nursing homes for the care of acute cases of general sickness in Scotland until well on in the nineteenth century, when, following the work of Lister, surgical practice had become so much safer.

5

Until near the end of the eighteenth century there was virtually no provision for the insane in Scotland. A notandum by Lord Fountainhall in 1681 was to this effect : " In Scotland, having no Bedlam, we commit the better sort of mad people to the care and taming of chirurgeons, and the inferior to the scourge." The establishment in 1782 of the asylum at Montrose, through the good offices of Mrs. Carnegie of Pitarrow, was the first of its kind. Before it was built, the magistrates were frequently under the necessity of confining lunatics in a common prison, " where they were liable to have their disorders increased by the publicity of the place of their confinement, and often exhibited the most shocking scenes of blasphemy and desperation." " The position of the Tolbooth in which lunatics were usually immured, was a source of daily grievance to the compassionate inhabitants of Montrose, more especially during an age that slowly recognized the supremacy of benevolence as a remedy in mental diseases." " But now," wrote Sinclair in 1825, " they are employed during their lucid intervals in some species of manufacture, or in painting, reading, gardening, and other amusing occupations." In his suggestions for the improvement of the health of Scotland, Sinclair counselled that in large towns infirmaries should be provided, and that " wherever the population is sufficiently numerous to require an infirmary, a lunatic asylum should likewise be established."

The asylum at Montrose had a curious history, in so far as it had originally associated with it an infirmary and dispensary for the sick poor, though the partnership was broken in 1839, when the new Montrose Royal Infirmary was opened. The original building stood close to the harbour, and though it was repeatedly extended it was constantly overcrowded, because of the great demand for accommodation, and as a result the condition of the patients was not altogether satisfactory. As early as 1822 reports of the visiting medical officers protested against the gradual accumulation of old incurable patients. In 1828 the patients were classified into eight groups—genteel females, furious and mild ; common females, furious and mild ; genteel males, furious and mild ; and common males, furious and mild. In 1834 the first full-time medical superintendent, Dr. Browne, was elected, and he soon objected to the connection between asylum and infirmary, chiefly because " the best part of the house is at present devoted to the reception of surgical and other non-contagious diseases." Dr. Browne had strong views on the treatment of the insane. He was greatly in favour of employment and against punishment and restraint.

The Act to Regulate Madhouses in Scotland (1815) required such houses to be licensed and inspected by sheriffs accompanied by medical men. In his report on Montrose Asylum in the autumn of 1835 the Sheriff of Angus recorded that the practice of introducing a fiddler once a week continued. " The Sheriff happened to be visiting when the females were dancing. The music seemed to give pleasure to all, whether dancing or not, and, for a time at least, seemed to change the current of their ideas. . . . One of them who is religiously insane, and, on ordinary occasions, very annoying to visitors, by declaiming to them very sternly on religious topics, was dancing merrily, with her Bible in her hand, and came up to the Sheriff, and made some observations as to turning their kirk into a ball-room, and laughed heartily."

From 1782 to 1824, 412 patients were treated in Montrose Asylum, and of these 129 were said to be " completely recovered " ; from 1825 to 1840, 294 patients were admitted, and 152 " completely recovered."

In 1855 the Royal Commissioners who visited the asylum found that the pauper patients were divided into four classes, beginning with the convalescent and quiet and descending by grades to the refractory and dirty. The ventilation of the dormitories was bad. It was then the custom in the asylum, when patients were violent and destructive, to remove all their clothing and to supply them with no clothes, coverings or bedding except blankets and straw. The house was badly supplied with water, which in summer was apt to fail altogether, and there was only one drain to receive all the sewage of the house, " which proves a great inconvenience to the servants."

Some of the male patients worked in the fields and some were engaged in picking oakum and making nets. A few females were occupied in the washing-house and laundry and others in sewing and knitting. By way of entertainment some of the patients had " the benefit of frequent excursions," and there was usually a dance once a week. Some of the trusted pauper patients were permitted to play quoits and bowls of an evening on the links, and there was a billiard room for the private patients.

No mechanical restraint was employed in the asylum, but instead there was resort to lengthened seclusion, sometimes continuing for weeks or even months. The seclusion cells were seriously unsatisfactory. It was said that the condition of the asylum was most injuriously affected by incurable and degraded cases sent in from Highland parishes only at the most advanced stage.

The Aberdeen Asylum, opened for the reception of patients in 1800, was instituted by the managers of the Aberdeen Infirmary for the accommodation of lunatics belonging to the town of Aberdeen and neighbouring counties ; the institution was governed by a body chartered to manage the Infirmary and Lunatic Asylum of Aberdeen. Despite repeated extensions the asylum was constantly overcrowded. It had accommodation for private patients as well as for paupers.

Mechanical restraint by means of the straight waistcoat or muffs was not used, but in its stead, as at Montrose, lengthy seclusion was employed. There were ten small airing courts and four " seclusion yards," which were paved with asphalt and were used for patients labouring under maniacal excitement. Some of the patients worked in the fields and some of the females helped with the work of the washing-house and laundry.

When the asylum was visited by the members of the Scottish Lunacy Commission in 1855, it was found that the patients generally seemed to be well looked after in their persons and clothing, and sufficiently fed. " Many of the paupers, however, especially those who are town-bred, complain of the porridge-diet for breakfast, for which the resident physician is not authorized to substitute tea."

The movement that led to the establishment of the Edinburgh Royal Asylum was largely instigated by Dr. Andrew Duncan and his colleagues of the Royal College of Physicians. Duncan first mooted the scheme in 1791, but there was difficulty in raising funds, and though in the year 1806 a grant was obtained from Parliament of £2,000 out of the fund arising from the forfeited estates, the asylum was not opened until 1813, and then only under difficulty. For a long series of years the want of funds and the difficulty of classifying patients in a small establishment practically excluded the poor from the asylum. In 1836 negotiations commenced between the town council and the managers of the asylum, with a view to transferring to it the whole of the patients then in the city bedlam. An arrangement was concluded whereby the managers undertook to erect additional buildings and to provide accommodation for the whole of the lunatic poor of the city. The building was considerably extended between 1840 and 1847, but it was invariably fully occupied. The managers were already heavily loaded with debt and applied to the Government for a loan to enable them to complete the asylum buildings. This application was unsuccessful, but having by a special Act obtained power to borrow, the managers went on in 1855 to extend the hospital further.

Private and pauper patients were admitted. The construction and furnishing of the asylum were better than in those at Montrose and Aberdeen. There were separate sick-rooms, two to each ward. Attempts were made to provide for the entertainment of the patients by concerts, dances, lectures, and occasional country excursions. Some of the male patients were employed in agricultural labour, carpentry, and tailoring, and some of the females in the wash-house and laundry and in sewing, but the provision of suitable employment was not so extensive as it might have been. Mechanical restraint was not used, but, as at Montrose and Aberdeen, seclusion was much employed. The asylum was always seriously overcrowded.

Up to the beginning of the nineteenth century there was no proper provision in Glasgow for the guardianship and treatment of the insane. Before that time a ward or two in the Town's

Hospital were devoted to the reception of the insane poor, but the accommodation was wretched. The "cells," as they were specially and aptly named, were horrible dens, cold and damp and dreary, simply places of restraint, since devoid of all positive function whether of treatment or even of humane guardianship. For the insane of the well-to-do classes there was no local provision of any kind. The first to make a movement for a separate institution were the directors of the Town's Hospital, for the state of the "cells" there had attained notoriety in the city. In 1804 the collection of funds to build an asylum commenced, and in 1810 the foundation-stone was laid. The hospital, then known as Glasgow Asylum for Lunatics, was situated in what is now Parliamentary Road, and in December 1814 the patients, forty-one in number, were transferred from the cells of the Town Hospital to the new institution. The new asylum was regarded as probably the best of its kind constructed in Britain, "and perhaps in Europe." The staff consisted of the superintendent and matron, a male and a female keeper, a porter, a man for attending to the furnaces of the heating apparatus, a cook, a housemaid, one woman employed in washing and one in sewing.

From Cleland's account of conditions in 1831 it appears that the number of insane persons in the Lunatic Asylum, Garngad House Private Asylum, and the Town's Hospital amounted in all to 264, of whom 212 were described as "insane," 11 as "idiots," and 41 as "silly in mind." The majority of the patients were in middle life.

The asylum in Parliamentary Road continued to do good work, but, like others of its kind, was seriously overcrowded. Until 1837 the office of superintendent was held by a layman, the medical work of the hospital being carried on by a visiting physician whose duty it was to visit the hospital three times a week, the medical records being written by the apothecary. About 1838 the directors decided that the time had come to provide a new institution giving more extensive and better accommodation.

The old hospital in Parliamentary Road and part of the grounds were sold to the directors of the Town's Hospital, and a new site of sixty-six acres purchased at Gartnavel. The foundation-stone of the new hospital was laid in 1842 with considerable ceremony. A procession consisting of representatives of the Town Councils of Glasgow, Paisley, and Greenock, and of parishes in the neighbourhood of Glasgow, representatives of the Merchants' House, the Trades House, the Clergy, the University, and the Faculty of Physicians and Surgeons, headed by a military band, and accompanied by a military guard, formed in George Square and marched to Gartnavel for the ceremony. For many years the hospital, in addition to providing accommodation for private patients, received rate-aided patients from Glasgow and the surrounding districts.

The number of patients admitted each year to the Glasgow Asylum never exceeded one hundred until 1836, when 122 patients were admitted. Thereafter the yearly admission rate showed a steady increase, and in the first year of the new hospital's work 327 patients were admitted. This increase was due in part to the removal to the asylum of many pauper patients, who before that time had been farmed out in Arran and elsewhere by parochial authorities. In 1846 there were 769 patients resident in the hospital, but a diminution in numbers began in 1848, due to the transference of pauper patients to lunatic wards erected in connection with the workhouses of some of the larger parishes.

Dr. MacNiven has provided some interesting notes about the types of mental illness dealt with in the earlier years of the hospital's existence. The supposed causes of mental illness in 1838 included, in addition to such causes as anxiety, drunkenness, grief, and heredity, " political excitement," " reading works of fancy," and " excessive mental exertion," while in 1842 the illness of two patients was attributed to " seeing an execution," and in one to " weaning without necessary precautions."

Dr. Hutcheson, the first superintendent, had much to say about the influence of social conditions on mental illness, and particularly of alcoholism. " Want and intemperance go hand-in-hand. Whenever a man falls below a certain point in physical comfort he becomes reckless, and sensual enjoyment forms his only pleasure . . . and I look on it to be a vain effort to attempt any moral or religious improvement unless at the same time the wants of the body be supplied."

A reading of the earlier reports of the hospital suggests that this was from the beginning conducted on humane and enlightened lines. Harshness and coercion on the part of the attendants were condemned, as were also depleting methods of treatment, such as blood-letting. An ample diet, fresh air, exercise, occupation and amusements, and sedatives to calm the mind were

The old Asylum of Montrose, first of its kind in Scotland

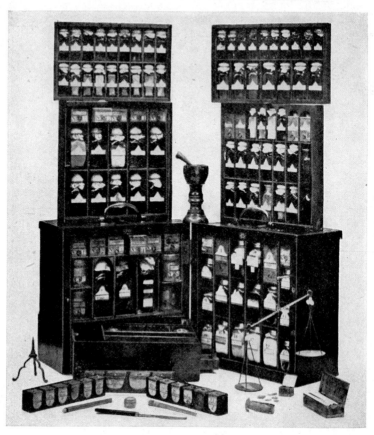

The medicine chest of Prince Charles Edward, showing the
elaborate equipment then in use

by courtesy of the Royal College of Physicians of Edinburgh

repeatedly mentioned as remedial measures. It was recognized that one of the most beneficial factors in the treatment of the insane was daily occupation, and there were occupational work-shops for weaving, tailoring, shoemaking, carpentry and saddlery, as well as facilities for sewing, carding, spinning and dressmaking. There were billiard rooms and a library ; and Dr. Hutcheson stressed the importance of reading and music as therapeutic measures. In his report for 1830 he wrote, " Did the forms of the Established Church, to which we are bound to adhere in religious services performed in the Asylum, permit the use of the organ, I am convinced that they would be more impressive and produce a most beneficial effect." Dr. Mackintosh, who was then super-intendent, reported in 1859 that the bagpipes were " occasionally played in the grounds for the benefit and pleasure of the patients from the Highlands of Scotland, whose spirits were elevated and cheered by the stirring sounds of the national instrument."

Mechanical restraint was abolished in the hospital as early as 1841, and the superintendent of the time declared that there was infinitely less violence and struggling, and less destruction of furniture, and that patients generally were improved in their conduct as a result of the abolition of restraint.

The governors of the Royal Infirmary of Dundee had long felt the want of a place of confinement for lunatics belonging to the city and to the neighbouring parishes, and in 1805 they appointed a committee to procure subscriptions for building an asylum. The foundation-stone of the edifice was laid in 1812 but the asylum was not opened for the reception of patients until 1820. The building as at first erected was of limited dimensions, and numerous additions were made subsequently. In his *History of Dundee* Thomson claims that Dundee Asylum was one of the first three in Scotland to adopt the policy of non-restraint in the treatment of its patients, and that the whole establishment was from the beginning conducted on the most modern of approved principles. One striking feature of the institution was the importance attached to occupational therapy. " Labour of many kinds, recreation, exercise, and some social intercourse among the patients are employed to promote their health and prevent the mind from brooding over its imaginary ills ; and thus a proper foundation is laid for other remedial measures, and powerful auxiliaries are engaged to render the medical treatment effectual." The chief occupations were weaving linen for sheeting and cotton bagging, picking manilla and hemp rope, mat-making, pumping water for the use of the establishment, gardening, domestic work, knitting, and shirt-making. "Those who are too old or infirm to work, or those whose rank in life is such that they have been unaccustomed to it, are furnished with a variety of amusements and other means of passing the time as agreeably as possible—reading, writing, music, billiards, hand-ball, and keeping pets." Thomson claimed that the Dundee Asylum "was the first in Scotland to carry out this judicious system of employment to any extent."

The number of patients continued to increase. In 1845 it was 208, and patients had to be declined. In the report for 1844–45 the cures were said to have numbered 477 out of 1,091 patients admitted since the opening of the hospital in 1820 (43·7 per cent.), and the average annual mortality for the same period was stated to be 6·1 per cent. "In conclusion," wrote Thomson, "Dr. Nimmo has performed several difficult operations most skilfully and most successfully. The patients on whom he performed the operation for rupture still live, and are in the enjoyment of bodily health."

When the Royal Commissioners visited the asylum in 1855 they found that of the 213 patients 40 were private patients. The asylum was particularly clean and well-ventilated but badly overcrowded, and often two patients were found together in rooms originally intended for one. Mechanical restraint was not employed, nor seclusion used to undue extent. "There is, however, a deficiency in the means of personal cleanliness, and recourse is had to objectionable contrivances in dress to counteract improper tendencies. The means of occupation are insufficient."

Murray's Royal Asylum for Lunatics, Perth, was opened in 1827 for 80 to 100 patients, and extensions for 60 more were added in 1834. The grounds surrounding the house were laid out in walks, gardens, bowling-green, and cricket-ground. In 1855 there were in the asylum 60 private and 75 pauper patients. A considerable number of the male patients found employment in the garden, and a few in shoe-making and tailoring, but the Lunacy Commissioners thought that on the whole there was a deficiency of books and objects calculated to interest the patients, and of the means of occupation.

The want of an asylum for the treatment of pauper lunatics in Moray had long been felt, and about 1826 the trustees of

Gray's Hospital proposed to the land-holders of the county that if they would contribute liberally towards the erection of a pauper lunatic asylum, and if the plan met with general approval, the trustees would grant ground for the purpose, give a handsome subscription towards the buildings, and assist in paying the wages of a keeper. This offer was accepted, and the asylum was opened in 1835 and extended in 1850. The medical officers of the asylum were shared with Gray's Hospital, and in 1855 the house contained 39 patients. Those from the county of Moray had a preference, and none from other counties were received until all from Morayshire had been accommodated. All the patients were received at pauper rates and none were admitted except through the Inspectors of Poor. The chief occupation of the male patients was agricultural labour, and the females were mostly occupied in sewing and in the laundry and wash-house. Means of amusement were very scanty and the supply of books small, but " the precentor attends for an hour every Wednesday for the purpose of playing the violin and singing with the patients."

The Crichton Institution, Dumfries, was opened for the reception of patients in 1839, and ten years later a second institution was erected on adjoining ground, named the Southern Counties Asylum, and receiving pauper patients only. The Crichton Institution accommodated 120 patients and the Southern Counties Asylum originally 150, but that number was soon exceeded. The Lunacy Commissioners thought very highly of the Crichton Institution, and especially of its facilities for recreation and amusement. The equipment and arrangements in the Southern Counties Asylum, though simpler, were also found to be satisfactory. Mechanical restraint was never used, except in the case of patients who refused to have food, and seclusion was not employed as a substitute. " This Asylum is very ably conducted."

In 1846 that part of Perth Prison originally occupied by the French prisoners of the Napoleonic wars was made available for the reception of the insane in consequence of a desire on the part of the managers of existing asylums to be relieved of the care of criminal lunatics. There was accommodation altogether for 35 males and 13 females, and in May 1835 the number of insane prisoners was 27. The Lunacy Commissioners did not like the arrangements which they found in the criminal lunatic wards at Perth : " The whole arrangements are made principally with a view to the security of the patients, and scarcely, if at all, with reference to their treatment as sufferers from disease." There was an almost complete lack of occupational recreation, and two patients were habitually under restraint. When they visited the prison again eighteen months later the Commissioners found three patients under restraint : " One had an iron chain placed round his waist, to which one hand was fastened ; another had a hand fastened in a similar way, and his legs were hobbled by rings placed round the ankles and connected together by an iron chain. The legs of the third were restrained in the same fashion."

There were four cells for lunatics on the ground floor of each wing of Inverness Infirmary. The cells consisted of stone vaults, which had no means of being warmed. The windows were strongly boarded up with only a small opening at the top for the admission of air and light. In winter there was no alternative between starving the patient with cold or keeping him in constant darkness. The cells measured $8\frac{1}{2}$ feet long by $8\frac{1}{2}$ feet broad and were about 9 feet high in the centre of the arch. The bedsteads were fixed wooden troughs with a bottom sloping towards the foot where a tray was introduced. At the head and foot were chains for the purpose of fastening the arms and legs of the patient. There were no water-closets or any facilities for washing.

The " cells " of the infirmary were used principally for the detention of patients until they could be sent to the chartered asylums in the south. Sometimes the Sheriff limited the period of their stay in Inverness to three weeks, but in the winter of 1854–55 a female patient was detained there for six months before being sent to Montrose Asylum, and during all this time she was kept in her cell with her hands muffled. The patients were not taken out for exercise, chiefly because there were no attendants to take the necessary charge of them. " There is indeed one man who is styled keeper of the lunatics ; but he is at the same time gardener, barber, and porter, and has neither the means nor the time to attend to the patients." The parishes paid at a rate of 1s. a day for their patients while they remained. " When they are sent to asylums in the south, they are generally accompanied by a policeman, and travel by the steamboat or outside the coach. . . . The parochial authorities complain much of the expense thus incurred."

The report of the Royal Commission on Lunacy classified the houses in which insane were received as falling into two groups—houses into which they were received under cognizance of the Sheriff, and houses into which they were received without such cognizance. Into the first group fell the chartered asylums, public asylums without a charter, poorhouses receiving patients either in separate wards or in common with ordinary paupers, private licensed houses, houses for single patients reported to the Sheriff, prisons and schools for idiots. The houses in which the insane were received without the cognizance of the Sheriff were unlicensed poorhouses, private houses not reported to the Sheriff in terms of the law, houses of relatives, and unlicensed private establishments. Altogether there were in Scotland on 14 May 1855 2,732 private insane patients and 4,642 pauper insane. These patients were distributed as follows :

	Private patients	Pauper insane
In chartered asylums . . .	652	1,511
In licensed houses	231	426
In poorhouses	9	667
In reported houses	10	31
In schools for idiots	12	3
In unlicensed establishments . .	18	6
With relatives	1,453	1,217
With strangers	297	640
Not under care of anyone . .	50	141
Total . .	2,732	4,642

While the conditions under which the insane lived in the chartered asylums were not always above reproach, they were, in general, very much better than the conditions prevailing in poorhouses and in private licensed houses. Some poorhouses " avowedly and habitually " received lunatic and fatuous patients, and almost all the others received casual patients from time to time. The sixteen Scottish poorhouses professing to receive insane patients were Falkirk, Dalkeith, Edinburgh City, Edinburgh St. Cuthberts, South Leith, Dunfermline, Kirkcaldy, Aberdeen, Old Machar (Aberdeen), Glasgow City, Glasgow Barony, Greenock, Paisley, Abbey (Paisley), Dumfries, and Rhinns of Galloway (Stranraer). All these poorhouses were visited by the

Royal Commissioners and all were criticized by them. The majority of their patients were mental defectives or had become "fatuous from age," but some were acutely ill. Thus, in St. Cuthbert's Workhouse, Edinburgh, there were 16 patients classified as curable and 66 as incurable. In most poorhouses admitting lunatics the attendants were paupers who received a shilling or so a week for acting in that capacity, and in the South Leith Poorhouse the two female attendants were remunerated by their children being received into the house. In many the fatuous paupers, not under warrant, were admitted without any medical certificate, the inspector of poor deciding whether a licence should or should not be taken out in any particular case. It was the duty of the house governor to receive all the patients sent in by the inspector of poor.

All the insane poor of the parish were received into the lunatic department of the Barony Poorhouse : none were sent to any chartered asylum or licensed house, and few, if any, were placed with relatives or strangers. The diet in the poorhouse was nominally according to the scale laid down by the Board of Supervision, but as there were complaints of scanty quantity the Parochial Board gave orders for an increase, which consisted principally of oatmeal. The lunatic wards at Greenock Poorhouse were said to constitute " a regular hospital for the treatment of insanity." Recent and curable cases were admitted as readily as others, and were permanently retained, unless they became extremely unmanageable, when they were sent away, not for their benefit but to get rid of the trouble and annoyance of keeping them.

There was great difficulty in securing admission to an asylum for poor patients who required such care. Several of the parochial boards of parishes in which there were poorhouses sought to establish at them wards for lunatics, but the Board of Supervision rightly took the view that these small establishments could not adequately take the place of properly planned mental hospitals, though undoubtedly preferable to the detention of pauper lunatics in private licensed houses. In 1851 the Board found it necessary to issue a circular pointing out that it was the duty of parochial boards and inspectors of poor to take care to send no poor person who was insane or fatuous to a poorhouse without having previously obtained the sanction of the Board and the licence of the Sheriff.

There were in Scotland in 1855 twenty-four private institutions licensed for the reception of the insane. Three of these were in Edinburgh, fifteen in the Musselburgh area, one in Aberdeen, and the others in the west of Scotland. The condition of lunatics in these licensed houses was determined partly by the rate of payment, but perhaps still more by the character of the proprietor : " as a class, those who receive pauper patients are totally unfit for the proper discharge of the highly responsible and delicate duties they undertake." The Royal Commission complained that licences had been granted to persons who had no knowledge whatever of the nature and treatment of insanity, who had no experience of nursing, and who were unprovided with sufficient capital to make satisfactory provision for the wants of those under their charge. At Musselburgh one proprietor had formerly been a victual dealer, another an unsuccessful baker, and another a gardener, while the last person who obtained a licence was a woman keeping a public-house, who had taken a second house for the reception of lunatics, " with the view, as we were told by her daughter, of keeping both for a while and continuing that which should prove the more successful speculation."

These houses varied greatly in size and contained anything up to ninety patients. Nearly all were overcrowded. Thus the licensed house of Lilybank, in Musselburgh, which was rented at £35 per annum, had a population of seventy-three patients, besides the family of the proprietor and the attendants. Proprietors of new houses sought to establish themselves by receiving patients at lower rates than those already in existence, and standards inevitably fell further. In some cases the proprietor of a licensed house was prepared to pay the travelling expenses and all other outlays incurred prior to the admission of pauper patients. The usual rate of payment for paupers in licensed houses was £20 per annum, while for private patients the rates varied between £20 and £350 per annum. There was no way of finding out the amount of food received by patients in these private houses. In the pauper houses the diet in general consisted of porridge and buttermilk, morning and evening, or of tea and bread, if the patient preferred them ; and of broth, with bread, potatoes and a small allowance of meat for dinner. The animal food, said to amount to about two ounces per patient, was always given in the broth. The food was usually served in a slovenly manner. The Royal Commissioners reported that although they could not ascertain the amount of food allowed to pauper patients in the licensed houses, they had no difficulty, on comparing their bodily condition with that of the same class of patients in the chartered asylums, in arriving at the conclusion that the latter were generally better fed.

According to the Annual Report of the Board of Supervision the number of fatuous or insane poor relieved during the year ending 14 May 1863 was 6,266. Nine years previously the figure had been 3,893.

The Royal Commission on Lunacy, reporting in 1857, found much to criticize in the provision for the insane poor of Scotland. The accommodation in asylums was barely sufficient for one-third of the insane. As a result, numerous private houses had been opened for the reception of pauper lunatics, and most of these presented gross abuses. Official visits were inadequate. The wards in poorhouses that had been opened to meet the demand for accommodation generally failed to afford proper means of treatment. Patients were often improperly detained in gaols for considerable periods. A large number of single patients were detained at home or illegally placed in the houses of strangers, often under very bad conditions. "A few are subjected to personal chastisement, some are permanently chained, others are placed in outhouses, or are locked up in small closets just capable of holding them." The inspectors of the poor assumed an un-warrantable power over pauper patients in keeping them at home or placing them in the houses of strangers, in selecting asylums for them, in removing them from asylums, and in removing them from a public asylum to a licensed house. Neither the Board of Supervision, the Sheriff, nor the managers or medical super-intendents of chartered asylums, exercised any check on this inordinate power assumed by inspectors. "In the treatment of the insane poor, curative means are frequently never considered by inspectors, who seem to think of nothing beyond safe custody, and the lowest possible expenditure."

The Commission made many concrete suggestions for the improvement of arrangements for the care of the insane, and from these arose in time the district asylums provided through-out Scotland, and a great tightening of machinery for safeguard-ing the interests of the insane.

Chapter XII

THE HEALTH AND WELFARE OF CHILDREN

I

INTEREST in the health and welfare of children is of recent growth, though the susceptibility of childhood to adverse social circumstances has long been known. In 1840 Cowan of Glasgow wrote that " the contrast between the labouring classes and those in easy circumstances is in no particular so strongly marked as in the relative number of the births and deaths of their children." Even sixty years ago child life was still regarded as of comparatively little value, interest being centred rather in the years of working output—an attitude of mind which touched the welfare of the young in many adverse ways. There was little time in the busy nineteenth century to give heed to the welfare of children, too often regarded as encumbrances for the few years before they could be put to work. Already in 1832 Cowan had quoted a prevalent view that smallpox, the chief cause of infant deaths at the beginning of the century, was " the poor man's friend," as it saved him the expense and trouble of a family. There was apparently a feeling that smallpox " or some other equally fatal malady, is essential to the comfort of the poor," and it was regarded as merely another manifestation of divine providence when the great epidemics of measles in the immediately ensuing years swept on to destroy many of the children who had through vaccination escaped death from smallpox.

Yet many centuries before the nineteenth there were evidences of effort to protect infant life. An ordinance of the Provincial Councils of the Church, held in Scotland in the thirteenth century, forbade mothers or nurses to place young children in the same bed with themselves, " by reason of the frequent dangers arising from this practice." In the sixteenth century the Presbytery had often to deal with the offence of " smooring bairns "—smothering children. There were many entries like this in the records : " Three women parochinaris of Cadder accusit of smooring their bairnis in the nicht are referrit to the Session of Cadder to be tryit thair." The delinquents were chiefly women, but on some occasions men appeared and were " rebuked for being art and part in smooring the bairn." These were cases in which the child had lost its life through the carelessness or intemperance of the parent. The punishment awarded was usually light ; for example, an entry of 27 April 1592 bears that the Presbytery " advises and resolves that smoorers of bairns mak thair repentance two Sondayes in sekcleith standing at the Kirk door." The offence was not easily stamped out—it continued for centuries—and there is an entry in the records dated 25 December 1647 to the effect that " a number of women in the toun having overlaid their children in their drunkenness, the Presbiterie advise that the old Act touching the repentance be revised and put in Execution." In 1690 an Act was passed anent murdering of children : " If any woman shall conceal her being with child during the whole space, and shall not call for and make use of help and assistance in the birth, the child being found dead or-missing, the mother shall be holden and reputed the murderer of her own child." A century and a half later, John Gibson, Surgeon in Lanark, reported to a committee then investigating the condition of the labouring population of Scotland, that there were a number of loose girls in the town and neighbourhood of Lanark, and that infanticide was by no means uncommon, although frequently managed so as to elude detection.

Hector Boece recorded in 1527 that in Scotland's heyday, then unhappily departed, " Ilk moder wes nurice to her awin barne "—if she could not nurse her child, grave doubt attached to its legitimacy ; and that strong measures were taken to preserve the vigour of the race : " He that was trublit with the falling evil or fallin daft or wod or havand sic infirmite as succedis be heritage fra the fader to the son, was geldit ; that his infeckit blude suld spreed na forthir. The wemen that was fallin lipper, or had ony othir infection of blude, was banist fra the company of men ; and gif sche consavit barne under sic infirmite, baith sche and hir barne war buryit quik [alive],"—an early Scottish essay in human genetics.

2

The comprehensive Poor Law Act of 1579, designed to punish strong and idle beggars, but to relieve the poor and impotent, contained a provision that if any beggar's bairns between the ages of 5 and 14 " shall be liked of by any subject of realm of honest estate," such person might have the bairn, by direction of magistrates or justices, to the age of 24 years in the case of a male child and to the age of 28 years in the case of a female child ; and if any such children departed, or were enticed away, from their masters, the same remedy lay against the child or his enticer as in the case of a " feit " servant or apprentice. An Act of 1597 extended the period of servitude to a lifetime, though it seems that there was difficulty in having these Acts rigorously applied. In 1617 there was another Act " anent the poor," and this laid it down that poor children were to be trained to labour, the children to be such as were certified to be poor and indigent and to have no means of living. These children " shall be bound and restricted to their masters, their heirs or assignes, in all kinds of service which shall be enjoined them, until they are past the age of 30 ; and they shall be under discipline to their said masters, and subject to their corrections and chastisements according to the merits of their offences, in all manner and sort of punishments, life and torture excepted." This Act contained a pious provision about the need for educating and training such children, but the emphasis was on servitude, and a thoroughly dangerous piece of legislation it was. Another pernicious development of the same year was the legalization of the practice of " arling " the children of colliers. An indigent collier could bind over his child at baptism to his master by accepting " arles " or earnest money, and the children were in fact commonly arled into slavery in this way. A later Act of 1661 complained that previous Acts anent the poor had been inefficient, and proceeded to set up companies for making " Linen cloth, Stuffs, etc.," ordaining that, " in each parish one or more persons be appointed at the charge of the heritors for instructing the poor children, vagabonds and other idlers, to fine and mix wool, spin worsted and knit stocking." Economic pressure on the poor was very great, and Graham records that for food children were in some cases actually sold to the plantations.

3

From the foundation of the Town's Hospital in Glasgow in 1733, many children were " relieved " by that institution, and during the period 1790–1830 the number shown in the accounts as being " on nursing wages " (put out to wet-nurse at the rate of 20s. per quarter) ranged between 105 and 1,072, the peak figure reached in 1820. In February 1802, illegitimate or adopted children were first admitted to the hospital on payment of £25, without any question being asked of those who presented them. From then until July 1818 the number admitted under this arrangement totalled 197 : of these 113 died, 52 were " at nursing," 12 returned to their friends, 9 were put out to apprenticeship or service, and 11 remained in hospital. The arrangement for the admission of such children was originally made " from motives of humanity," but it came to be " greatly abused " by persons sending infants from the most distant parts of the country, and frequently in a diseased state. In November 1818 the governors resolved that in future they would not admit children of this description except those whose parents had a domicile of three years' standing in Glasgow, and that the charge for admission should be £40, " being the minimum sum charged in Edinburgh." At Michaelmas 1819 there were 355 adults and 58 children in the Town's Hospital, as well as 212 children belonging to the hospital but boarded in various parts of the country. The board for the first year, exclusive of clothes and education, was 30s. per quarter, and 25s. thereafter. The superintendent of the hospital visited these boarded-out children annually, though such information as is available about the administration of the parent establishment scarcely suggests that this visitation was likely to be a powerful safeguard. One girl from the hospital was indentured as late as 1843 to a Kirkintilloch manufacturer, being bound for five years to " serve and obey " ; for every day she was off work during that time she was to serve two days free at the end of her five years' engagement, " which absent days shall be liquidated and proved by the master's word or oath if required . . . in place of all other proof." These children were often the victims of gross cruelty. The whole question of the management of the city poor in Glasgow was reviewed by a Committee of the Town's Hospital in 1817. The committee reported that boys were sent out from the hospital at the age of 9 or 10, when they were bound apprentices for the space of seven years, " for the consideration of food and clothing, except during the last year, when they are allowed a percentage on their earnings " ; and the committee obviously had some misgivings about this arrangement, for they added that, " It may be questioned whether they do not sometimes leave the house too young." The committee found that in the previous year, of above 100 children in the hospital, 30 girls were employed in making lace, and 20 boys and girls in tambouring, the remainder, except the very young, in picking oakum and cotton. They complained that these children were not really being prepared for a vocation in life ; the girls " are not prepared for service, and the boys go away equally awkward in their line."

In 1783 David Dale established his mills at New Lanark, long the best of their kind ; but even they depended largely on child labour, mainly orphans from Edinburgh. The children worked eleven and a half hours a day for six days a week—from six o'clock in the morning till seven o'clock at night, with a break of half an hour at nine o'clock for breakfast, and of an hour at two o'clock for dinner—being " educated " for nearly two hours at the end of their day's work. Information about this education, and many other interesting aspects of the labour of children at New Lanark, is contained in Mr. Dale's replies to questions addressed to him in 1796 by the chairman of the Manchester Board of Health. The questionnaire and the replies are printed on pages 93–6. Even allowing for the humanizing influence of Robert Owen, who took over the mills from his father-in-law in 1799, it is hard to take at its face value the statement, made fifty years later, that " the Company also supply excellent schools for the young, where all the necessary, and some of the ornamental, branches of education are taught at a very trifling expense." That Owen was aware that working conditions might seriously injure health—and especially the health of child workers—is apparent from his famous " Address to the British Master Manufacturers," in which he pleaded that no child should be employed under the age of twelve :

I think an intelligent slave master would not, on the sole principle of pecuniary gain, employ his young slaves even ten hours of the day at so early an age. And we know that judicious farmers will not prematurely put their young beasts of burden to work : and that when they do put them to work it is with great moderation at first, and we must remember too, in a healthy atmosphere. But children from seven to eight years of age are employed with young persons and women of all ages, for fourteen or fifteen hours per day in many of our manufactures, carried on in buildings in which the atmosphere is by no means the most favourable to human life.

The year 1802 saw the passing, by Sir Robert Peel's government, of the Health and Morals of Apprentices Act, which, with all its limitations, represented the first attempt to improve the lot of pauper children employed in cotton and woollen factories.

The Act forbade the employment of children at night, or for more than twelve hours by day ; demanded the provision of facilities for the elementary education of apprentices, and of sufficient clothing ; the whitewashing of factories twice a year, and their adequate ventilation. Two inspectors or visitors of the scheduled factories were to be appointed from among justices of the peace, one of them a clergyman. But the Act did not work well, despite its frequent amendments, and a Royal Commission was set up to investigate the whole position. The chief recommendations of the Commission were the limitation of working hours for all under 18 years of age, shorter hours for children under 13 years of age, a provision that children under 13 years of age should attend school, the appointment of professional inspectors of factories, and the issue of special rules applicable to particularly dangerous trades. The Factory Act of 1833, the outcome of this report, ordained that no children were to be employed under 9 years of age, that none between 9 and 13 years were to work for more than 8 hours a day, and that for those between 13 and 18 years the period of work was not to exceed 12 hours per day. The limitation of child employment did not, however, apply to lace and silk factories. In Forfar flax mills children who could just walk worked so long as they could be forcibly kept awake. By a new Factory Act of 1844, certifying factory surgeons were first appointed to examine workers under 16 years of age as to their physical fitness for employment, and employment of children under 8 years of age was prohibited in all factories. An Act of 1847 limited the hours of employment of women and young persons in cotton factories to 10 per day, but despite all these measures child employment continued on a large scale, and the factory inspectors reported that during the period between 1857 and 1862 adult male labour had decreased by 18 per cent., while child male labour had increased by 53 per cent. and child female labour by 78 per cent.

An Act had been passed in 1840 to prevent children from being sent up chimneys as brushers or cleaners, but it was only partially observed and many children continued to be burned, sometimes to death, in this occupation. In 1863 it was reported that the number of boy sweepers was on the increase, because magistrates hesitated to impose the fine of £5 imposed by the Act on the masters of children used in this way.

The lot of children in colliery districts was still worse. Children of 6 toiled all day underground for half a crown a week ; in 1825 an Act was passed to procure a 12-hour day for those under 16. In evidence to a Government Commission in 1840 Dr. Alison, who had been in practice in Tranent, wrote of children there of 7 or 8 being employed as " bearers " or " putters " in the pits, working for 10 or 12 hours at a time, some during the day, some at night, according to shift. " These poor children," he wrote, " present little of the buoyancy of youth, seem even comparatively careworn, and are often so little and so stunted as to appear younger than they are." Dr. Alison's neighbour in Inveresk thought that women should be discouraged from working in the mines when they had a young family to attend to at home. Both doctors agreed that the practice of drinking whisky in these districts was begun at a very early age, many mothers giving their children toddy as soon as they were born as a specific for " gripes " and indeed for the great majority of children's diseases and complaints. Children of 8 or 10 years of age often took a glass of toddy just as readily as their parents. " Nothing is done without whisky. The infant's head, the moment it is born, is washed with whisky ; as soon as it begins to cry, toddy is poured down its throat. . . . I have known boys about the age of 10 or 12 years in the habit of getting intoxicated occasionally. On extraordinary occasions, such as the ' New Year ' or ' Fair Day,' it is common for boys still younger to get intoxicated."

The publication in 1842 of a report on the employment of women and children in underground mines and collieries drew attention to the exhausting and degrading conditions of that work, and led to the passing in the same year of an Act which excluded women of all ages, and children of both sexes, from work in the mines.

It is not surprising that under such social conditions children fared ill. Symons, in the Report of the Select Committee on the Health of Towns, wrote that in Anderston two out of three children between the ages of 3 and 12 received no education, and that in Glasgow very young children were put to work at an early age at light operations in weaving. The factory regulations did not extend to hand-loom weaving or spinning at home or winding on the cops, which was usually the work of children. " They are employed at age 8 and taken into mills about the same age, despite the fact that the Factory Act prevents them being taken younger than 9." He added that the children of Glasgow appeared to be very emaciated, though not perhaps more so than in Manchester.

The rapid industrial development and the severe economic depression of the Hungry Forties encouraged, or perhaps compelled, the mothers of young children to take up factory work. Sometimes the children were left at home unattended, sometimes in the care of an older member of the family not yet sufficiently mature to be left with that responsibility. As an experiment a public nursery was established in Glasgow for the care of children whose parents were prevented by their work from taking care of them at home, or of children who were orphans. Healthy children, from eighteen months to six years of age, were admitted at the nominal charge of 1s. 6d. per week, and " So successful, indeed, has been the undertaking," said an early annual report on the venture, " that there is no doubt Glasgow will not long be the only city in this country that can boast of a nursery institution."

Commenting on the census of 1861 the Registrar-General calculated that 25 per cent. of the children under one year of age of workers engaged in the manufacture of cotton died in the course of a year, while the corresponding figure for the children of agricultural workers did not exceed 12 per cent. ; in the cotton trade father, mother, and all children above ten years of age were drawn away to the mills, so that the care of the infants devolved on " incapable old women or on mere children," and the Registrar argued that the occupation of the parent was therefore the direct cause of the mortality of the children. The medical officer to the Privy Council urged with little success that nursery accommodation should be provided in association with factories so that the worst of these abuses might be avoided.

4

Dr. Hutcheson, the first physician-superintendent of the Glasgow Royal Mental Hospital, held advanced views on education and training in childhood. In his report for 1842 he wrote : " By education I do not understand the common routine at present being pursued in families and in school, which is better calculated to confirm or call forth the predisposition of insanity than to eradicate it. To be of service it must be founded on more enlarged views, both of the physical and of the mental constitution of man. It must be begun on the first days of existence, and continue until all the powers of mind and body be fully developed." He went on to lay down rules for the upbringing of children, believing that much depended on the example set to the child by its nurse.

In 1816 David Stow established a Sunday evening school in which he gathered for conversation and biblical instruction the poorest and most neglected of the children in the Saltmarket of Glasgow, and eight years later, under his influence, a society was formed to establish a week-day training school in Drygate which ultimately became the first normal college in the kingdom for the training of teachers. Stow specially valued the playground, or " uncovered schoolroom," as a place where, under right super-vision, good physical and moral training might be secured.

In 1846 an educational census was taken by Sabbath School teachers in Glasgow, and it emerged that of children above six and under sixteen years of age the proportion attending day schools was 46 per cent., the proportion of children not at school and unable to read was about 25 per cent., and the proportion of children who could write was only 30 per cent. Even so, the general level of education in Scotland at that time cannot have been worse than that south of the Border, for in his report for the year 1863 the Registrar-General pointed out that only 10 per cent. of men and 22 per cent. of women were unable to write their names in the Marriage Register in that year. " These proportions," he said, " though not all that could be wished, contrast favourably with those of England ; for only 76·22 per cent. of men and 66·91 per cent. of the women who married in England in 1863 were able to sign their names ; while 23·78 per cent. of men and 33·09 per cent. of the women, not being able to write, were obliged to sign by mark." Judged by this educational criterion, Inverness and Ross and Cromarty appeared to be the most backward Scottish counties.

Sheriff Watson of Aberdeen established there in 1841 a ragged school for vagrant boys, and, two years later, another for girls. Other schools of the same kind were opened in Edinburgh by Dr. Robertson, but it was the pleading of Dr. Guthrie that gave the greatest impetus to the ragged school movement. In his Edinburgh pastorate Guthrie soon recognized that the most effective results were to be obtained among the young, and following his " Plea for Ragged Schools " in 1847, the " Original

Ragged Schools " were established in the city for the class whom he called " city arabs."

The Dean Orphanage in Edinburgh sprang from the Orphan Hospital and Workhouse, founded in 1742, and Cauvin's Hospital, founded by a one-time teacher of French in Edinburgh (1825) " for the endowment and maintenance of a hospital for the support and education of boys."

In the eighteen-forties proposals were put forward to establish in several parts of the country industrial schools for the children of poor parents, with a view to their education and instruction in some trade or occupation by which they might be " enabled honestly to earn their own subsistence." Schools of this type, voluntarily financed, had been established on a limited scale in Aberdeen and Perth with good results, though in 1850 Sheriff Watson (of Aberdeen) reported that many of the children who went to the industrial schools in that city are " dwarfish in body and mind . . . puny, pigmy, feeble, and deformed creatures." In Aberdeen the number of juvenile vagrants fell from 397 to 14 following the opening of the schools.

In Edinburgh Bailie Mack presented to the Parochial Board a report on the subject of Schools of Industry, in which he said that in the course of his duty as a magistrate he often had brought before him boys and girls of very tender years, as from 5, 6, or 7 years of age, charged with street begging and sometimes with pilfering and stealing. He had always great reluctance to commit these children to prison, and the youthful offenders were generally dismissed with an admonition as to their future conduct. But they soon came back, and ultimately, if they had attained the age of seven years, he had " no alternative but to send them to prison." He thought it would be of great value if a plan could be devised by which these children might be taken charge of and admitted and trained to some industrial employment, which would be a great boon to the children themselves and would free the inhabitants of an annoyance and nuisance to which they were daily subjected. Bailie Mack's attention had been called to the success that had attended the establishment of Schools of Industry in Aberdeen. The Edinburgh Parochial Board remitted to a committee further consideration of the matter, and it was suggested that the children for whose benefit and reformation these schools should be instituted might be divided into three classes : (1) boys and girls under 14 years of age, found prowling through the streets and apprehended by the police for begging, who had no known place of residence and whose parents were unknown ; (2) children whose parents would be anxious enough to rear their children properly but were unable to do so through their extreme poverty ; and (3) boys and girls totally destitute who had been convicted of theft. It was felt that these three classes of children could all be regarded as themselves " objects of parochial relief " in terms of the Poor Law Act, and it was recommended by the committee that two industrial schools should be established in Edinburgh by the parochial authorities, one for boys and one for girls. It was later decided by the Parochial Board that suitable premises in the neighbourhood of the poorhouse should be hired by the Board for the establishment of one such school.

In Glasgow, representatives of the Town Council, the Parochial Boards, the Town's Hospital, the House of Refuge and the Night Asylum conferred about the establishment of industrial schools, and early in 1846 a report was prepared on the subject by Andrew Liddell, Convener of the Council Committee. The report accepted the value of industrial schools and suggested that they should deal with much the same types of children as indicated in the Edinburgh report. It was thought that day scholars could be supported at a cost of about 1s. 3d. per week. Mr. Liddell quoted that sum as the cost of food, being the mean between that of the industrial schools at Aberdeen, where it was 1s. 2d., and the Night Asylum, Glasgow, where the cost of each inmate was 1s. 4d. a week. He considered that this sum would cover the extra outlay because the produce of labour, though it should yield no more than it did in Aberdeen, viz. 7d. per week, would cover all other cost, including teacher's salary, school rent, gas, coal, etc. It was thought that 30s. or 40s. per annum might be taken as the probable extra cost of those who required to be lodged and clothed—" One complete dress of strong and substantial material which could be had at from 20s. to 24s. ; mending and washing with lodging can, with care and economy, he had for 15s. to 20s." The proposal was that the parishes of Glasgow, Barony, Govan, etc., should act in concert to carry out this venture, and that if the measure was taken up by the parochial boards in an open and liberal spirit, thereby providing shelter and education for every destitute youth, the police magistrate would find his duty of ordering the streets to be cleared of all vagrants an easy matter.

The first Industrial Schools Act of 1854 empowered courts

to commit a vagrant child not exceeding 15 years of age to an industrial school irrespective of whether the child had committed an offence.

In 1760 the first school in Britain for the deaf and dumb was founded in Edinburgh, and about 1800 the Blind Asylum in Edinburgh was opened ; in those days smallpox was the chief cause of blindness.

In 1860 the Board of Supervision issued a circular " as to the Education of Deaf and Dumb Pauper Children and the Instruction of Blind Pauper Children." The circular pointed out that such an amount of education as was necessary to fit these children for the performance of their religious and moral duties, and might enable them to become not only innocuous but useful members of the community, was a part of the relief to which pauper children were by law entitled. It recognized that the necessary educational facilities could be afforded only by special means of instruction ; parochial boards were under an obligation to provide this if facilities existed in their parishes, and they were enjoined to do so on moral and economic grounds even where it involved making suitable arrangements elsewhere.

5

Imbecile children were often left in unsuitable homes or boarded out under bad conditions, and in their annual report for 1853 the Board of Supervision recorded that a building had been erected at Baldovan, near Dundee, at the private cost of Sir John and Lady Ogilvie, for use as an institute for the cure of imbecile and idiot children, in the mode recommended and pursued with great success by Dr. Guggenbuld of Abdenberg, Interlaken. The institute would not be endowed, but would be maintained partly by subscriptions and voluntary contributions, and partly by the board paid for the pupils. It was proposed to receive pupils of two classes at different rates and thought probable that the directors might be able to receive poor children at a rate so moderate that in many cases parochial boards might send pauper children to be instructed there with ultimate advantage, even from a pecuniary point of view. It was hoped that the institution—the first of the kind to be established in Scotland— would be ready to receive patients in the course of 1854. " We do not doubt," the Board said, " that many pauper children who, by treatment in such an institution, might have been made capable of maintaining themselves, have, for want of such means of instruction, remained helpless burdens on their parishes through their lives." Shortly afterwards an idiot school was opened in Edinburgh, and in 1862 the Royal Scottish Institution for the Care of Mentally Defective Children was established.

Boarding-out of necessitous children has been practised in Scotland for very many years. Often children were placed in unsuitable homes. The great development of industry and the increase in destitution about the middle of last century invested the problem with a new urgency, and the Board of Supervision was driven to inquire into the whole matter by an unfortunate case of neglect of a boarded-out child in St. Cuthbert's Parish of Edinburgh, this case being the subject of a criminal prosecution. From the inquiry it emerged that in many urban parishes destitute orphans and deserted children, instead of being collected in poorhouses, were dispersed in surrounding rural districts, boarded out in the homes of working-class families and, from time to time, visited by an inspector appointed by the Parochial Board for that duty. The Board concluded that while it was evident that the risk of neglect in particular cases was much greater than if such children had been collected in one or two establishments, while the amount of literary instruction imparted to them would generally be less than in a well-regulated establishment, and while, in a majority of cases, if not in all, " the children would fail to acquire habits of cleanliness and order so perfect as might be taught in a training school," yet it was probable that the results obtained in this country by boarding-out were on the whole preferable to those reached even in well-regulated establishments where pauper children were gathered together. Living in working-class homes, the children soon developed domestic attachments, ceased to be a separate class of the community, and were " speedily absorbed and lost sight of in the mass of the labouring population."

A few years later the Board of Supervision published a report by one of its officers on the boarding-out of pauper children from Glasgow and other towns in the island of Arran. It appeared that there were about 130 such children, boarded-out chiefly with crofters and cottars. These children were welcomed by the islanders, for in the houses of the crofters there was usually a " roughness " (a plentiful supply) of wholesome provisions, and the addition of two or three children made no very great difference in the family consumption of food, while their board, paid regularly in cash, was of considerable importance to the crofter in helping him to pay his rent. The allowance usually paid in respect of each child was 10s. or 12s. a month, with clothing and school fees provided. The inspector was of opinion that, except perhaps in one or two isolated instances, no more natural arrangement could be made for looking after these children, though he doubted whether the arrangements for their medical care were satisfactory. He quoted as a good example of a satisfactory foster home one in which were a crofter and his wife, their adult son and daughter, and four pauper children—two brothers aged 11 and 7, and the other two, also brothers, aged 11 and 8. The house which this family occupied consisted of the byre, the kitchen, with two beds, and the inner room with two beds. Beds and general furniture were said to be good, and the children apparently happy ; " there was ample show of provisions." The inspector was convinced that this boarding-out arrangement was a good one for the children ; the natural dispositions of the foster-parents were kindly and hospitable, visits of inspection were frequent, and there was a notable improvement in the well-being of the children. The pale face and inert expression sometimes observable in poorhouse-bred children were exchanged for a healthy complexion and an intelligent expression.

There had apparently been some misgiving in Arran about the growth of the practice of boarding-out children from the city on the island, and it was recognized that questions of social policy might arise if the practice came to be further developed— the effect of the introduction of unhealthy elements into the island population, and the future liability of these children on the receiving parishes—but the inspector summed up the matter in these words : " In the meantime, it appears to be unquestionable, that a present benefit is conferred on these poor children, and that the crofters and small farmers in Arran are not only benefited by the cash payments on their account, and enabled to pay their rents more easily than they could do without them, but have also a present and prospective supply of servants and labourers whose wages are at the lowest."

In 1863 the physical condition of children in the Linlithgow Poorhouse was reported by a visiting officer to be unsatisfactory, though he had been unable to discover the cause of the trouble. The Board of Supervision nominated Dr. Littlejohn as commissioner to inquire and report : " He found the sanitary condition of the house, the diet, and accommodation satisfactory, and the airing yards good ; but recommended the introduction of more active and joyous games, and that the children should be taken out for exercise on a wider range two or three times a week."

6

For centuries, severe, almost barbarous, measures had been practised by the Church against immorality and illegitimacy, and these continued into the nineteenth century, but with little effect ; Johnston believed that some part of the high illegitimacy rate was a direct outcome of conditions and practices of feudal times. In Aberdeen in 1574, 27 per cent. of births were illegitimate, while in Perth in 1580, 40 per cent. of children baptized were born out of wedlock. This state of affairs was not confined to any one stratum of society. It was common among the nobles and among the clergy. In 1558–59 the Synod of Edinburgh enacted that neither prelates nor any other ecclesiastics should directly or indirectly give with their illegitimate daughters in marriage to barons or landowners, any greater sum than one hundred pounds yearly of the Church's patrimony. The clergy were enjoined " to remove their oppen concubines." Patrick Hepburn, Bishop of Moray, had seven illegitimate children—five sons and two daughters—" all acknowledged in one day."

As was to be expected, the attitude of the Church to illegitimate children was not conducive to any great zeal for their welfare, and this attitude was carried forward to the days when the relief of destitution came to be a function of the parochial boards. It was reported about 1840 that "the authorities do, as a general rule, resist all claims made on behalf of illegitimate children, from a desire to avoid the encouragement of vice by too ready advances made at the public expense." But in 1858 the General Superintendent of Poor in Scotland reported that cases of women receiving relief for their illegitimate children were exceedingly numerous and were yearly increasing, the number of children ranging anything up to six per mother. He regretted that there was little feeling of shame, either in the unfortunate creatures themselves or with the people at large, that there was no hesitation in engaging this class as servants, and that " even persons in a superior position, and some whose profession it was to set a moral example, had this class as servants." He concluded that the facility of obtaining parochial relief for illegitimate children tended to immorality, though he did not consider that immorality could be attributed entirely to it, for the manner in which the humble classes were brought up from their infancy, all the family sleeping in the same room, often in the same bed, and the bothy system of housing farm labourers lowered the moral feeling and tended to make the young an easy prey. Seeking to explain the high proportion of illegitimacy among the labouring classes in 1855, the Registrar-General expressed the view that the bothy system of housing farm workers was not such an important factor as that prevailing on smaller farms where young unmarried workers lived very much with the family ; and he put forward the theory that the relatively low incidence of illegitimacy in some Scottish counties corresponded with a low educational standard in these counties, with the result that in them marriages, albeit improvident, were more frequent than in the more highly educated areas, and the illegitimacy rate correspondingly lower.

In 1863 the Registrar-General reported that 10 per cent. of all children born in Scotland were illegitimate, and that illegitimacy seemed to be on the increase. He regarded it as a singular fact that Scotland stood almost alone among the nations as a country where illegitimacy was more common among the rural population than among those in the towns. The counties in the south-western and north-eastern parts of the country yielded the highest proportion of illegitimate births, the figures reaching a height in the counties of Wigtown (16·9 per cent.), Banff (16·7 per cent.), and Aberdeen (16·2 per cent.). He drew attention to the fact that about every year the proportion of male children born was higher among illegitimate than among legitimate children. Taking everything into account, he concluded that illegitimacy in Scotland was a very different thing, and had different causes, from illegitimacy on the Continent of Europe, where it probably depended mainly on prostitution and on the large number of women kept as mistresses, whereas in Scotland it depended principally " on the young having premature intercourse before they were in a condition to get married," a circumstance aggravated by the fact that with the passing of the Poor Law Act in 1845 many houses were pulled down to prevent the poor from acquiring settlements, and as a result many young people who wished to be married were unable to find houses.

Though accurate statistics are available only from the time of the introduction of Registration of Births, Marriages, and Deaths in 1855, Mortality Bills prepared from parochial registers under the authority of the magistrates afford information about the numbers buried in Glasgow—and, for what the information is worth, reputed causes of death—for many years before that date. The Mortality Bill for 1791 showed that in that year there were 1,508 burials in the city (apart from 43 inmates of the Town's Hospital), as well as 928 from the parishes of Gorbals, Calton, and Anderston. Of the 1,508 burials in the city, 968 (or 64 per cent. of the total) were of children under 10 years of age. In 1830 the total number of births in Glasgow was 6,397, plus 471 still-births. In the same year the number of burials entered in the registers of the burying grounds of the city and suburbs numbered 5,185, of which 471 were the still-births already mentioned, 877 were deaths of children in the first year of life, 1,123 between the ages of 1 and 5, and 253 between the ages of 5 and 10. The number of still-births had risen steeply. In 1821 there was 1 still-birth for every 21 births, a figure comparable with the mean of the nine principal towns in Europe, but by 1831 the proportion had risen to 1 still-birth for every 14 births, a figure exceeded only by Strassburg. Mean mortality under 5 years of age during the years 1822–30 was 1 in 90; but from 1831–39 it was 1 in 72. Child mortality, which had been tending to fall in the years before 1830, began to increase again after that year. Up to 1800 smallpox was the greatest single cause of child death, accounting for over 30 per cent. of all the deaths under 10 years of age, and in the few years preceding that date it appears to have been more fatal to children in Glasgow than anywhere else in Britain. With the adoption of vaccination at the turn of the century the picture changed completely, and in the ten years 1803–12 the percentage of deaths of children under 10 due to smallpox fell to less than 10. On the other hand, deaths from measles and scarlet fever combined to be largely responsible for the deaths of children. During the years 1835–39 there were in Glasgow 1,056 deaths from scarlet fever, of these 97 were in the first year of life, and 853 between the ages of 1 and 10. It was estimated that about one patient in twelve contracting the disease died from it. During the same period there were in Glasgow 2,482 deaths from measles, and of these

528 were in the first year of life and 1,929 between the ages of 1 and 10.

In 1838 just over one-half of the 6,932 deaths in Glasgow occurred among children under 10 years of age, a proportion very similar to that prevailing fifty years previously, and when to these are added the 583 still-births which occurred that year the total loss of infant life can be described only as appalling. As late as 1863 just over 60 per cent. of all the deaths in Glasgow occurred among children under 10 years of age. In Scotland as a whole, 120 of every 1,000 infants born alive died before completing the first year of life. The rate of infantile mortality was higher in towns than in country districts, and varied considerably from town to town ; thus, of the eight principal towns in Scotland, it was lowest in Perth (117), and ranged upwards to 163 in Glasgow and 193 in Greenock, where, however, there was in that year a formidable outbreak of smallpox which accounted for about one-eighth of the infant deaths. Premature debility was responsible for 22 per cent. of the deaths of children in the first year of life. The other chief causes of child death were the common infectious diseases (whooping cough, smallpox, enteritis, scarlet fever, diphtheria, and croup), respiratory diseases, and tuberculosis. Robert Adam wrote in 1813, " Next to the smallpox formerly and the measles now, Chincough is the most fatal disease to which children are liable." So far as can be judged, the chief changes in cause of child mortality between 1838 and 1863 were a relative decrease in deaths from bowel complaints among young infants, an increase in deaths from respiratory diseases among children under 5, and an increase of deaths from scarlet fever among children of all ages.

This tale of increasing sickness and death among young children does not make encouraging reading, but already in 1863 forces were mustering that were ultimately to effect a great improvement. Enlightened opinion, like that of Sheriff Allison of Glasgow, vigorously denounced the " vicious state of society " that was killing off the infants ; the Factory Acts, despite their slow and halting progress, were beginning to reduce the worse abuses of child employment, while the new sanitarians, chief among them Gairdner in Glasgow and Littlejohn in Edinburgh, were beginning to make their plea for more space for the children, and more of the facilities that would help to make possible a reasonably happy childhood.

AUTHORITIES REFERRED TO IN THE TEXT

Aberdeen, Book of. Edited by David Rorie for 107th Annual Meeting of British Medical Association, 1939

Aberdeen Philosophical Society, Transactions of, 1892, p. 60

Balfour, Wm. *Heads of Cases of Rheumatism and Complaints allied to it, successfully treated by Compression and Percussion after all other Remedies had failed* (Edinburgh, 1827)

Barbe, L. A. *Sidelights on the History, Industries, and Social Life of Scotland* (London : Blackie, 1919)

Barnet, T. R. *Reminiscences of Old Scots Folk* (Edinburgh : Foulis, 1913)

Begbie, J. *On the Causes of Death in the Scottish Widows' Fund Life Assurance Society* (Edinburgh : Constable, 1866)

Bennett, Professor. *Monthly Journal of Med. Science* 1851, p. 266

Boswell, J. *Journal of a Tour to the Hebrides with Samuel Johnson, LL.D.*

Briscoe, H. *Report of General Board of Supervision* (Edinburgh, 1858)

Brown, A. *History of Glasgow and of Paisley, Greenock, and Port Glasgow* (Glasgow : Paton, 1795)

Brown, P. H. *Early Travellers in Scotland* (Edinburgh, 1891). *Scotland before 1700* (Edinburgh, 1893)

Campbell, G. D. *Eighth Duke of Argyll, Scottish Diaries and Memoirs 1746–1843* Edited by J. G. Fyfe (Stirling : Mackay, 1942)

Carlyle, A. *Ibid*

Cathcart, E. P. *Communal Health* (Glasgow : Craig and Wilson, 1944)

Chadwick, E. *Report of Poor Law Commissioners on an Enquiry into the Sanitary Condition of the Labouring Population of Great Britain* 1842

Chalmers, A. K. *Transactions of Royal Sanitary Association of Scotland* 1926

Chambers, R. C. *Domestic Annals of Scotland* (Edinburgh : W. & R. Chambers)

Cleland, J. *The Annals of Glasgow* 1816. *The Rise and Progress of the City of Glasgow* 1820. *The Former and Present State of Glasgow* 1840

Cockburn, Lord. *A Letter to the Lord Provost on the Best Ways of Spoiling the Beauty of Edinburgh* 1849. *Memorials of his Time*

Comrie, J. D. *History of Scottish Medicine* (London : Bailliere, Tindall and Cox, 1927)

Coutts, J. *History of the University of Glasgow*

Cowan, R. *Remarks suggested by the Glasgow Bills of Mortality* 1832. *Vital Statistics of Glasgow illustrating the Sanitary Condition of the Population*

Creighton, C. *A History of Epidemics in Britain* (Cambridge, 1891)

Cullen, G. M. "Concerning Sibbens and the Scottish Yaws." *Caledonian Medical Journal* April 1911, p. 336

303

Dick, G. "An Old Board of Health." *Health Bulletin, Department of Health for Scotland* July 1945

Dingwall, Burgh Records of

District Surgeons of the Parishes of Glasgow. *Facts and Observations on the Sanitary State of Glasgow* 1846

Duncan, A. *Memorials of the Faculty of Physicians and Surgeons of Glasgow 1599-1850* (Glasgow, 1896)

Dundee, *British Association Handbook* 1912

Edinburgh, 1329-1929 (Edinburgh : Oliver and Boyd, 1929)

Eyre-Todd, G. *History of Glasgow* (Jackson, Wylie, 1931)

Fyfe, J. G. *Scottish Diaries and Memoirs, 1746-1843* (Stirling : Mackay, 1942)

Gairdner, W. T. *Report to the Board of Police on the Health of Glasgow* 1863

Galt, J. *Annals of the Parish*

General Board of Supervision of Poor, Scotland, *Annual Reports of*, 1846-1863

Glaister, J. "Epidemic History of Glasgow 1783-1883." *Proceedings of Philosophical Society*

Gordon, J. F. S. *Glasgow Facies* (Glasgow : Tweed, 1872)

Gregory, J. C. "Report of a Case of Peculiar Black Infiltration of the Whole Lungs, Resembling Melanosis." *Edinburgh Medical and Surgical Journal,* xxxvi, 1831

Guthrie, T., *vide* Fyfe. *Scottish Diaries and Memoirs, 1746-1843*

Hamilton, Dr. *Medico-Chirurgical Transactions,* xxi (Glasgow)

Home, G. *Edinburgh* (London : A. & C. Black, 1927)

Hunter, R. *The Water Supply of the City of Glasgow* (Glasgow : Menzies, 1933)

Hutchison, R. *Transactions of the Highland and Agricultural Society of Scotland,* ii, 4th series (Edinburgh : Blackwood, 1869)

Johnston, T. *History of the Working Classes* (Glasgow : Forward Publishing Co)

Jones, Wm. *The Expectation of Life in the City of Glasgow* (Glasgow : Anderson, 1925)

Kermack, W. R. *Nineteen Centuries of Scotland* (Edinburgh : W. & A. K. Johnston, 1944)

Lang, A. *A History of Scotland* (Edinburgh : Blackwood)

Lugton, T. *The Old Lodgings in Glasgow* (Glasgow : Hedderwick, 1901)

Lunacy, Report of Scottish Commissioners on, 1857

Macgregor, A. *Old Glasgow* (Glasgow : Blackie, 1880)

Mackenzie, A. M. *The Kingdom of Scotland* (London : W. & R. Chambers, 1940)

Mackintosh, J. *History of Civilisation in Scotland* (Paisley : Gardner, 1893)

McKellar, A. *London and Edinburgh Monthly Journal* September 1845, p. 645

McLean, H. A. "Notes on Some Old Glasgow Institutions with Medical Associations." *Glasgow Medical Journal* 1910, p. 188

McNeill, Sir John. *Report General Board of Supervision, Scotland* 1853

Marshall, Wm. *Lancet* 1834, ii, p. 271

Marwick, Sir Jas. D. *Glasgow : the Water Supply of the City* (Glasgow : Anderson, 1901)

Mill, J., *vide* Fyfe. *Scottish Diaries and Memoirs 1746–1843*

Miller, Captain. "Papers relative to the State of Crime in Glasgow." *Proceedings British Association, Glasgow Meeting* 1840, p. 170

Nicholls, Sir George. *A History of the Scotch Poor Law, in connexion with the Condition of the People* (London : Murray, 1856)

Owen, R. *To the British Master Manufacturers*, p. 142 (Dent)

Paul, H. *The Glasgow Mortality Bill for the Year ending 31 December 1838*

Perry, R. *Observations on the Sanitary State of Glasgow* 1846

Poole, R. *Memoranda regarding the Royal Lunatic Asylum and Dispensary of Montrose 1821*

Registrar-General, Scotland. *First Annual Report* 1863

Reports on the Sanitary condition of the Labouring Population of Scotland. Presented to Parliament 1842. (Contributions by Adamson, J., Alison, S. S., Allison, W. P., Anderson, G., Arnott, N., Baird, C. R., Burton, J. H., Cameron, J., Chambers, Wm., Forrest, W. H., Gibson, J., Kilgour, A., and Galen, J., Laurie, W. L., McLellan, R. D., Stevenson, W.)

Robertson, D. *A History of the High Constables of Edinburgh* 1924

Rorie, D. "The Stone in Scottish Folk Medicine." *Caledonian Medical Journal* July 1911, p. 410

Russell, J. B. *The Evolution of the Functions of Public Health Administration in Glasgow* 1895

Sage, D., *vide* Fyfe. *Scottish Diaries and Memoirs 1746–1843*

Scotsman, Leader, 7 May 1863

Simpson, Sir J. Y. *Evidence to Health of Towns Committee. Antiquarian Notices of Syphilis in Scotland. On Some Magical Charm Stones or Curing Stones. Archaeological Essays*, edited by John Stuart (Edinburgh, 1872)

Sinclair, Sir John. *Analysis of the Statistical Account of Scotland* (Edinburgh : Constable, 1825)

Skeen, Gilbert. *Ane breve description of the Pest* (Edinburgh, 1568)

Smith, A. *Wealth of Nations* ii, p. 439 (Oxford, 1869)

Smollett, T. *Humphrey Clinker* (Nelson)

Stark, J. "Epidemic Fevers of Scotland." *Trans. of Epidemiological Society of London*, ñ, 2

Strang, J. *Bursaries, Schools, Mortifications, and Bequests* (Glasgow University Press, 1861)

Sutherland, Dr. "Report on Measures adopted for Relief of Cholera in Glasgow, 1848–49 " ; Appendix to a *Report of the General Board of Health on the Epidemic*

AUTHORITIES REFERRED TO IN THE TEXT

Symons, J. C. *Reports from Assistant Hand-Loom Weavers' Commissioners.* Parliamentary Paper issued 27 March 1839

Thomson, J. *History of Dundee* 1847

Thomson, J. B. *Edinburgh Medical Journal* 1858

Thomson, Wm. *Medico-Chirurgical Transactions, Glasgow,* xx, xxi

Turner, A. L. *The Royal Infirmary of Edinburgh* (Edinburgh : Oliver and Boyd, 1929)

Watt, R. *An Enquiry into the Relative Mortality of the Principal Diseases of Children and the Number who have died under ten Years of Age in Glasgow during the last thirty Years* 1813. Facsimile Reprint by John Thomson in Glasgow in 1888

Webster, Rev. A. *Census of Population and of the Proportion of Men able to bear Arms throughout Scotland* 1755. Manuscript with Curators of Advocates' Library

Wilson, Rev. J. M. *Gazetteer of Scotland* (Edinburgh : A. Fullerton, *circa* 1860)

Wright, J. N., and Snodgrass, N. S. *Scotland and its People : a Symposium* (Edinburgh : Oliver and Boyd, 1942)

INDEX

Aberdeen Asylum 273

Aberdeen, bridewell at 224 ; costs of cottages in 60 ; Den Burn in 164 ; edict of Town Council of against venereal disease 108 ; effect of industrial schools on number of vagrants in 294 ; freedom from plague of 2, 106 ; malignant sore throat in 134 ; measures against plague in 102–3 ; monastic hospitals in 255 ; nationality of citizens of 72 ; sanitary condition of 163–64 ; Shore Porters Society 87 ; typhus fever in 117 ; water supply 154 ; workhouse discontinued 181

Aberdeen Infirmary 259; patients treated in 265

Aberdour parish refuses medical relief 251

Abernethie, James, medical officer in Glasgow 232

able-bodied and disabled 172

Adam, Robert 51

Adamson, Dr., on measles at St. Andrews 133, 134

age and distribution of population 65, 67, 69

agricultural workers, housing of 45

ague 82, 131, 132 ; attributed to Union with England 131 ; cure of 228 ; decline of attributed to improvement in drainage 82

Aird, Alexander, of Dingwall 156

Aldcambus leper hospital 98

Aldnestum leper hospital 98

ale, as common drink 15

Alison, Dr., advocates hospital at Tranent 239 ; on diseases of miners 90 ; on effects of child labour in mines 291

Allison, Professor W. P., on causes of typhus fever 117, 118 ; on conditions in Canongate poorhouse 213 ; on developing concept of preventive medicine 97

almshouses, conditions in 214

Anderson, Wm., and the Board of Supervision 205

apothecaries attached to Court 231 ; and surgeons 235

apprentices in shipyards, medical care of 28

Arbirlot, cholera prevention at 123

Arbroath, costs of cottages at 60 ; influenza at 132

" arling " of miners' children 287

Arnot, Hugo, on condition of Edinburgh Tolbooth 223

Arnott, Dr. Neil, on fever and housing conditions 57 ; on fevers prevalent in Edinburgh and Glasgow 118

Arran, boarding-out of Glasgow children in 297, 298

Ashley buildings, Edinburgh, as example of better housing 53

assessments for relief of poor 195

asylum, places reserved in, for new cases arising 207

asylums, private, bad conditions in 284

Ayala, Don Pedro de 40

Ayr, cost of erection of cottages in 60 ; dispensary arrangements in 242 ; quality of bread in 39

Badges authorizing infirm to beg 166, 167

bakehouses, working conditions in 92

Baldovan Institution, Dundee 296

Balfour, Dr. Wm., on treatment of rheumatism 82

Ballantyne of Dryhope, blood-letter of Yarrow 230

banqueting, regulation of 17

Barbreck's bone as cure for insanity 228

Barra, difficulty of poor relief in 203 ; inspector of poor at 197 ; lack of meal in 29

Begbie, Dr. J., on causes of death among contributors to Scottish Widows' Fund 75

beggars 20 ; badges to be issued to 166 ; children of, liable to be seized 287 ; disposal of in Berwickshire 188 ; punishment of 168

307

colliers "arled" 287 ; "on nursing wages" 287, 288 ; poor relief granted to 204 ; poor, to be taught to spin 287 ; premature employment of 289 ; sold to plantations 287

chincough, fatal to children 302 ; in Glasgow 112, 134, 302

cholera 2, 3, 123–30 ; Acts 123 ; at Carron 128 ; at Dingwall 126–27 ; at Edinburgh 128–29 ; at Glasgow 125–26, 128–29 ; at Wick 127 ; Boards of Health set up 124–27 ; hospital at Mill End, Glasgow 124 ; hospital at Surgeon's Square, Edinburgh 129 ; measures for prevention of 125–26 ; stimulates development of health policy 2 ; preventive measures at Arbirlot 123 ; spread influenced by conditions 57

Christison, Dr., on condition in Canongate poorhouse 213

Church, attitude of, to lepers 99, 100 ; opposes assessments for poor 187 ; Provincial Council of, on overlaying of children 285 ; resources for relief of poor at end 18 c. 6, 186 ; "city arabs" 294

City Workhouse, Edinburgh 219

cleanliness of streets and dwellings, Acts to secure 50

cleansing of streets of Edinburgh 137–39

Cleland, J., analysis of age-sex distribution of population, 1821, 67 ; on overcrowding in Glasgow 58 ; on those most susceptible to typhus fever 4

clengers 106, 107

clergy and practice of medicine 230

Cockburn, Lord, criticizes public washhouse on Calton Hill 158 ; on effects of manufactures on the people 14 ; on inmates of Trinity Hospital 175 ; on the class of unemployed poor 192

coffee, "radical" 24

Coll, on difficulty in levying assessment for poor relief 196

collector for poor appointed in Glasgow 170

Commission to review administration of poor relief 194

Commissioners in Lunacy and Board of Supervision at variance 209

common lodging-houses 60–3 ; licensing of 62 ; risk of infectious disease in 10

consumption and heart disease as causes of death 78

consumption in 18 c. 83 ; prevalence of, in large towns 84 ; in Western Isles 84

control of drinking in 15 c. 15

correction houses 173, 268 ; master of, given extensive power 173

cost of maintenance in poorhouses 220

cottages, costs of, in Scottish towns 60

Cowan, Dr. R., advocates establishment of medical police 57, 143, 240 ; on fever and housing conditions 56 ; on differential birth and death rates 285 ; on relation between epidemic disease and poverty 97

Cowane's hospital, Stirling 255

Craig, James, plan for New Town of Edinburgh of 51

Craigentinny meadows 159

Cranstounhill Water Company 151

Crawfordjohn, housing in 41

Crichton Institution, Dumfries 279

crime, and poverty 191–92 ; decreasing in Glasgow, 1839, 225 ; incidence related to health of community 225 ; in relation to housing in Glasgow 58 ; in Edinburgh 226–27

criminals, aliment to, in gaol 224

Crombie's Land, Edinburgh, condition of 53

Cromwell, Oliver, orders cleansing of Edinburgh 138

croup 135, 136

Cumyne, James, Medical Officer in Aberdeen 232

Cunningham, Patrick, charged with blood-letting 235

curing stones 228, 229

Curry, the King's jester, "suspect of pestilence" 102

Dale, David, employs child labour at New Lanark 289

David, King, flees from plague 101

Davidson, Sheriff 208

deaf and dumb persons in 1861 census 86 ; school for, in Edinburgh 296

Dean of Guild Court 54–6

Dean Orphanage, Edinburgh 294

Deanston mill, working conditions in 89 ; works doctor employed for 89

PRINTED IN GREAT BRITAIN AT
THE PRESS OF THE PUBLISHERS